D1174527

PRENTICE-HALL INTERNATIONAL SERIES IN MANAGEMENT

Baumol	*Economic Theory and Operations Analysis*
Churchman	*Prediction and Optimal Decision: Philosophical Issues of a Science of Values*
Clarkson	*The Theory of Consumer Demand: A Critical Appraisal*
Greenlaw, Herron, and Rawdon	*Business Simulation*
Holt, Modigliani, Muth, and Simon	*Planning Production, Inventories, and Work Force*
Miller and Starr	*Executive Decisions and Operations Research*
Pfiffner and Sherwood	*Administrative Organization*

PRENTICE-HALL QUANTITATIVE METHODS SERIES
Dr. W. Allen Spivey, Editor

Brown	*Smoothing, Forecasting and Prediction of Discrete Time Series*
Cyert and Davidson	*Statistical Sampling for Accounting Information*
Hadley and Whitin	*Analysis of Inventory Systems*
Kemeny, Schleifer, Snell, and Thompson	*Finite Mathematics with Business Applications*
Massé	*Optimal Investment Decisions: Rules for Action and Criteria for Choice*
Stern	*Mathematics for Management*

PRENTICE-HALL, INC.
PRENTICE-HALL INTERNATIONAL, INC., UNITED KINGDOM AND EIRE
PRENTICE-HALL OF CANADA, LTD., CANADA
J. H. DE BUSSY, LTD., HOLLAND AND FLEMISH-SPEAKING BELGIUM
DUNOD PRESS, FRANCE
MARUZEN COMPANY, LTD., FAR EAST
C. BERTELSMANN VERLAG, WEST GERMANY AND AUSTRIA
HERRERO HERMANOS, SUCS., SPAIN AND LATIN AMERICA

Prentice-Hall, Inc.   Englewood Cliffs, N.J.

Robert Goodell Brown

Arthur D. Little, Inc.

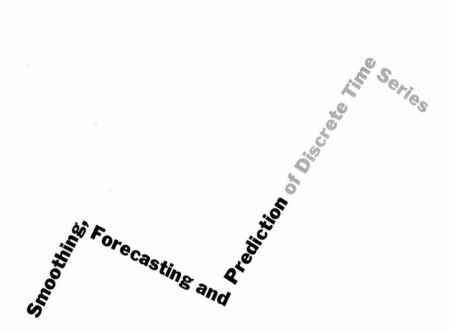

Smoothing, Forecasting and Prediction of Discrete Time Series

PRENTICE-HALL INTERNATIONAL, INC. *London*
PRENTICE-HALL OF AUSTRALIA, PTY., LTD. *Sydney*
PRENTICE-HALL OF CANADA, LTD. *Toronto*
PRENTICE-HALL FRANCE, S.A.R.L. *Paris*
PRENTICE-HALL OF JAPAN, INC. *Tokyo*
PRENTICE-HALL DE MEXICO, S.A. *Mexico City*

© 1962, 1963 by Robert Goodell Brown

All rights reserved. No part of this book may be reproduced in any form, by mimeograph or any other means, without permission in writing from the publisher.

Library of Congress Catalog Card Number 63-13271

Printed in the United States of America. C.

Preface

"These hieroglyphics have evidently a meaning. If it is a purely arbitrary one, it may be impossible for us to solve it. If, on the other hand, it is systematic, I have no doubt that we shall get to the bottom of it."

Adventure of the Dancing Men

In recent years, the rapid rise of technology in industry and in government has created both the need and the means for effective use of high-speed, internally programed, digital computers. As computers are employed more and more to carry out the routine data-processing functions for a business, or for the Defense Department, there is a stronger and stronger pressure to develop means for handling all the steps in the problem routinely. No intermediate print-outs, that delay the processing, should be required. The information should be "untouched by human hands," from the original input to final output. As Sir Walter Scott wrote* in 1830, "The times have changed in nothing more than in the rapid conveyance of intelligence and communication."

* *The Heart of Midlothian.*

In many applications, computers were first employed solely for routine data processing: the preparation of payrolls, maintenance of inventory lists, posting production progress, and recording of stock status. These applications require that information be printed out, either in summary or in detail, for someone to look at and make a decision for some sort of action. Operations research studies have made it possible to pass from the use of computers for bookkeeping to their use for control: production scheduling, stock replenishment, capital budgeting, air defense, and fire control systems. Each of these applications requires an estimate of what will happen in the future. Men with sufficient skill, judgment, and experience can do a reasonable job of predicting the future, given enough time and information. These men are frequently reluctant to admit that a computer can be taught to forecast well. A reluctance to exploit the speed, capacity, and flexibility of a computer has been noticed among pilots who were skeptical of bombsights and fire-control systems, and among stock analysts when first faced with a modern integrated data-processing system.

A computed forecast may not always be more accurate than a human prediction. It can be obtained so much faster and so much more cheaply, however, that it may be advantageous to sacrifice some accuracy if necessary. More frequently, the machine's forecasts, on the average, are more accurate than the conventional human predictions, by a measurable amount.

The scope of this book is limited to the current state of the art of programming digital computers to compute forecasts of discrete time series. The analysis of the entire control system that makes use of the forecast is beyond this book. We are concerned primarily with what the control engineers call the *open-loop* characteristics of one box that accepts current observations of the time series and delivers a forecast of the probability distribution from which future observations will be drawn. The analysis and development of these techniques has been kept sufficiently general that they can be applied to a very wide variety of integrated control systems.

Objective forecasts, of the type that can be programed for a computer, are dependable and unemotional; their response to changes in the external environment can be studied in advance and systems can be designed from these studies; the computations are consistent and therefore controllable across a wide variety of problems. Since perhaps 80 to 95 per cent of the problems encountered are quite routine, they can be handled by the computer. Thus, the analyst has from five to twenty times as much effort available to spend on the exceptions that really do require his skill, judgment, and experience.

In 1959, the McGraw-Hill Book Company published my *Statistical Forecasting for Inventory Control* which reported the state of the art at that time, with special reference to inventory control applications. Research in the problems of statistical forecasting has proceeded steadily since then, and much more powerful methods have been developed, particularly in the description of a time series by much more general classes of functions. Of especial interest to businesses with seasonal demand should be the class of trigonometric functions that make it possible to describe any cyclical process accurately and easily.

The organization of this book has been something of a problem to me. The objective of our research has been the development of practical methods that can be applied to real problems in the government and in business. Therefore, the primary results should be presented in a "How to" fashion that the men who are directly concerned with the problems can understand. On the other hand, these results stem from some intricate reasoning that can be carried out accurately only in the language of mathematics, and not everyone can speak that language fluently. The better the reader understands where the results came from, the surer he is of applying them correctly.

As each new topic is introduced, there is a non-technical summary of the major results to be obtained. Where possible, I have given a plausible argument that is intended to make the results seem reasonable. Numerical examples are also used to make a point clear. There are work sheets so that you can work out additional examples by hand. These work sheets can easily be converted to computer programs. With diligence and patience, almost anyone should be able to get a sufficient understanding of the procedures to apply them and to get the correct answer.

Complete mathematical derivations are also given, with the formulas and tables necessary to extend the range of coverage beyond the problems that can be illustrated by examples. A standard college background in mathematics should be sufficient for an understanding of the principal results in the more technical sections. Only a professional mathematician, however, will fully appreciate the results and be able to extend them to new areas. The topics of interest to the mathematician primarily are written in more technical language than that used in discussing the problems and procedures for dealing with them. Such sections also assume that the reader has a more advanced background. The text is larded with exercises to help stimulate thought about the problems.

Whenever you feel that you are getting in over your head, skim the material for a while, until the discussion becomes less theoretical. Occasionally, you will find that you must go back and work on an earlier section to get the material needed as a foundation for something later. The classroom teacher will find it advisable to skip some material and to cover the remainder in a sequence that suits the needs of the class.

A teaching sequence that has been successful is first to cover one complete, although elementary system based on Chapters 1, 4, 8, 22, 23, and 25, followed by units on data (Chapters 2 and 3, Appendix A); time series models and the characteristics of smoothing systems (Chapters 4, 9, 10, 11 and Appendix B); general exponential smoothing and forecasting (Chapters 12, 15, and 16), Error Measurement (Chapters 19 and 20). At the end of the course, the class can take up special topics, such as probability models (Chapters 5, 13, and 17), the direct forecasts of Chapter 18, and optimum linear filters (Chapter 21).

A number of concepts are used in this book. The reader who is familiar with these concepts in other areas should have no difficulty. The reader who is aware that he is going to encounter new concepts should have no difficulty in getting a sufficient understanding of them from the context. Some of the following concepts are trivial, some are quite deep. I have found that they have created problems for people who are not aware that they *are* new to them: probability distribution, functions, least squares, simulations, systems analysis and design, transforms, and so on.

A number of formal manipulative techniques are also used freely in this book. The reader who wants to go deeply into the developments discussed here should have a good working knowledge of algebra, the calculus, mathematical statistics, and matrix algebra. If the reader knows something about computer programming, he will more fully appreciate the reasons for some of the development. It is not necessary, however, that he be a professional programer. Two techniques are used in some depth: z-transforms and the regression analysis. Since these are not generally understood clearly, a brief review of the essential developments is included in the appendices.

Each of the six major parts of this book thoroughly discusses the alternative choices facing the systems designer in (1) deciding on the sources of the data to be used; (2) the model to represent the data; (3) the smoothing technique to estimate values for the model from the current data; (4) the forecast obtained from the model; (5) the measurement of error in the forecasts; (6) the applications of the forecast and error measurement to a particular decision problem. For a particular application, many of these alternatives may not be relevant. The teacher may therefore organize the material around a single thread that selects one alternative in each section, leading to a particular system for forecasting. When that system is well understood, he may then go back over some of the alternatives that might have been considered at each stage of the design.

Much of the work leading to this book has been carried out in the course of industrial assignments by the Operations Research Section at Arthur D. Little, Inc. During 1961 and 1962, the Bureau of Supplies and Accounts has supported basic mathematical research in the techniques of forecasting under Contract Nonr-3406(00). I should like to express my appreciation for the support and encouragement offered by Captain Ed Scofield, SC, USN, Commander Herb Mills, SC, USN, and Messrs. Randy Simpson and Jim Prichard.

I gratefully acknowledge the help of many colleagues and acquaintances who have made numerous comments and suggestions. Especial mention must be made of Professor G. E. P. Box of the University of Wisconsin, Professor Ronald A. Howard of MIT, Professor Sebastian Littauer of Columbia University, Mr. Warren Briggs of The RAND Corporation, and Messrs. Jim Loughney and Peter Woitach of IBM's Systems Research Institute. Dr. Robert Barringer, Michel Carré, Gordon Crook, Dr. James Dobbie, Dr. Ernest Foernzler, Frank Hulswit, Mrs. Elizabeth Hutton, Dr. Richard Meyer, Lawrence Parker, Dr. Stefan Peters, Peter Strong, and Miss Joan Sullivan at Arthur D. Little, Inc., have contributed greatly in suggesting novel ideas, developing proofs, and carrying out detailed examples. Miss Norma Moulton has coped admirably with the unenviable task of typing and retyping the manuscript.

Chris Kentera, Robert Carola and Norm Stanton of Prentice-Hall have made the work of publishing this book seem, to the author at least, a simple task and a great joy.

The quotations at the beginning of the various sections are taken from the Sherlock Holmes stories by Sir Arthur Conan Doyle, and are used by permission of Sir Arthur Conan Doyle's estate.

ROBERT G. BROWN

Table of Contents

1 Introduction 1

Section I   Data 19

2   Sources of Data 23
3   The Sampling Interval 42

Section II   Models 49

4   Time Series Models 57
5   Probability Models 78

Section III   Smoothing Techniques 85

6   Criteria 91
7   Exponential Smoothing 97
8   Choosing the Smoothing Constant 106
9   Multiple Smoothing for Higher-order Polynomials 123
10   Analysis of Characteristics 145
11   Adaptive Fitting of Transcendental Functions 158
12   General Exponential Smoothing 174
13   Probability Models 199

Section IV   Forecasting   207

14   **Lead Times**   213

15   **Forecasting with Time-Series Models**   218

16   **Variances of Coefficients and Forecasts**   227

17   **Forecasting with Probability Models**   242

18   **Special Direct Forecasts**   248

Section V   Error Measurement and Analysis   263

19   **The Normality of Forecast Errors**   271

20   **Forecasting the Allowance for Error**   291

21   **Optimum Linear Filters**   306

Section VI   Exploration of Alternatives   321

22   **Work Sheets for Hand Computations**   325

23   **Planning the Exploration Program**   333

24   **Computer Simulation Programs**   341

Section VII   Applications   355

25   **Safety Factors for Inventory Control**   363

26   **Rally Handicaps**   383

Appendix

A Regression, Autocorrelation, and Spectral Analysis 387

B The z-Transform 403

C Samples of Time Series for Practice 413

D Mathematical Tables 435

Bibliography 451

Glossary of Mathematical Symbols 463

Index 464

Work Sheets

1 MOVING AVERAGES 100

2 EXPONENTIAL SMOOTHING 103

3 LEAST SQUARES 126

4 MANUAL LEAST SQUARES COMPUTATIONS 129

5 DOUBLE EXPONENTIAL SMOOTHING 131

6 TRIPLE EXPONENTIAL SMOOTHING 137

7 TRIPLE COEFFICIENT SMOOTHING 141

8 GENERAL EXPONENTIAL SMOOTHING 197

9 VECTOR SMOOTHING 204

10 INSTALLATION RATES 225

11 DEMAND-DURING-A-LEAD-TIME 252

1 Introduction

"The emotional qualities are antagonistic to clear reasoning."

The Sign of the Four

You're driving an automobile. You glance at the gasoline gauge and decide to drive on past a service station. In that decision you have weighed your estimate of when you'll next pass another station and your estimate of the rate of consumption of gasoline, and decided that your present supply is greater than the consumption until the next replenishment opportunity. You can do these computations quite subjectively and can afford to carry a quarter tank of gasoline that is never used, just to be quite sure that even if you make a reasonable error you won't get into trouble.

A businessman may have to make similar decisions for each of thousands of items he keeps in stock. It is vitally important for him to be able to reduce his investment in unused stocks. Objective computations of the probabilities of consuming stock at various rates and objective computa-

1

tions of the time to the next replenishment opportunity can sharpen the decision of when and how much to order.

You're out hunting. You see a duck, aim ahead of him, and fire. In taking aim, you have weighed your estimates of the relative speeds of the duck and your shot; the aiming point is placed so that it will take the duck as long to reach that point on his path at his speed as it will take your shot to reach the same point. Again, you do these computations quite subjectively and perhaps miss once in a while.

The pilot of a fighter plane has the same problem. In wartime, however, he cannot afford to miss, and the speeds involved are so much higher, the distances so much greater, that objective computations can greatly increase his successes.

I participate in sports car rallies. The members of my club have more or less well-defined feelings about the relative capabilities of the contestants who enter any particular rally. These estimates are based on very subjective appraisals of past performance and could probably place any particular team in the right one of the four quartiles of the standings at the end of a rally.

The club was at one time concerned with setting handicaps, based on a fair assessment of the performance of each of more than 100 members of the club. In order to handle the volume of work and to be absolutely fair and unemotional it is necessary to have reproducible objective computations.

War, business, sports, and every-day life present countless other situations where one must somehow estimate what will happen in the future, as a basis for reaching a decision or taking action. In some instances, the estimate is reached subjectively; in others, an objective computation is advisable. In this book, I use *predict* to refer to the subjective estimates, and *forecast* to denote an objective computation. The book might well have been called *Smoothing and Forecasting of Discrete Time Series*, for it has very little to say about predictions. Predictions are sometimes used as an input to forecasting, and forecasts are sometimes a basis for a prediction; the discussion of predictions centers around these relationships.

Based on the Latin origins of the word, *to predict* is to "say beforehand." The Norman heirs to Latin were typically the ruling or managing class, and since it is an obligation upon good management to anticipate unusual change, I use *predict* to refer to subjective estimates of the future, especially the anticipation of novel factors. The impact of a new product on the market, the effect of competitive action (including evasion of an enemy target), a change in the national economy, the onset of war: these all require predictions. Many operations research studies have had the objective of making such predictions more objective. The skill, experience, and judgment of a good manager are required for really good predictions, so that only a few time series can be successfully predicted. These series may be crucial: the total sales of a company, or over-all production schedules.

In contrast, *to forecast* is of Saxon origin, to "throw ahead," implying that there is something in hand to be thrown. Specifically, we shall take this something to be past data about production, demand, prices, or the track of a missile, which can be projected into the future. At the working level, which once was the province of the conquered Saxons, people are concerned with details: each product made in the factory, each target in a large raid, each member of a sports car club. Hence, it seems etymologically more appropriate to use the Saxon term for the routine, objective, computations that (1) throw past data into the future and (2) because they are routine, can be applied to a great many series.

The distinction is not sharp and is by no means universal. Webster's *Collegiate Dictionary* says "*predict* is commonly used where inference from facts (rather than occult processes) is involved. *Forecast* connotes conjecture rather than inference." On etymological grounds, however, I shall take the liberty of using *predict* to mean management's occult conjectures, and *forecast* to refer to inference from data.

My good friend and neighbor, Jay W. Forrester, also uses the two words in the opposite sense from mine. In *Industrial Dynamics*,* he uses *prediction* to mean the employment of formal models for predicting the specific future values of the time series of interest. *Forecasting* is distinguished as meaning any of the more informal processes by which estimates are made about the future.

The reader should know that the two words have very specific meanings here, and that other usage may be contradictory. Having made the distinction, I shall have very little to say, that is, constructive about *how* to predict, except to get more skill, better judgment, and longer experience. The discussion of error analysis, in Section V, can be equally well applied to predictions or to forecasts, so that the appropriate margin for error can be computed in either case. If this measurement of error is fed back to the person responsible for making the predictions, he will have a natural tendency to try to profit by his mistakes and so improve the quality.

The October, 1961, issue of the Pacific Supply Letter, issued by the Navy's Fleet Supply Office, had a very pertinent article, "What Is Your Prediction?"

One of the toughest jobs a Leading Commissaryman has is to predict, with a high degree of accuracy, just how many mess patrons will be enjoying the tempting, tasty meals prepared by his master chefs. [The article suggests a set of 5″ × 8″ cards with two spaces for each meal.] In one area you record the

* Cambridge, Mass.: Technology Press, M.I.T., 1961.

number of men you are estimating will eat that meal. In the other section you record the actual number of men that were fed. . . .

By comparing the estimated number against the actual number of men fed, you have a quick method of knowing whether or not you are a good "guesstimator." If the two figures are considerably out of phase, think of all the reasons why your "guesstimate" was off. Did you forget that it was payday? How many are at school, away from the ship for dinner? Was it raining? Did liberty start early or late? Go on from there, analyzing the many other things that affect meal attendance. Now that you have made this analysis, compare the actual number of men fed against the number authorized. Does the difference run in a pattern? If so, corrective action on your part may be in order.

Most ships will find that a system such as the one described above will be of great help to the "guesstimator." Above all, if you are not keeping a written record of the actual number of men you feed at each meal, you are omitting one of the best tools of the "guesstimator's" trade.

Subjective predictions enter into the problem of making objective forecasts in either of two ways. On the one hand, the predictions may constitute part of the data from which the forecast is computed. On the other, the objective forecast may be one of the many sources of information on which the predictor exercises his judgment.

The smoothing techniques to be discussed in Section III revise the coefficients to be used in forecasting with each successive observation. The emphasis is on the revision of a previous set of coefficients. Therefore there must be an initial set of coefficients from which to start the process; these initial conditions must frequently be predicted. For example, when a new product is launched there is no historical information from which to compute the initial conditions.

Some of the models discussed in Section II relate the observations to other time series, as independent variables. Predictions from one or more sources can be included in such models.

The forecast is an estimate of what future observations will be *if the underlying process continues as it has in the recent past.* Whenever a responsible manager knows of some factor that will change the underlying process, he can and should modify the forecast accordingly. The results of the computations on past data give him a point of departure from which to predict changes. Note that since the forecast procedure is formal and objective, one knows exactly what has been taken into account and what has not.

This book does not pretend to cover the entire field of all methods of forecasting. All the methods covered here are in actual use and have proved to be successful when applied correctly. The approach is that of the systems engineer **rather than the economist.** The late Charles S. Roos, one of the founders of the Econometric Society, classified the forecasts used for, and by, business into five categories:*

(1) *Naïve*. These are unsophisticated, scientifically uninstructed projections. They include . . . random methods, guesses, straight-line or mathematical trend projections, autocorrelations, and harmonic analysis.

(2) *Leading Indexes*. These are indexes or time series which usually (or always) change before a change in the index or aggregate to be forecast. For example, shipments of goods precede earnings; and industrial contract awards always precede industrial construction.

(3) *Comparative Pressures*. These methods usually involve ratios or differences. For example, the ratio of inventory to sales, production to capacity, new orders to production, or shipments to new orders. They may involve the difference between demand and supply.

(4) *Opinion Polls*. These are the weighted or unweighted averages of naïve forecasts, or of forecasts made by people who have information and techniques of forecasting not available to the polltaker.

(5) "Econometric" is a word coined to mean the union of economic theory and mathematics, statistics, and accounting. Econometric methods of forecasting, to be successful, must be concerned with truly dynamic theories of economics.

Under these descriptions, all the methods in this book would be grouped as "naïve," for they deal with mathematical trend projections and autocorrelations. I am sure, however, that some of the methods will seem to be sophisticated; their development has certainly been scientific. The bibliography gives some of the principal works that deal with Roos' other four categories; they are not discussed further here.

The forecast systems discussed are intended to be part of some larger control system. The final analysis and evaluation should be made with the forecast in its proper context, but the "open-loop" characteristics investigated here can be very important in narrowing the choices to be explored in the more elaborate environment and in suggesting the proper corrective action if the first design leads to some undesirable characteristics.

In designing a statistical forecasting system, bear in mind the uses to which it will be put. In particular, it is necessary to know how stringent the requirement for accuracy is, as a function of the lead time. A ten-year projection of total company sales cannot be very accurate in detail, but it does not need to be. Suppose a commitment is made, such as building a new plant, on the anticipated volume of sales five years in the future. If the volume materializes in four years or six, instead of five, no great penalty will be incurred. Particularly, that far in the future, there is ab-

* See Bibliography, page 451.

solutely no requirement for a forecast of the sales for each individual item in the line.

The shorter the lead time covered by the forecast, in general, the greater the need for accuracy and for detail. In Section VII, we shall discuss how to estimate the expected risk incurred from using a given forecast procedure. Since every forecast is inherently subject to error, there will be some cases when the future event is larger than forecast, and other cases when the event is smaller than forecast. Usually the penalties for being over forecast are different from the penalties for being under forecast. A bias can be deliberately introduced to minimize the expected sum of these penalties.

The need for such a bias has been long recognized intuitively by businessmen in their inventory control policies. "Instead of the traditional department store motto of 'Thick on the best, thin on the rest,'" says Sol Cantor of Interstate Department Stores, "the discount operator says, 'Thick on the best, to hell with the rest.'"* In Section VII, we shall make this intuitive recognition more formal and thereby sharpen control.

Perhaps the expected risk, even when it is at a minimum, is unacceptable. There are two ways to reduce the minimum risk. One is to design a forecast system that will have greater accuracy. There is a limit to the maximum accuracy that can be achieved, and a tremendous increase in effort is needed to go from a very good system to the optimum system. Even in the optimum forecast system, some margin for error must be allowed.

The other way to reduce risk is to shorten the lead time. It is almost always possible to forecast over a short lead time with greater accuracy than over a long lead time. A tentative commitment may normally be made sufficiently far in advance to allow for its orderly fulfillment. If actual events are nearly as forecast, then the original plan can stand. There is almost always a later opportunity to modify the original commitment, possibly at some cost. These opportunities can be exploited to advantage.

In another context, guided missiles were developed to shorten the lead time required for making the final correction to the path of a projectile. The general plan of action is set when the missile is launched. If the estimate of the target's path changes—from better information or because the target changed course—the missile's path can be changed correspondingly. Guided missiles are more expensive than conventional shells and should be used only when the increased effectiveness warrants the cost.

Consider the problem of controlling the stock of items in an inventory. A forecast of demand during a normal lead time will generate routine replenishment orders. It is possible to think of a system that allows safety

* *Fortune*, quoted in *The New Yorker*, May 12, 1962.

stock sufficient to give only a very small chance of a shortage. When less safety stock is provided, the chance of a shortage rises.

For the few Class A items that each sell a great deal, one philosophy counsels releasing routine orders on the basis of a rather thin safety stock; the buyer follows the actual demand closely. Whenever later information indicates the possibility of a shortage, the delivery is expedited. In effect, such expediting reduces the lead time at which the final commitment is made. The expense of this action must be weighed against the expense of carrying the stock that would reduce the need for such action.

Another important characteristic of the forecast, in relation to the control system, is its stability. We can formalize the notion later, but for the moment, we can say that, in a stable system, whenever the forecast is modified in the light of additional information, the new forecast shouldn't be very different from the previous ones. Wild fluctuations in the observed data should be smoothed out. Obviously, the forecast must respond to a sudden shock, but the effect should die out gradually. It should never be possible for a shock to make the forecast "blow up," and it is desirable to prevent a shock from making the forecasts oscillate.

On the other hand, the forecast must have *some* response to a shock. If the shock is the onset of totally new conditions, the forecast should respond as rapidly as possible. Unfortunately, the requirements for stability in the face of random fluctuations and for rapid response to real changes conflict with each other. The system designed must strive for the appropriate compromise between these objectives. We suggest the use of two or more modes of operation—one stable and one responsive—with a monitor to select the appropriate mode currently.

All the measurements of accuracy, stability, and response must ultimately be tested in the control system. The characteristics of the rest of that control system will affect the characteristics of the forecast system. In this book, we can study only the open-loop characteristics of forecasts. A thorough understanding of these will be of great help when it comes to the final matching of the forecasts with the control.

The principal burden of this book will be the techniques of forecasting, or rather of the methods of developing a forecasting system. The philosophy is something like building a model crane with an Erector set: choosing among alternative components to build a complete unit. There are six major considerations in the design of any forecasting system. In each of these stages there are usually many alternatives. A complete system is designed by selecting one alternative at each stage and matching it into a system. In a way, the book is a catalog of the alternatives available. Your job is understanding the alternatives so that you can select the proper matching set of six components to build your own forecast system.

The number of possible systems is very large, and we cannot possibly describe them all. Think of this book as a department store with six floors. We shall describe everything on each floor, one at a time. Then you take a trip, buying something on each floor. (If necessary, you can skip a floor or design some new alternative to what is described here.) The last section on applications illustrates some of the combinations you might select, but by no means all of them.

Only one of the six stages, smoothing, involves the novel and intriguing subject of elegant computational techniques. In some cases, these elegant techniques are little more than a formalization of the methods of subjective prediction and hence yield only slight improvement in the efficiency of getting precisely the same results as before. The merit of objective, routine forecasting in those cases is not one of better accuracy. But there are other important criteria, including

The time taken in getting the forecast.

The objectivity of the computations (which may lead to better control and greater uniformity).

The understanding of what will happen to the forecasts when unforeseen events occur and of how to make the appropriate compensation.

The real opportunity for improvement of an existing forecast system frequently lies in a study of the data used, the model that describes the data, or the measurement of forecast error. A little thought and common sense can lead to enormous improvement. We shall try to stress results, which are of concern to the whole organization, rather than the mathematical elegance that impresses a few technicians.

These six stages in the design of a forecasting system are described in the six major sections of this book. The following summaries may help to orient the reader in seeing how the parts may ultimately fit together into an integrated whole. The sections are (1) Data; (2) Models; (3) Smoothing Techniques; (4) Forecasts; (5) Error Measurement; (6) Decisions under Uncertainty.

1. *Data.* The forecasting problems with which we are concerned can be thought of in this way: We have a sequence of numbers and are required to compute some estimate of what future numbers in the same sequence will be. Then one more actual number is observed, and the computations are repeated.

When the sequences of numbers are orderly in some way, then the forecast can be obtained very simply. For example, predict what the next number will be in each of the following sequences:

(a) 17, 17, 17, 17, ?

(b) 1, 2, 3, 4, ?

(c) 1, 4, 9, 16, ?

(d) 2, 6, 12, 20, ?

(e) 2, 2, 4, 4, ?

(f) 103, 87, 95, 122, ?

The problem of statistical forecasting assumes that the source for these numbers has been settled and one must deal with them. The systems designer may have an opportunity to alter the source or the method of reporting the numbers in a way that will greatly simplify the forecasting problem. Section I is intended to help him think through these alternatives. The numbers should be a current and accurate representation of the basic process that is of concern. Sources of random fluctuations should be found and eliminated, insofar as possible. In some cases, it may be appropriate to transform the raw data in some way that will make the result a reasonably steady sequence of numbers, in which the variation is small compared with the average level and in which successive fluctuations are not correlated. Correlation of the data with a leading series is a special case of transformation that will be treated in Section III.

In general, we shall be concerned with sequences of numbers that do have some element of random fluctuation—like (f) in the examples above, in contrast to the earlier ones. The numbers can be measurements of any of a wide variety of physical processes: customer demand, raw material prices, missile positions, rainfall, lap times in a race. If the measurements are good representations of the process, the forecast can be good. If the measurements obscure the real process, no amount of statistical computation will lead to a good forecast.

2. *Models.* The successive values observed could be recorded in a table, like any of those given in Appendix C. The table by itself is not directly useful in forecasting what future observations may be. Of course, one could look at the table and estimate averages, trends, cyclic components, and so on, but these are representations of the data, not the data themselves.

It will be helpful to the systems designer to plot a sample of the data so that he can look at the whole collection at once. Figure 1.1 is a plot of the data in Table C.1, where the observed values are plotted as a function of time. The numbers fluctuate up and down, but there is not much evidence of any secular long-term trend. One might be tempted to forecast the next number as most probably equal to the average of the numbers observed so far. (The average of all the numbers in Table C.1 is 98.65.) This forecast is based on a very simple model of the data: the single number which is defined as the average.

A model is not necessarily an exact description of the way the process "really" works. A model railroad usually runs on a track that completes a loop: real railroads hardly ever do. Yet the model railroad can be used to illustrate the problems of making up freight trains in a switch yard. The model is an abstraction of the real problem that is useful for studying some aspect of it. But not all aspects: you can't tell how the door slam will sound from a clay model of a car. A model used as the basis for a forecast is not an exact description of the process that generates the numbers: it is merely a useful abstraction of the set of observations.

The plot of the data against time is not the only useful way of looking at the data. Figure 1.2 is another graphical representation of the same data. The numbers observed so far have all fallen between 51 and 153. Figure 1.2 shows the fraction of the numbers that fell below any given

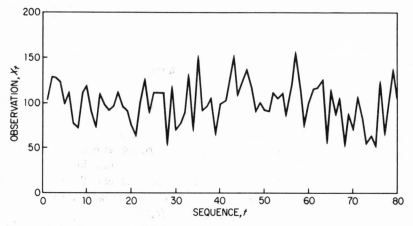

Fig. 1.1 A sample sequence of data.

value. None of them were below 50; all of them were less than 154; half of them were less than 101, and so on.

From the plot in Fig. 1.2, we might abstract the following description: a symmetrical distribution with mean 98.65 and standard deviation 29.65. A little further investigation would add the fact that the serial correlation between successive observations had a coefficient of 0.33. This description is a model. Another model might add the word *normal* to describe the type of distribution.

The ultimate objective of the forecasting process is obtaining an estimate of the probability distribution for some future event. If the distribution cannot easily be described by the usual mathematical functions, and if it does not change rapidly with time, then it may be appropriate to fit an empirical probability model (like Fig. 1.2) to the data. In many cases, however, the significant problem is that the mean (and perhaps some of the other parameters) of the distribution is changing significantly with time, whereas the distribution itself can still be described as one of a particular family of standard types.

In Section II, we shall be particularly concerned with the cases where the change in parameter values can be represented by some explicit function of time. Figure 1.3 (p.12) shows some of the typical mathematical models that will be used to describe local segments of a time series. Linear functions can be used to describe series that are growing (or declining) steadily.

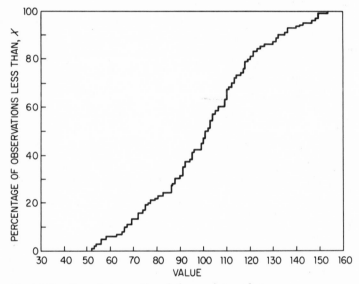

Fig. 1.2 Fraction of observations below a given value.

Quadratic functions can be used where the growth rate is changing. In a physical situation, such as tracking a target, linear functions can be used for constant velocity and quadratic functions for constant acceleration.

Exponential functions are used when the series is growing like compound interest—usually in some way related to the population or the national economy. Trigonometric functions are very useful models of seasonal variation: by taking enough terms of a Fourier series, the periodic wave can be made to conform to any desired shape. These same functions are required to describe the elliptical orbit of a ballistic missile.

In the samples of data given on pages 8 and 9, the models would be rather obvious in most cases. (a) Constant model, $x_t = 17$. (b) Linear model, $x_t = t$, where t is the time from the beginning of the problem. (c) Quadratic model, $x_t = t^2$. (d) Another quadratic model, $x_t = t + t^2$. (e) This one is a little difficult. If the observations had been 2 for as far in the past as one could see, then the forecast might be a string of 4's. If the preceding observations had been two 0's, then the forecast might be 6, 6, 8, 8, and so on. If the numbers represented sales of some commodity, and there had been a special promotion just before the third period, then the forecast might be 0, 0, 2, 2, and so on. In this case, the data themselves are not sufficient evidence on which to base a choice of a good model—more information is likely to lead to a better forecast. Finally (f) is quite irregular,

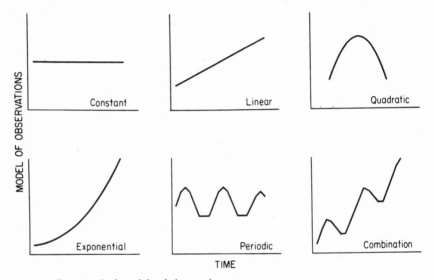

Fig. 1.3 Some typical models of time series.

and one would want much more information—either about this series, or about similar series for related items—before choosing a model that should give good forecasts.

When the data are regular and related to a physical process, the problem of forecasting may become so simple as to disappear. When sophisticated models are required, however, there are powerful and efficient techniques for getting good results. Nevertheless, the systems designer is still required to have some skill in selecting the appropriate model.

When the data come from a physical process that is well understood, then the model of that process will be the best basis for forecasting. For example, Kepler's laws give an excellent description of the path of a ballistic object. Even when the laws governing the process are not known, a good understanding of the process will furnish a good basis for forecasting. A case in point is the description of weather patterns in terms of the movement of air masses. In the fields of seismology, oceanography, and communications, it is sometimes possible to describe the data by a joint probability distribution, from which the theoretically most accurate forecast can be obtained (see Chapter 21).

When we pass to the realm of economics and business control systems, in contrast, there is not yet a sufficient understanding of the underlying processes that govern demand for finished goods or the prices of raw materials, and the model is largely a superficial description.

3. *Smoothing.* We shall regard smoothing as the process of revising estimates of the coefficients in the model in the light of successive observations of the data. For example, if one has selected a constant as the model for a particular time series, he has the problem of deciding the best numerical value of that constant on the basis of the information currently available. The statistician might think of the process as one of curve fitting; the electronics engineer would consider the problem to be one of filtering out noise to recover a signal.

A common way of fitting a constant is by averaging the data. One may average all the data from the start of the series. One can assign weights to the observations at various times in the past and compute a weighted average. When the series is changing slowly, it is common to average only the most recent N observations: a moving average.

In Section III, we shall discuss in some detail exponential smoothing and its extensions as methods for fitting any of a very wide class of models to a set of data. These methods have been developed with the following objectives in mind:

(a) *Accuracy:* the model is fitted to the data by least squares, with the criterion of fit being discounted in time.

(b) *Efficiency of computing:* the arithmetic is very fast on any computing machine, and only one word of information per degree of freedom in the model needs to be stored from one observation to the next.

(c) *Flexibility between stability and response:* the choice of a value for the smoothing constant dictates the effective number of observations taken into account in smoothing. When many observations are used, the forecasts will be stable; when few observations are used, the forecasts will respond rapidly to changes in the input data.

It is feasible to design a system with two modes of operation—one stable and one responsive—together with a monitor to determine which mode is preferable now. We shall also discuss some of the characteristics of the more familiar moving averages and least squares techniques for comparison with exponential smoothing.

4. *Forecasting.* When one has good estimates of the values of the coefficients in his model of the data, it is simple to evaluate that model at any future time. In most cases, that evaluation would be the forecast.

As we shall show in Section IV, however, it is possible to fit one function to past data in the smoothing process and forecast the future with some other function. For example, one might fit a quadratic function to observations of a target's path (to allow for turning), but forecast along the tangent to that curve—if the apparent curvature could be attributed to noise in the data. As an instance of management prediction, one could compute the limits the target could reach if it accelerated to its maximum capability.

In some cases, absolute simplicity of computation is required above all else. For example, in the control of inexpensive Class C items in an inventory, there should be a realistic order point, but it is not worth much effort to refine the basis for setting the order point. Some special methods for getting forecasts in these cases are discussed in Chapter 17.

5. *Error Measurement.* No forecast or prediction can ever be entirely accurate. Allowance for the necessary and sufficient margin for error can be critical in planning the conduct of a business or in designing the effective radius of a weapon. In this book, the discussion of data collection, model selection, smoothing, and forecasting is, to some extent, an extension and formalization of conventional lines of attack on the problem.

Section V contains some very novel and powerful means of estimating the distribution of errors in the forecasts (or predictions). It is important to distinguish between the distribution of the observed data around their mean and the distribution of the forecast errors around *an estimate* of the mean. In many cases, the errors in forecasting are normally distributed even when the observed data do not come from a normal distribution.

A normal distribution is completely specified by its mean and standard deviation. That is, when one has an estimate of these two parameters, it is possible, with the use of tables, to estimate the probability that any given event will occur. The tack taken in Section V is based on the special circumstances of the forecast error problem. If the forecasts are unbiased, the mean forecast error should be zero. Therefore, we check to see whether the mean error is sufficiently close to zero to accept the hypothesis that the forecasts are not biased.

It is simpler to compute the mean absolute deviation than to compute the standard deviation. This statistic is entirely equivalent, but because of the peculiarities of the absolute value of a variable, it has not been studied thoroughly in the statistics texts. Since it is useful in practice, we shall investigate the properties of the mean absolute deviation and their relations to the corresponding properties of the more widely used standard deviation.

The autocorrelation function for forecast errors can be computed from the characteristics of the forecast filter. Therefore, we shall discuss optimum linear filters in the context of forecast errors (Chapter 21) rather than for original data.

6. *Decisions under Uncertainty.* The span of interest of a forecasting system properly begins with the input data or observations and ends with the estimate of the parameters of the distribution from which future observations will be taken. This forecast will then be used, in some sort of control system, as a basis for deciding among alternative courses of action. (If the forecast is not going to be used, then it isn't worth spending much effort on its preparation.)

The types of control system that require forecasts are so diverse that any complete catalog is beyond the scope of this book. In designing the forecast subsystems, however, it is important to be aware of how the forecasts are to be used. Therefore, in Section VII, we shall discuss some typical applications.

The forecast systems that can be developed using the notions discussed in the book will provide an output that is either a probability distribution or the values of parameters from which a probability distribution can be constructed. That is, the system says, "I don't know what will happen. No one can know in advance what will happen. But here are the odds you should bet on any event within the possible range." This attitude toward the problem is quite different from the common one that talks about "the" forecast (which is usually a forecast of the mean of the distribution).

When only "the" forecast is available, the control system must base its decision on that one number: for a production plan, a reorder level, or an aiming point. When the system provides a probability distribution over the range of possible events, it is possible to plan to act on some number in this range, other than the mean.

Three decision problems may help illustrate different ways to take account of uncertainty in present estimates of the future:

(a) The raincoat problem: You're about to go on a trip on which it will be a nuisance to carry a raincoat if you don't need it, but even more of a nuisance to be without one if it rains. The weather forecast can be expressed only as a probability, P, that it will rain and a probability, $1 - P$, that it won't. There are two courses of action: to take the coat or not to take it. For each of the four possible combinations of coats and weather there is a payoff. Knowing these payoffs and the probability P, how would you decide whether to take your coat?

(b) The newsboy problem: A mathematically-inclined newsboy can forecast the probability $f(N)$ that he will have exactly N customers tonight. He must buy some number W of papers. If it happens that he buys more papers than there are customers $(N < W)$ he loses $c(W - N)$ cents on the excess. On the other hand, if it happens that there are more customers than papers, he loses a potential $p(N - W)$ cents in lost profit.

In the raincoat problem there were only two alternatives. The newsboy had a large collection of alternatives among which to choose $W = 0, 1, 2, \ldots, 50, \ldots$ to maximize his profit.

(c) The shotgun problem: The duck hunter, the skeet shooter, and the deer hunter each aims at the point where the target is most likely to be by the time the shot reaches the same point. The duck may change course so that the center of the shot misses him, but a few pellets at the edge of the pattern may have enough energy to bring him down. The deer can't change course that much during the time of flight, and it requires all the energy of the shot to bring him down. The skeet bird can't change course, but the competitor may have some aiming error.

The decision problem here is the spread of the shot, where a wide dispersion makes up for uncertainty about the relative position of the center of the pattern and the target, but at the expense of a much lower energy at any point in the pattern.

Most of the applications discussed in Section VII will be of the form:

Plan of Action = Forecast of Mean +
$\qquad$ (Safety Factor) $\times$ (Mean Absolute Deviation)

The safety factor may be positive, negative, or as a special case, zero. It may be selected to yield a theoretical economic balance among conflicting objectives, or it may be solely a means for implementing current management policy. There is an advantage to expressing the margin for safety as the product of the safety factor and the mean absolute deviation. One could set the safety margin entirely as a matter of judgment—it is frequently done. The mean absolute deviation is a normalizing factor, so that one decision regarding the safety factor will be correctly implemented in a very wide variety of particular cases, thus eliminating the need for many separate decisions. Furthermore, a great deal is known in advance about probability distributions when the variable is measured in multiples of the mean absolute deviation. Therefore, one can study what would happen if the safety margin were to be changed.

Don't abandon all common sense, however, in favor of nice mathematical theories. The whole purpose of setting the safety margin at some level is to secure particular operating results. Initially, the selection of the safety factor will be based on the theoretical model of what should happen. In practice there will be many small differences between the actual facts of the case and the assumed model. Most of the time, the theory should come close to actual practice, but there will be some cases of wide divergence. When it becomes clear that a larger margin for safety is required to get the desired operating results, go ahead and change the safety margin. Ignore the theoretical basis on which it was set initially. This means, of course, that you must provide for keeping track of what does happen for comparison with what you thought should happen. Otherwise it will not be possible to make the adjustments that need to be made. The Pacific Fleet Commissaryman referred to earlier in this chapter is a case in point.

Another matter which should be of great concern to the systems designer is beyond the scope of this book. The use of the forecast may affect the forecasting problem. That is, the plans based on the forecast are quite likely to interact with the external environment and hence alter the characteristics of the future observations. The exploration of these phenomena is the subject of industrial dynamics.*

EXPLORATION OF ALTERNATIVES. Section VI discusses a variety of methods for exploring the effects of combining alternatives in different ways. There is nothing rigid about the preceding six steps to forecast systems design. I have found them to be a useful check list to make sure that all relevant points are covered. When circumstances warrant, the designer should not hesitate to omit some one of these steps—there are several examples in this book that do so. It would be very unusual if the exact answer to every problem that could be encountered in practice were given somewhere in this book. The designer should expect to have to improvise, to extend, and to modify the material given here in order to match the needs of the particular problem with which he is faced. I only hope that this exposition of the basic principles will give him sufficient understanding to be able to see how to develop his own techniques.

The work sheets in Section VI are intended to show how a basic system can be set up and tested in such a way that any section of the system can easily be replaced by some alternative, so that the effects of the alternatives can be compared. This ability to replace individual components is essential for the continual growth and improvement of the system. New techniques will be developed; new problems will arise; and new understanding of how to cope with the problems will emerge. Most control systems are much too large to redesign the whole program. If the system is designed on a modular principle, pieces of it can be redesigned and introduced with minimum disturbance to the rest of the system.

The only characteristic that can't be easily changed is the content of

---

* Jay W. Forrester, *Industrial Dynamics* (Cambridge, Mass.: Technology Press, M.I.T., 1961).

the information that is transmitted from one part of the system to another. We shall stress forecasting on the principle that an observation $x(T)$ is furnished at time T to the forecast computation, which in turn furnishes an estimate of the mean $\hat{x}(T + \tau)$ and of the mean absolute deviation $\Delta(T)$ to the part of the control system that decides on some plan of action $= \hat{x}(T + \tau) + K\Delta$. The processing of the input to provide the output can take a wide variety of forms.

"No data yet," he answered. "It is a capital mistake to theorize before you have all the evidence. It biases the judgment."

A Study in Scarlet

Forecasting is a process in which one is concerned with a sequence of numbers, a discrete time series. Some of the numbers in this sequence have been observed and are known. The forecasting problem is estimating the probability distribution from which further numbers in the sequence will be drawn. The estimate is modified with each new observation.

In this section, we shall discuss some of the problems involved in getting these observations for use in a forecasting system. Particular attention will be paid to data on demand for a stock item which would be required for an inventory control system, since there are several sources of "noise" that tend to obscure the true pattern of demand and some of these sources can be eliminated.

Samples of typical sequences of observations are needed during the design of the system. Appendix C gives tables of the data used in the various examples discussed in this book as one source of samples on which to try out alternatives. In Section VI, we shall discuss the generation of synthetic sequences for exploration, evaluation, and demonstration of system operation. If the control system for which the forecasts are required is to operate in real life, it must be robust; that is, it cannot be sensitive to the exact characteristics of the data used as inputs. Therefore, it is not necessary to put a great deal of effort into getting a clean sample of data during the design stage. It *is* necessary to have the best data possible for the regular operation of the system.

The forecasting system is a sort of "black box" that can be studied by itself. In actual operation, of course, it must be "plugged into" the real world. There are two ends at which the forecast system meets the real world. One is the input, which we discuss in this section; the other is the output, discussed in Section VII.

We can give here only a general discussion of the problems of interconnection, with a few typical examples. The systems designer, with a thorough understanding of his control problem and the characteristics of the forecast system he wants to use, must design the particular interconnection that is best for his situation.

Chapter 2 discusses the desirable characteristics of the data used as a basis for forecasting and some of the measures that can be taken to improve the quality of this information. Chapter 3 discusses the sampling interval between successive revisions of the forecast.

2 Sources of Data

This is the age of little humorous signs on the walls of offices and shops. One very pertinent sign is frequently seen on the wall over the head of the man designing an integrated data-processing system. It says simply

GIGO

The accountants have had their LIFO and FIFO inventory valuation systems for a long time, but GIGO is a new acronym. Translated, it stands for Garbage In, Garbage Out. In other words, an integrated data-processing system is no better than the data it is given to process.

The particular data used as input to the forecast system define the application. In order to discuss forecasting in general, we shall talk about discrete time series that may represent demand, prices, positions, temperatures, or any of a host of other physical or economic measurements. If the control is to be effective, the data must be a good representation of the actual process being controlled. The forecasting problem is easiest when the time series can be adequately represented by simple functions of time.

It is not always possible to get all these desirable properties. Sometimes, however, a little ingenuity will make it possible to get data from a different source or to report the data in a different way. Such modifications of the control and reporting system, external to the forecast subsystem, are a rich source for major improvement in over-all control.

DISCRETE TIME SERIES. In this book, we are concerned only with smoothing and forecasting discrete time series. The basic processing cycle starts with the observation of one more piece of information. There is time to carry through all the calculations necessary to modify the estimate of the distribution of future observations and to take any appropriate control action before the next observation is taken.

Real-time computation of the forecast is a basic premise in this book. There is much material on time-series analysis* in which the entire time series is presented at one time, as in an electrocardiogram, a seismograph record, or a fifty-year history of the stock market. We shall examine such records in order to understand the problem presented by a time series, but the principal objective is to design a forecasting system that will revise the forecast after each observation.

Throughout this book, we consider continuous processes only to the extent that the information arrives in discrete samples. For example, the path of an aircraft is continuous. Air Traffic Control, however, will observe the plane's position only at intervals. Even with a scanning radar, there are only a very few actual observations per minute. If the controller must rely on pilot's reports when he passes over certain checkpoints, the information may be much more sparse.

We shall distinguish between a *continuous process* (such as the flight of an aircraft) and *discrete samples* of information about the process. The temperature and pressure in a chemical process may vary continuously, and there may even be a continuous graph plotted by a recording instrument. Still, if the operator comes around only periodically to look at the graph and to adjust the controls, this is a discrete system. Note also that the sampling interval may not be uniform in time as measured by the calendar or by a clock. Observations of the state of the system may be reported only when some specific event occurs, like the passage over a checkpoint or an operator's tour.

The process may be continuous, in the sense that there is a value that

---

* See, for example, Proceedings, Symposium on Time Series Analysis, Brown University, June 11–14, 1962.

can be observed at any time, but the observable value takes sudden jumps. Suppose we define "the" price of a security on the stock exchange as a value halfway between the lowest offer and the highest bid. At every instant of time there is a price which the specialist can observe. This price takes sudden jumps as new offers and bids are recorded.

The trader, however, cannot observe this price continuously. Brokers and professional traders get irregular samples on the ticker at the time of each transaction. The general trading public gets regular samples of the closing price in the daily newspaper. There are also weekly and monthly reports that give regular samples at even longer intervals.

Sometimes the basic process is inherently discrete. Production occurs in batches; shipments arrive in truckloads; and demand arises as a sequence of pulses: finite quantities at discrete (irregular) intervals. If one were to observe processes such as these continuously, most of the time there would be nothing to observe. Occasionally there would be a pulse, for which the size and timing could be observed.

These processes are rarely observed continuously. The individual pulses are accumulated for some period, and then the total is reported: demand from all customers during the day; all material received this week; production this month. It is customary to report an observation of production, shipments, or demand at regular intervals, such as a day, week, or month. It is not necessary for good control to report regularly. In Chapter 18, we shall discuss the reporting of demand only when additional material is received into inventory: an irregular observation triggered by a specific event.

When the process is continuous or quasi-continuous, the data represent the state of the process; hence, the forecast estimates the state at some future time. When the process is basically a series of discrete pulses, the data represent the sum of the pulses during one sampling interval. Usually the forecast estimates the total of these pulses during some other interval of time.

In order to be quite general in the discussion of the smoothing and forecasting processes, we shall think of the data as being a discrete time series represented* by x_t. The subscript t may be thought of as standing for time: the next observation will be taken at time $t + 1$. Hence the unit of time is the sampling interval. It may be a second, a day, or a year. (Chapter 3 discusses the choice of the proper length of the sampling interval when there is a choice available.) It may even be a sequential numbering of the observations, which are taken only when a specific event happens. Examples of time series make a diverse list:

---

* In some chapters, it is more convenient to use the notation $x(t)$ so that subscripts are available for indices other than time.

Customer demands on an inventory
Stock market prices and trading volumes
Target positions in a weapons system
Weather data
Individual's performance in sporting events
Learning curve data
Quality attributes in manufacturing
Time intervals between successive events
Yields from a chemical process
Automobile gasoline consumption

DATA MUST REPRESENT PROCESS. The duck hunter knows that he'll get better results by looking at the duck than by watching its reflection on the surface of the lake. Weapons systems people spend a great deal of effort in improving radar (or other tracking devices) in order to get an accurate measurement of the current positions of the targets. In these cases, it seems obvious that the data are the best measurement of the process that can be obtained.

Production planning and inventory control systems, however, don't always put the same emphasis on clean data. The control of production and inventories should be based on a forecast of demand: what the ultimate consumer really would take, if he could get it. All too often, the only data available are something like shipments to customers or orders from distributors. These data can be used quite effectively in design studies to see how demand data would be forecast if they were available. Usually, orders and shipments show much more erratic changes than demand does, so that a system designed to cope with those changes will certainly work well with actual demand data.

But although the available data are useful for the study and design phase of a job, they can be very poor for the real operation of the control system. There have been several cases where the principal improvement in control over inventories came not from better forecasting techniques but from getting clean data about demand.

For example, some companies still say (in effect), "We can't possibly find out what the actual consumption is; why, we don't even have a record of our own customers' demand. We do need a better basis for planning production, but all we have is a record of what we've shipped to distributors. Can you use that?" For study, of course, one can use shipment data; but for the routine operation of the new control system, shipment data are very bad.

If management feels the need for improving its production planning, it must be aware of an unduly large file of back orders or of several customers who went elsewhere when the item they wanted was not in stock. Shipments are a very distorted picture of actual demand, therefore, and production plans based on shipments will continue to be distorted.

Most management today is aware of this distinction, although it may not always be aware of the importance of rectifying the situation. There is another even more dangerous problem, however, of which few seem to be aware. This is the effect of independent inventory management decisions at each echelon of the distribution chain between the ultimate consumer and the manager who is studying his planning problems: a distributor, a manufacturer, a parts supplier, or a raw-material producer.

Think of the distribution pipeline as a long pipe. At several stages there are men who use their skill, experience, and judgment (and perhaps some science) to manipulate pumps and valves to regulate the flow of water in the pipe. At the far end, a little water occasionally drips out of the pipe and is consumed. The producer can see only the fluctuations in water pressure at his end of the pipe and yet must try to infer the net rate of consumption. It may be cheaper in the long run to pay for a water meter at the far end than to try elaborate techniques of forecasting from poor data.

In the appliance industry, it is common practice to include a warranty card with each appliance. The customer is urged to fill in the card and send it back to the manufacturer to register himself for service. It is usually true that the customer will get the service he needs, even if he hasn't registered. Some enlightened manufacturers are using these cards to estimate the current rate of consumption, as contrasted with the current rate of orders from the top middleman. A newsprint mill samples the size and circulation of its customers' newspapers to determine actual consumption patterns (which are obscured by the purchasing agents' inventory manipulations).

Exercise. How can one use warranty cards returned to estimate current consumption, even when only roughly a third of the cards are returned? Would it help to code the manufacturing date on the card?

The following analysis may help to show the degree to which these intermediate inventory management decisions may cloud the pattern of consumption. In particular, we are interested in getting an estimate of the variance in the data created by ordering in quantities that exceed current use. (On the first reading you may want to skip to page 32.)

Assume that there is a probability, p, that a retail store sells one piece of a given product in unit time, and probability, $q = 1 - p$, that it doesn't sell any. The expected sales per unit time are therefore p, and the variance is pq. If there are n stores that all order from the same warehouse, the total quantity ordered from the warehouse in unit time will be a sample from a binomial distribution with mean np and variance npq.

Now suppose that, instead of ordering one piece from the warehouse every time the store sold one, the store orders a pieces and then waits until it has sold all a. The expected store order per unit time is still p (if the inventories are to remain in balance). Therefore, the probability that the store orders must be $p' = p/a$, and we can let $q' = 1 - p'$.

If there is a chance, p', that a store will order a units and a chance, q', that it will order nothing, the expected order is $p'a = p$ (as before). The variance is

$$a^2 p' q' = p(a - p)$$

The quantities ordered from the warehouse will now be samples from a new binomial distribution, with mean np and variance $np(a - p)$.

Suppose that there are $n = 5$ stores ordering from one warehouse and that $a = 3$ pieces are ordered at one time (instead of one):

Probability One Piece Is Sold in One Period	Expected Quantity Ordered	Variance if Ordered as Used	Variance if Ordered 3 at a Time	Ratio
p	$\mu = np$	$\sigma_1^2 = npq$	$\sigma_2^2 = np(a - p)$	σ_2/σ_1
0.08	0.4	0.368	1.168	1.78
0.4	2.0	1.2	5.20	2.08
0.8	4.0	0.8	8.8	3.32

Let us take the analysis one stage higher. If the stores order from the warehouse exactly what they need to replace sales, and if there are m warehouses that order from the plant exactly what they need to replenish demand from the stores, then the total demand on the plant will be a sample from a binomial distribution with mean mnp and variance $nmpq$.

But most warehouses claim that they can't afford to order in each period just what was demanded of them. It is "more economical" to order b pieces at a time and then wait until all b have been used before ordering more. Following a similar analysis, we find that the variance of the quantities ordered from the plant is increased from $nmpq$ to $mnp(b - np)$. Let $m = 5$ warehouses and $b = 12$ pieces per order.

Probability One Piece Is Sold in One Period	Expected Quantity Ordered	Variance if Ordered as Used	Variance if Ordered $b = 12$ at a Time	Ratio
p	$\mu = nmp$	$\sigma_1^2 = nmpq$	$\sigma_2^2 = mnp(b - np)$	σ_2/σ_1
0.08	2	1.84	23.2	3.55
0.4	10	6.0	100.	4.08
0.8	20	4.0	140.	5.92

We set up a very simple simulation, whose sole purpose was to illustrate how perfectly rational rules—viewed at one stage in the process—can make the overall supply problem much more difficult. The situation simulated is not intended to be realistic, but it does help explain some of the phenomena noticed in actual data.

In the present problem, we constructed the following situation. At the bottom of the supply pyramid are 125 units, called *ships*. Each month any ship uses one piece of an item, with probability p, or uses none, with probability $q = 1 - p$. Hence, the total usage in any month is a sample from a binomial distribution with mean $125p$ and variance $125pq$. The number of trials is large enough that a normal distribution should be an adequate approximation to the binomial distribution.

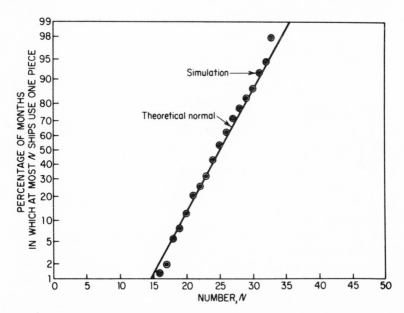

Fig. 2.1 Distribution of the number of pieces used by ships per month.

Figure 2.1 compares the actual distribution of usage in 151 months with a normal model based on $p = 0.2$; mean $np = 25$; standard deviation $\sqrt{npq} = \sqrt{20} = 4.47$.

A ship does not order one piece each time it uses one; after an initial transient (discussed below), however, when the inventory has become stable, the ship orders 2 pieces every other time it uses one. According to the preceding analysis, the distribution of quantities ordered should have mean 25 and variance $(125)(0.2)(1.8) = 45$. In 151 months of the simulation, the actual mean quantity ordered was 25.7, and the variance was 41.

Figures 2.2 and 2.3 show how the quantities ordered by our "fleet" of 125 ships contrast with the quantities actually used. The pattern in Fig. 2.3, however, is still not too bad a set of data from which to forecast.

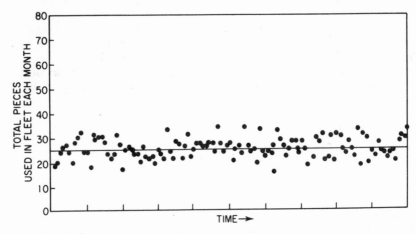

Fig. 2.2 Actual usage.

In our simulation, we let each group of 5 ships order from one "supply ship," so that there are 25 "supply ships." The total demand on a supply ship is the total ordered by its 5 ships. Of course, the supply ship won't order exactly the amount demanded of it if it follows conventional inventory theory.

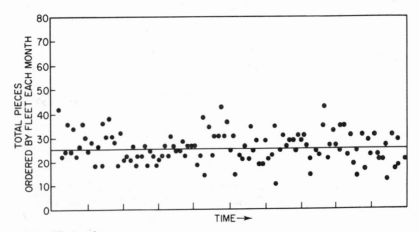

Fig. 2.3 Fleet orders.

Since there are 5 ships placing orders, the expected demand on any supply ship in one month is only one piece, with variance $(5)(0.2)(0.8) = 0.8$ pieces. We assumed that this is a fairly cheap item, so the supply ship will order an eleven-month supply, or 11 pieces.

Figure 2.4 is a plot of the sum of the quantities ordered by all 25 supply ships: a far worse picture than Fig. 2.2 from which to infer future demand.

The average quantity ordered is still the 25 pieces per month actually used, but the standard deviation has increased from ±4.5 pieces per month to ±14.3 pieces per month.

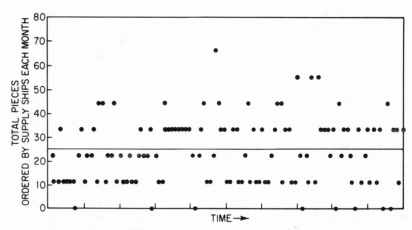

Fig. 2.4 Supply ship orders.

The simulation also had 5 groups of 5 supply ships ordering from shore stations, 5 shore stations ordering from one control point, which finally orders from a vendor. After the inventories had stabilized, the standard deviation of shore station orders (ordering at 51 pieces a time) was 33.8. The control point's orders on vendors (at 241 pieces per order) had a standard deviation of 74.6—nearly 3 times the average quantity actually consumed in one period.

A very interesting by-product resulted from this simulation. The rule was that if any inventory was at, or below, the order point, an order was to be placed for a sufficient multiple of the order quantity to bring the available stock above the order point. (The order point was set equal to the demand placed on the unit in the past four months.)

Since the simulation started with everything at zero, there was quite an initial transient. We allowed four months for this transient (since the order points were four months demand) before printing out the data.

In some of the early runs, the shore stations and the control points never placed an order for 100 months because initially each ship had ordered 2 pieces to bring inventory above the order point of zero. Hence, each supply ship ordered 11 pieces to fill these orders. The 5 shore stations had demand for 55 pieces and therefore ordered 102 (twice the standard of 51), which meant that the control point had to place an initial order for 723 (three standard orders).

On the second month, every unit had shown some activity, so the order points increased, setting off another wave of orders. This process was repeated for the first four months until order points were at the desired level; but now the inventories were so high throughout the system that many units didn't order at all for several months.

It was thirty-four months before the shore stations resumed ordering on the control point, and the inventory there was so high that the control point didn't order from the vendor until the ninety-sixth month.

These difficulties could be avoided if actual usage at the consumer level were reported back to each stage in the supply chain. The delays and amplifications caused by basing plans on the orders received from the next lower level can create severe instability in the control system. Industrial dynamics is primarily concerned with such effects as have been noted, for example, in the textile industry.

SCREENING UNUSUAL DATA. Data transmitted and transcribed by people are always subject to error; unfortunately, so are data processed by machines. (One hopes that the machine's error rate is lower, but don't count on it without making a thorough check.) Small errors in the data will be very hard to find, but on the other hand, they usually don't make too much difference.

Larger errors can be detected. Some thought should be given to pre-screening the data to make sure that the numbers used by the forecast system as input data do not contain egregious errors.* An order-processing activity may be trained to distinguish between normal demand and extraordinary demand. Any data that are identified at the source as extraordinary can be used to affect the stock status records but would not be included in the data used by a routine forecast system. For example, if a warehouse normally supplies repair parts to garages around town, it can expect demand for one, two, or even half a dozen units (or packages). Such demand is normal. When someone builds a new garage, he will require a very large amount of several items all at once as an initial stock. Such demand would be noted as extraordinary.

The forecast system itself will detect large departures from normal. Since the system forecasts the probability of observing any of several different levels in the future, it is possible to provide for an exception report whenever the system encounters an observation that is very improbable. The report asks that the circumstances be checked before the routine computations proceed.

Exercise. How would you guard against inadvertently omitting an observation (such as by dropping a punched card on the floor), and how would you distinguish the omission from a legitimate zero? Is it ever possible for the observed data legitimately to be negative?

* See F. J. Anscombe, "Rejection of Outliers," *Technometrics*, 2, No. 2 (May, 1960), 123–47.

UNDERSTANDING THE PROBLEM. The first step in designing a forecast system is examining the available data and deciding whether they do give an adequate representation of the process that is to be controlled. It is advisable to return to the examination of the input data as other phases of the study are taken up. For example, when the first tentative system has been described, it may be worthwhile to run a dual simulation. On one run use the data that are readily available. On the other run use synthetic data that have the characteristics that might reasonably be assumed for better data. (For example, one might contrast the use of data at the top echelon of a supply chain with some simple model of the actual pattern of consumption.) Compare the costs of the actions taken on the basis of either of the two alternative sets of data. The difference in cost will give a reasonable order-of-magnitude estimate of the expense that might be worth incurring to get the better data.

Frequently, once one has been convinced that better data are worthwhile, inexpensive ways can be developed for getting them. The appliance manufacturer's warranty cards are an example.

When you do manage to get a bit of real data, don't immediately rush off and stuff it into the nearest computer. Chew on it for a while, roll it over, and get the full flavor of the problem. There are some economic advisers whose principal technique of prediction is getting so thoroughly steeped in the data that it becomes "intuitively obvious" what the future will be.

One of the easiest ways to become thoroughly familiar with the characteristics of the data is to plot them as a graph. It is well worth the time and effort to plot the data yourself rather than to have it done by a clerk. As you plot each point, you'll find yourself trying to guess what the next one will be, and that is the whole objective of a forecasting system. If you can analyze—even subconsciously—what you go through in trying to predict, you'll have a much better appreciation of what it is you must teach the computer.

Plot sample sequences against time, and look at them. Is there any apparent tendency toward long-term trends, seasonal variation, or other stable patterns? Or could you visualize the data as samples all from the same population? Should the time index be elapsed calendar time or the sequence number of the observation?*

Summarize the data in a histogram. Is the distribution skew or symmetrical? Is there one mode, or are there significant secondary modes? Can you think of any reason why there should be two separate processes that combine to give the observed values? Would they account for the

---

* M. F. M. Osborne, "Periodic Structure in the Brownian Motion of Stock Prices," *Operations Research*, 10, No. 3 (May–June, 1962), 345–79.

separate modes? (For example, demand data may have one mode generated by retail customers and another by a few very large distributors. Normal radar returns are quite different from specular reflections.)

Compute the mean, variance, and the autocovariance (see Appendix A). Are the fluctuations superimposed on the basic patterns serially independent, or is there a significant autocorrelation? Compute the lagged cross correlations between the data and other available series that may be causally related.

The objective, of course, is getting data that really represent the process to be controlled and that have a simple pattern in time that can be adequately described in terms of simple functions. The superimposed fluctuations should be independent (that is, have zero serial correlation), and have as small an amplitude as possible.

Systematic versus Random Variation

A most important feature of the data to look for (in anticipation of Section II) is the separation into systematic and random components. The systematic components will be exploited in the forecast, since they can be represented as deterministic functions of time. In Chapter 4 we shall discuss time-series models in some detail, especially polynomial models, exponential models, and sinusoidal models.

If the data could be represented by a simple average over time, then the first differences between successive observations should fluctuate randomly around zero. If a straight line would be a better model, then the first differences will have a non-zero average, but the second differences will fluctuate around zero. In general if the nth differences are zero (on the average), then the model will be a polynomial of degree t^{n-1}, and the average of the $(n-1)$st differences will be an estimate of the coefficient of that term in the model.

Exercise. Plot the data on IBM common stock prices (Table C.5) as a time series. Compute the mean, variance, and autocovariance of these prices. Also plot the first and second differences and compute their means, variances, and autocovariances. Sample the data weekly during the period June 29, 1959, through May 16, 1961, for these computations.

Sometimes there may be a systematic trend in the higher-order differences. Then perhaps the data are growing exponentially. Instead of differences, investigate whether the ratios between successive observations fluctuate near unity.

Exercise. Plot the annual data on revenue passenger miles (Table C.7) as a function of time on semilogarithmic paper. Compute the mean, variance, and autocovariance of the logarithms of the data and of the differences between logarithms.

The data may have a strong periodic component, where the pattern of the data repeats itself after every p observations. Since appearances may be deceptive, the first step should be to check that the variation is strictly periodic. Start with each observation in turn and add the total of p successive observations. If the original data were periodic, with period p, then the moving totals will have no periodic variation. Compute the power spectrum (Appendix A) for the data and for the moving totals to find the frequencies that have significant contributions.

Exercise. Compute the power spectrum for the monthly imports by Company B (Table C.9).

Perhaps the most interesting problems to tackle are those where some combination of several types of model is required. We shall use the number of passengers carried, by months, on commercial aircraft in international traffic as a prime example. The basic data are given in Table C.10.

Exercise. Plot the data from Table C.10 as a function of time. Estimate the degree of the polynomial required to represent the secular movement in the moving twelve-month totals. Compute the power spectrum for the seasonal component (the ratio of the actual datum in a particular month to the polynomial base as of that month).

Transformations

One of the factors to investigate is whether the data you have are related to any other time series that you can know in advance. In what follows, we shall discuss transformations of demand data, based on the ratio and the difference between the demand and another time series that "explains" some of the sudden shifts in the basic data. We shall also talk about scale transformations required by non-uniform measurement techniques. In Chapter 11, we shall investigate multiple regression among several related series.

INSTALLATION RATES. In the garment trades, manufacturers have long recognized that the fraction of all customers who require a given size changes very slowly with time. The size ratios are quite dependable for

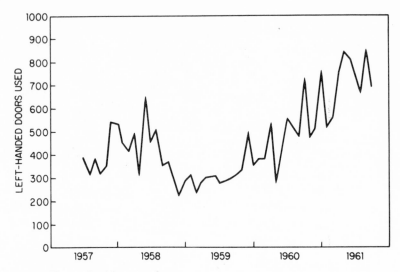

Fig. 2.5 Usage of refrigerator doors.

production planning and inventory control. The needs or wants of the population change much more slowly than do production schedules or even product lines. A company that makes electronic accounting machines may find that the percentage of customers who require an optional carriage drive on the tabulator is also very stable, and therefore easy to forecast.

Let us illustrate the concepts with the choice between left-hand and right-hand doors on a refrigerator. From time to time, the historical pat-

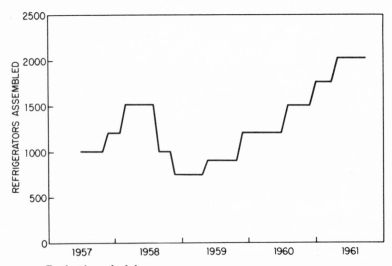

Fig. 2.6 Production schedules.

tern of left-hand doors used in the refrigerator plant (Fig. 2.5) shows sudden jumps and drops. Beginning late in 1959 there appears to be a significant upward trend. These changes would be hard to forecast in advance.

Figure 2.6 shows the production schedules for the total number of refrigerators assembled during the corresponding period. This schedule is known sufficiently far in advance to be useful in forecasting the requirements for doors. Notice that a large part of the rise and fall in the usage of doors might well be explained by similar changes in the production schedule.

The installation rate is the ratio of the usage of a particular option (or size) to the total production of the relevant product line. In many cases, as with the left-hand doors for refrigerators or size-14 dresses, the installation rate can be assumed to be relatively constant in time (Fig. 2.7).

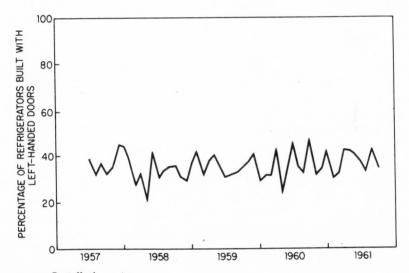

Fig. 2.7 Installation rates.

It is simple to forecast what the installation rate is most likely to be in the future. The required number of doors can then be obtained by multiplying the forecast rate by the production schedule. (You can use the data given in Table C.3 as a source of material for practicing alternative techniques of forecasting using installation rates.)

Exercise. In the case of the refrigerator doors, would you forecast left-hand and right-hand doors, or just one? Which one? If there were three alternative models of radios for an automobile, would the same reasoning apply? What about shoe sizes?

The installation rates might not always be constant in time. For example, some of the high-cost options on automobiles (such as automatic transmissions and air conditioning) show a high installation rate early in the model year, which drops steadily through the year. There are two plausible explanations: Cars produced early in the year are sold to people who think of the car as a status symbol, whereas those who buy late are more apt to be bargain hunters who do not want the expensive features. Also cars produced early go on display in the dealers' showrooms, and it is good marketing to have all the features available.

Nevertheless, if the pattern changes steadily throughout the model year, it will be easier to forecast if the effects of changes in production schedule have been eliminated.

An extension of the notion of an installation rate may be appropriate to adjust the observed data to the number of working days in the month or the number of hours that stores are open.

PREDICTION BIAS. Many large manufacturing corporations sell parts to other corporations that assemble products or distribute them, rather than to the ultimate consumer. The larger customer accounts may furnish a projection of their requirements to help the manufacturer plan his production and procurement. It is not unlikely that if these estimates are predictions, they will show a rather consistent bias. One customer, who is congenitally pessimistic about business prospects, may always understate his true needs and have to ask for more at the last moment. Another may be pessimistic about the availability of supply and predict his requirements high. The feeling may be, "No matter what I'll really need, I've got 'em producing enough to be able to deliver what I want."

The true requirements will change from time to time, just as the production schedule for refrigerators. If there were no real changes in the pattern of demand, it would be a waste of time to furnish projections of anticipated demand. If the bias in the predictions were constant, or nearly so, it could be forecast.

Exercise. Should the bias be computed as the difference between the customer's prediction and the actual requirements, as the ratio, or as the relative difference? How would you decide? Should separate forecasts be made for each customer, or only on the net total for the product? How can you take account of the small customers who don't furnish an estimate at all?

SPORADIC DEMAND. A manufacturer of oil field equipment had to keep controlled stocks of spare parts. Some very large and expensive parts are seldom used. For example, there is a large ring gear, costing $3000. When it is needed, it must be available quickly—there isn't time to make another one. Yet it is impossible to use two at once. It makes little sense for production planning and inventory control to compute that the average use of ring gears is 0.02 pieces per month. It's either 1 or it isn't. When we plot demand as a time series, we get a long string of zeros and an occasional 1—a very poor pattern to try to describe.

Turn the problem around. Every time there is a demand, you get an observation of the time that elapsed since the previous demand. This generates a sequence of large numbers that are very likely to be represented by a steady exponential distribution. Therefore, by computing that the mean time between demands is fifty months, you can immediately determine that 98 percent of the time the next demand will occur at least a month after the previous one.

SPORTS CAR RALLIES. The preceding examples illustrate a few of the many ways that demand information can be transformed in order to present a simpler problem to forecast in an inventory control system. An analogous problem in an entirely different field is the choice of a coordinate system for tracking missiles and satellites. The methods of making the necessary coordinate transformations are well known* to those concerned with the problem and of minimum interest to those who aren't, so we needn't go into them here.

The following example has been chosen because it illustrates how to construct a standard scale on which to measure the observations, so that successive samples in the time series will be truly comparable in a way that relates to the basic process.

An average-speed rally is an event in which from 20 to 75 cars participate. Each car is given a set of instructions to guide it over a complicated course of roads at specific speeds. At three or four points (unknown to the contestants), the actual time of arrival is noted and later compared with the theoretical time based on the correct course and the correct speeds. The score is based on the differences between the theoretical time of arrival and the actual: the closer the actual time to the theoretical, the better (lower) the score.

During 1959, the Touring Club of New England explored the use of handicaps, based on the past records of performance for each member. Ted Patton participated in 26 rallies during 1957–59 and earned scores ranging from 17 to 938 points. The difference in difficulty of these rallies means that 938 was not the "worst" score, nor was 17 the "best."

The successive scores are plotted in the upper part of Fig. 2.8. The data are given in Table C.4, as a source of numbers for further examples. Table C.4 also shows the median score of all contestants in each rally and the number of entries. Obviously, it doesn't take as much skill to place

---

* I. I. Shapiro, *The Prediction of Ballistic Missile Trajectories from Radar Observations* (New York: McGraw-Hill Book Company, Inc., 1957).

fifth in a rally with 10 contestants as it would in one with 100 contestants, and a handicap should be based on some measure of skill.

It was found that in each rally the scores earned by the contestants could be described very well by a lognormal distribution; that is, the logarithms of the point scores were normally (gaussian) distributed. (As

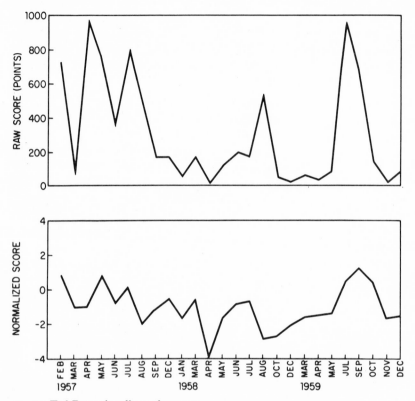

Fig. 2.8 Ted Patton's rally performance.

an interesting sidelight, the standard ratios* were the same over more than 50 rallies studied, although the medians varied tremendously.) Therefore, it was decided that a reasonable measure of skill would be the probit corresponding to the rank or standing of each team. That is, in each rally we ask, "Based on the probability distribution of all scores, how likely would the average contestant be to get a score as high as this one?" The less probable it is to get a score that high, the higher the evidence that skill was involved. Figure 2.9 is a nomograph that was constructed to con-

* R. G. Brown, *Statistical Forecasts for Inventory Control* (New York: McGraw-Hill Book Co., Inc. (1959)), 197–216.

vert standings into a linear measure of skill. The lower plot in Fig. 2.8 shows Patton's scores in these normalized units.

Notice how much more regular—and therefore forecastable—the normalized scores are. His performance on the April, 1958, rally was significantly better than usual, whereas, in the January rally of that same year,

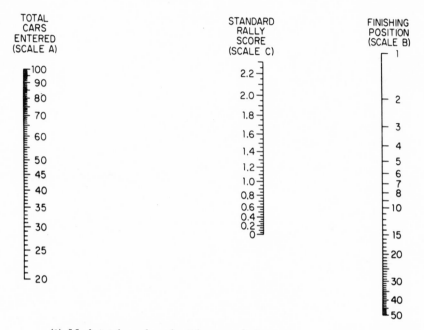

(1) Mark total number of entries on scale A.

(2) Lay a straightedge from Scale A to finish position on Scale B.

(3) Read score on Scale C where straightedge crosses it.

    (a) Upper half of rally: count from first place; score will be negative (−).

    (b) Lower half of rally: count from last place; score will be positive (+).

Fig. 2.9 Nomograph for converting finish position to standard score.

he had had another very low numerical score, which was just about average when translated into skill. His performance on the September, 1959, rally (670 points) was really worse than either the July or October rallies, with 940 and 131 points respectively.

3 The Sampling Interval

The basic unit of time used throughout this book is the sampling interval. At time T we observe x_T. The next observation is x_{T+1}, available one sampling interval later. In a weapon system, the sampling interval may be as short as a fraction of a second. In a chemical control system, the process may be sampled every hour. Traders in the stock market study the prices and volumes once a day. Manufacturing schedules may be revised monthly, or financial budgets revised annually.

We do assume that the sampling interval is long enough so that the forecast can be revised in real time, and so that some control action can be taken before the next observation in the sequence. "Action" in this sense implies the opportunity to make some change; frequently the change in the control system will be zero.

The length of the sampling interval appropriate for revising the forecast may be quite different from the interval required for other purposes. For example, it is common to post demand data daily to reflect current stock status. Monthly, or even quarterly measurements of total demand may be adequate for revising the forecast used in controlling the stock.

In this chapter, we consider the problem of choosing a particular sampling interval if the interval is not already fixed by factors outside the scope of the present study.

One consideration that applies to the sampling of a long continuous process is the *aliasing* of higher frequencies. Nyquist's sampling theorem* states that it is theoretically possible to reproduce all signals up to frequencies having at least two observations per cycle. In practice, it may take a dozen observations per cycle to reproduce the pattern adequately. The effects of variation with a higher frequency are confounded, or aliased, with those due to lower frequencies. A longer sampling interval tends to have a damping effect on the control system. High-frequency phenomena are not noticed, and therefore the system cannot respond to them.

Rule of Thumb

In Chapter 13, we shall discuss the lead time that the forecast should cover. One of the factors to be considered is the minimum lead time for making firm commitments. There is a latest time when final adjustments can be made to plans. The lead time extends from then until the effect of those changes is felt. For example, the time of flight for a shot from a gun is such a lead time. Once you have fired at a duck, you can't change the path of the pellets.

The length of the minimum lead time is a natural measure of the tempo of the system being controlled. It may be a few seconds for shooting at ducks, a few months for manufacturing appliances, or a few years for building a major capital plant. As a rough rule of thumb, the sampling interval for revising the forecast should be between a quarter and a tenth of the minimum lead time in the system; that is, there should be from four to ten opportunities per lead time to modify the forecast.

When the lead time is very short, there may be only one opportunity to modify the forecast per lead time. The calendar may make it convenient to revise the forecast 12 or 13 times a year, when the lead time is on the order of one year.

Optimum Sampling Intervals

Operations Research is concerned with optimization problems. They follow a fairly common pattern, which we shall encounter several times in this book. Conceptually, one can draw a graph with the ordinates representing cost (or some other measure of effort or penalty). There are three curves on this graph. The first curve on the graph rises to the right and

* H. Nyquist, "Certain Topics in Telegraph Transmission Theory," *Trans. AIEE,* pp. 617–44, April, 1928.

represents elements of increasing cost. A second curve rises to the left and represents elements of decreasing cost. The third curve is obtained, point by point, as the sum of the ordinates of the other two. It represents total cost.

At some point—which can, of course, be at one extreme of the range—in the range of the problem, the total cost will have a minimum, and that point is called "the optimum." So much of the problem is quite routine and is used so often that it might be worthwhile to make a rubber stamp of the curves. On each new problem, take a sheet of clean white paper and carefully stamp the curves on it (Fig. 3.1). Then all that remains is to

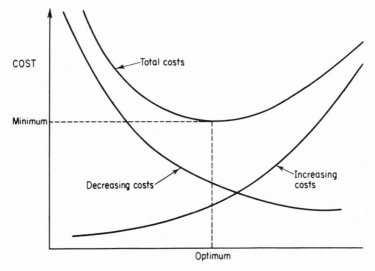

Fig. 3.1 The rubber stamp of operations research.

identify the independent variable, which is to have the optimum value. Of course, one must also determine the exact shapes of the curves and a few other messy details before the problem is completely solved. It's a handy way to start thinking about the problem, though.

At the moment, we are concerned with the design of the proper sampling frequency for the data. Let us think through, qualitatively, how the proper frequency could be investigated.

First consider the costs that will increase with the length of the sampling interval: the cost of not noticing a change in pattern. In an airport, where planes maneuver rapidly, the surveillance radar scans quite rapidly, compared with the rate at which observations are required en route. An air defense radar might scan traffic more rapidly than a simple traffic control radar, since enemy targets would be likely to take evasive action.

Observations should be frequent enough to cope with real changes in the situation being observed. The Navy tends to look at its demand for supply items once a quarter, whereas many industrial manufacturers revise their forecasts monthly. In the style trades, where the market can shift suddenly, a week may be a more appropriate interval. Professional traders in the stock market get daily reports (or even two hourly summaries) of trading activity.

Now let us consider two types of cost that should decrease as the intervals between successive observations are made longer. (We assume that the intervals are always long enough so that the forecast computations can be carried out to the point where some sort of decision for action is made before the next observation.) The first decreasing cost is the annual cost of doing the computations. In the case of a very large inventory, this cost may be significant. It may be measured in machine time available, or opportunities for other jobs foregone, rather than in dollars. If it takes eight hours to process the files completely, it obviously is very expensive to try to forecast every day; no other work could be carried out on the machine.

The second decreasing cost is related to the structure of the original process. In a process where the data are inherently discrete, it is possible to sample so often that there is nothing to look at. For example, a daily report of the trading volume of Christiana Securities would yield little novel information; on a very high fraction of the days, the report would be zero. In most inventories there are a great many items for which there is only occasional demand; the sampling interval should be long enough to give a reasonable chance that some demand has occurred since the previous observation.

There is an analogous problem in the design of the scanning rate for a radar. If the scanning rate is made too high, there will be too few pulses reflected from the target to get a good signal.

If the sampling rate is too high, it will be difficult to see the pattern and hence harder to forecast very far into the future. If the basic process generates a series of pulses which are accumulated and observed periodically, then the average quantity observed will be proportional to the length of the sampling interval. If the data have no serial correlation, the variance will also be proportional to the length of the interval, so that the standard deviation grows only as the square root of the length. Hence the longer the interval, the clearer the average level of the process.

The basic consideration in selecting the sampling interval should be balancing the risk of not noticing a change quickly against the inherent variability of the data and the cost of revising plans frequently. As with most situations that could be plotted like Fig. 3.1, the region in the neighborhood of the optimum is very flat. The actual interval selected can be quite different from "the optimum" without changing total costs appreciably.

Example. The following example illustrates the computation of variability as a function of the sampling interval. An analysis was carried out for 10 parts stocked by the Navy for repair of ships' equipment. The actual demand was recorded in each of eighty successive weeks, and the standard deviations of these numbers were computed for each of 10 parts. Then the data were grouped as if the demand had been reported only once per two weeks, once per four weeks, and once per eight weeks. The standard deviations of the reported demands were then calculated for each possible reporting interval and expressed as a multiple of the standard deviation computed for weekly reports.

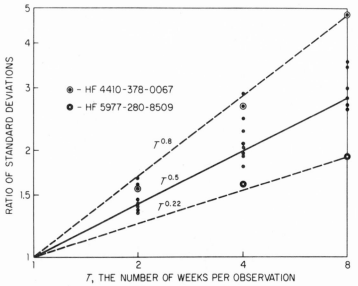

Fig. 3.2 The standard deviation of demand observed every T weeks.

Figure 3.2 shows how the standard deviations grow as a function of the reporting interval T. The ring cup (HF 4410-378-0067) shows a significant serial correlation in the demand, and hence the standard deviation grows proportionally to $T^{0.8}$, whereas the brush electrical contact HF (5977-280-8509) has some negative correlation, and the standard deviation is proportional to $T^{0.22}$. The central tendency, however, is for the standard deviation to grow as the square root of the reporting interval.

In general, the analysis goes as follows: Let the time series be a sequence of observations x_t. Without loss of generality, we can assume that the mean is $\bar{x} = 0$. Suppose the series has a known autocorrelation function

$R_{xx}(\tau) = \overline{x_t x_{t+\tau}}$; by definition, the variance is $\sigma^2 = R_{xx}(0)$. These statistics are given for some basic unit reporting interval. (Refer to Appendix A for a discussion of the autocorrelation function.)

Suppose we now change the reporting interval to some multiple k of the basic unit. The new sequence of observations will be

$$y_n = \sum_{t=kn}^{k(n+1)-1} x_t$$

The autocorrelation function for the new sequence will be

$$R_{yy}(\tau) = \overline{y_n y_{n+\tau}} = \overline{\sum_{t=kn} x_t \sum_{t=k(n+\tau)} x_t}$$

where there are k terms in the summations.

This reduces to

$$R_{yy}(\tau) = \sum_{j=0}^{k-1} \sum_{k=0}^{k-1} R_{xx}(k\tau + j - k)$$

The variance of the derived sequence is

$$\sigma_y^2 = R_{yy}(0) = \sum_{j=0}^{k-1} \sum_{k=0}^{k-1} R_{xx}(j - k)$$

If the original series were random,

$$R_{xx}(\tau) = 0, \ \tau \neq 0, \quad \text{so} \quad \sigma_y^2 = k\sigma_x^2$$

In the particular case of $k = 2$, for general correlation of the data

$$\sigma_y^2 = 2\sigma_x^2 + 2R_{xx}(1)$$

Exercise. Table C.2 gives a sequence of individual demand transactions on an inventory. The dates are artificial in that there are exactly twenty days in each month, so that the four weeks would include dates 1 to 5, 6 to 10, 11 to 15, and 16 to 20. Summarize the data by weeks and by months. Compute the variances for daily, weekly, and monthly reporting. Do the results conform to $\sigma_y^2 = n\sigma_x^2$?

When the basic process is continuous, the mean and the variance of the observations are not affected by the sampling frequency. (Unless one encounters the phenomenon in a scanning radar that the beam sweeps by the target too fast to get a good look.)

Exercise. Sample the prices of IBM common stock daily, weekly, and monthly in the period June 29, 1959, through May 16, 1961. How does the variance of the first differences depend on the length of the sampling interval?

"I don't mean to deny that the evidence is in some ways very strongly in favour of your theory. I only wish to point out that there are other theories possible. As you say, the future will decide."

Adventure of the Norwood Builder

The gasoline gauge shows that there are 2 gallons still in the tank, so you decide to drive on to the next filling station, which *must* be within 20 miles. Let's examine the reasoning behind that decision a little more closely. You never want to wait until the tank is bone dry before getting more gasoline. Allow 1 gallon as a reserve against all sorts of unforeseen events: the gauge may not be accurate; the next open station may be farther away than you think; or the driving conditions may be such that you'll burn more than a normal quantity of gas in the next 20 miles. On the average, the other gallon will carry you another 20 miles, so there's no need to stop now. In this section, we look a little more closely at why an average rate of 20 miles per gallon (or whatever the figure is for your car) is a useful sort of forecast.

The businessman has the same problem of estimating the average rate of usage over some replenishment lead time. Frequently he says that the average rate in the future will be the same as the average rate in the recent past. We shall look at this notion of an average rate, and also at the statement that it's an average computed *in the recent past*. Sometimes a simple average rate of usage is not sufficient: demand may be growing so that future demand will be greater than it has been in the past; demand may be seasonal, so that the average rate of usage depends on the season of the year. It will be our task to examine various other models that represent these patterns adequately.

When you shoot at a duck, you mentally calculate that his path during the time of flight of your shot will be like the path he has just been flying.

His future velocity is going to be like the velocity you are now observing. Again, note that it's the velocity that you are *now* observing. You may have seen the duck a long way off and watched him meandering all over the sky before he came within range. It is of no concern what the duck's various velocities were a long time before you shoot—it's only the present velocity that is useful in predicting his immediate future path. The model you have of his flight path is a simple average velocity, equal to the recent observed velocity. His position, of course, is a linear function of time.

Such a simple explanation is, of course, entirely inadequate when it comes to tracking ballistic missiles. A most significant era in the history of astronomy was the early seventeenth century when Kepler discovered that the path of the planets was an ellipse with one focus at the center of the sun and that the radius from that focus to any planet swept out equal areas in equal times. That sort of model (with due allowance for minor perturbations) is required for tracking missiles in the Mercury Project and orbiting satellites.

The forecasting problem starts with some process that generates a sequence of observations: the data. Ultimately we shall want to forecast the probability distribution from which future observations will be drawn. Our immediate next step toward that goal is representing the systematic changes in the sequence of past observations to date by some sort of model which can be projected into the future.

We shall require that the model be a good representation of the data in any local segment of time, close to "now." The model need not represent the data a very long time in the future, if by *very long time* we mean beyond the forecast lead time. In buying gasoline, one is not concerned with the fact that in five years' time the mileage will have dropped from 20 miles per gallon to perhaps only 14 miles per gallon. The phenomenon of decreasing gasoline mileage will be taken into account by revising the forecast in the light of later experience.

Similarly, with observations taken a very long time in the past, the current model need not represent them at all well. Your estimate of the duck's velocity when you shoot at him bears no relation whatever to his velocity five minutes ago.

What we mean by *a very long time ago* is a little harder to define exactly. The relevant period of past time depends on the length of the forecast lead time, the complexity of the model used and, sometimes, of some of the statistical characteristics of the sequence of observations. If the forecast lead time is long, then in general, the model should represent the data well for a long historical period. A simple model may be a reasonably good representation over short enough time intervals. An elaborate model should be an equally good representation over much longer intervals.

This book is primarily concerned with non-stationary time series, so that ancient data are not relevant to current conditions. The forecast is to be revised with each new observation; hence, the models used are not required to represent data over a long span of time.

In a curve-fitting problem, one is given an entire set of data all at once. The objective is then to find the simplest curve that describes the entire sequence. Therefore the data can be visualized as a graph like Fig. 4.1. This book deals with a different problem. We shall look only at small segments of the graph through a moving window. We can see a few points through the window, but the rest of the sequence is blocked out.

The window has a vertical dividing line: to right are "future" observations, and to the left "past" observations. We want the model to represent only these few points well. Call the dividing line "now." As time passes, we have to move the window along to the right, so that the dividing line stays at the current observation. Some past points which were once visible are now blocked out, and some future points which were beyond the forecast lead time now are of concern.

If the forecast is to be successful, the model must represent the future points visible through the window. Of course, we are not allowed to use these points in our forecast computations. We merely say that when time has elapsed so that we do know what the future observations are, it will turn out that the model was a good representation.

It may be hard to find a model that does represent data over a long enough span of time. If the model is a poor representation, then the distribution of forecast errors will have a large variance. In Section VII, we shall discuss ways of using the forecasts to minimize the risk of being wrong. If the distribution of forecast errors has a large variance, then this minimum risk will be high. Only a certain amount of improvement can be obtained by more elaborate models and more refined forecasting techniques. Perhaps steps can be taken to make the data a cleaner representation of the physical process to be controlled—which will make the forecasts more accurate and reduce the minimum attainable risk. If not, the only hope for improvement is to shorten the forecast lead time, that is, to alter the control process so that the final commitment to action can be deferred until a later date. High-velocity ammunition and guided missiles have been developed to decrease the chance of an unpredictable change in the target's path during the blind time between final adjustment of the plan and the effect of the action. Manufacturers in the style trades react to changes in the market much more rapidly than can John Brown, shipbuilder in Glasgow.

Plans may still be made long in advance and followed through if there is no sign of change in the process. But it is possible to modify the original plan at a late date and so decrease the chance of a large forecast error. Manufacturers who have trouble forecasting well enough for good purchasing and production-planning decisions may find it worthwhile to decrease the lead times to an interval over which they can forecast well. If expediting is allowed, it represents a shorter lead time for the final commitment to a production plan. If there's no change in the pattern of demand, the original plan goes through. If there is a change, the plan can be modified (although at a cost).

Astronomers can forecast the path of a planet centuries ahead, if required. There is almost no chance of an unforeseen disturbance to the path. They can forecast the path of an orbiting satellite for several weeks or months, but there are various disturbances that can alter the path significantly in time. When it comes to forecasting the path of a manned aircraft, however, one can forecast only a volume of space in which the target will be found in the next few minutes. The boundaries of this volume are defined by the aircraft's physical capability to maneuver. The actual location of the aircraft within this space depends on whether the pilot tries to evade or not. The size of the volume grows enormously with the lead time: nothing useful can be said about the location of an airplane this afternoon.

Most business forecasting problems are like tracking a manned aircraft: there is a very great chance of some major change in the pattern of demand, and the size of the likely changes grows enormously with the length of the forecast lead time.

We shall discuss two basic types of models in this section. Chapter 4 is concerned with time-series models, such as the average gasoline mileage for an automobile, or the elliptical orbit of a ballistic missile, or the exponential growth in the number of airline passengers. One thinks of the process as being described by a function of time. The deterministic process is observed in the presence of "noise," the unpredictable difference between the observed data and the "true process." The differences will be positive and negative and average to zero. Successive differences may be correlated or statistically independent. Something may be known about the distribution from which the noise samples are drawn—Section V deals with the problems of estimating the characteristics of the noise. Noise can be caused by inaccuracy of the method of observation (which may be inherent in the physical process involved or caused by using faulty equipment). The differences between a particular model and the observation are called *residuals*. The residuals include the noise, plus any deterministic variation not included in the model, plus the effects of inaccuracies in estimating values of the coefficients in the model.

Chapter 5 deals with a different kind of model. In this case, we focus attention on the probability distribution itself, in contrast to the previous approach which looked at the values of one or more parameters of the distribution (such as the mean and the standard deviation). It's something like trying to guess when you'll be home from the office any night.

You generally leave about 5:00. Sometimes you can get out a few minutes early, and sometimes the boss catches you at 4:45 for a "fifteen-minute" meeting. When the weather is good and there have been no accidents, you can drive home in thirty-five minutes. Sometimes, for no apparent reason, traffic is slow—it may be the backwash from an accident on a parallel route, or an ornery policeman at a crucial intersection. Then it takes up to forty-five minutes to get home. Occasionally, when a sudden snowstorm comes up, it takes an hour and a half to get home.

Your wife can be quite sure that you won't be home before 5:20, and equally sure that you will be home before 6:30. In between those times, there is some probability distribution that says "there is a probability $P(t)$ that he will be home before time t, where $P(5:20) = 0$, and $P(6:30) = 1.0$. There may, for example, be a fifty-fifty chance that you get home by 5:40, so that $P(5:40) = 0.5$. By long experience, your wife has built up some sort of estimate of this probability distribution, which might be represented by Fig. 5.1. Your wife estimates the probability that you will arrive by time t, not the mean and standard deviation of the poisson distribution.

These probability models have applications in some industrial inventory control systems, where the probability that demand during a lead time will be less than some level X cannot satisfactorily be described by any of the standard probability distributions. This is particularly true near one end of the range of the distribution. The stock people want to know whether to set the reorder point at X. If $X = 60$ pieces is correct, then there should be a 5 percent chance that demand during a lead time will exceed 60 pieces. We shall see some examples where the problem cannot be approached by describing the demand by any of the practical formal distributions.

A *model* is an abstraction of reality that preserves the characteristics of interest and suppresses other characteristics. Any sequence of observations could be represented by either a time-series model, or by a probability model. The correct choice depends on which sort of characteristics is more useful in forecasting the distribution from which future observations in the same sequence will come.

4   Time-Series Models

A communications engineer is concerned with data that might be the voltages in a telephone circuit or the strengths of the echoes received from a target by radar. The actual observations are considered to be the result of combining two components: a "true" process, or message, and the "noise." The process is a deterministic function of time, and that function is the significant characteristic of the data. The noise has some probability distribution, with zero mean.

The economist may be concerned with periodic observations of demand, productivity, prices, and so on. He wants to describe these observations by components, such as "trend," "cycle," "seasonal," and "irregular." Again, the trend, cycle, and seasonal variations represent an underlying process. The irregular component is the unpredictable (or not-to-be-predicted) variation, which can be described by a probability distribution having zero mean.*

---

* Economists sometimes use models that multiply these effects: $Y = TCSI$. In this chapter, we consider only models that are the sums of such components. The product of components can be changed into the sum of equivalent components by taking logarithms of both sides of the equation.

$$\log Y = \log T + \log C + \log S + \log I$$

or
$$y = t \quad + c \quad + s \quad + i$$

In either case, one can describe the process that generates the observations in terms of a set of significant patterns in time, plus an unpredictable random element. In a physical process—as in tracking a ballistic missile—the proper model to represent the observations is obvious. In economics and weather forecasting, however, the true process is not well enough understood. There are too many factors, with complex interactions, to allow derivation of an equation that describes the process underlying the observed data. In these cases, one must choose a descriptive model that approximates local segments of the observed time series well enough to get a useful forecast. Even so, the better one understands the basic mechanism governing the process being forecast, the better one can set up a useful model.

This chapter is divided into three principal parts. The first discusses algebraic models. The simplest case of an algebraic model is an average, as in the duck's current velocity or the current rate of gasoline consumption in a car. That is, we say that future observations will be samples from some distribution. It is significant that the mean of this distribution is constant (or nearly so) at least over the lead time for which we require the forecast. In any local segment of the time series, we can represent the observations well enough by the average level. We will allow, however, that in two widely separated segments of time, the averages may have different numerical values.

From averages, we turn our attention to straight lines. That is, we describe the time series by saying that the mean of the observations is increasing (or decreasing) with time at a constant rate. If the duck is flying at constant velocity, then his position is a linear function of time. From there, we shall generalize the algebraic models into any polynomial function of time, to describe the duck's position under constant, or even changing accelerations.

The second part of this chapter is concerned with transcendental models. The first such model is the exponential, which describes a process that is growing at a constant percentage rate, like compound interest. Then we shall consider trigonometric models, to describe periodic fluctuations: what the economist calls *cycles* and *seasonals*.

Finally, we shall comment on the use of multiple regression to find relationships between the observed data and some other time series which is known in advance, but which is not described by any simple mathematical function of time. These models generalize the notion of an installation rate discussed in Chapter 2.

Note that in each case the values of the parameters in the model are allowed to change slowly and at random. This feature will be inherent in deriving the smoothing techniques (Section III) for estimating the values of these parameters from the observed data.

Algebraic Models

CONSTANT MODELS. Look at Fig. 1.1, Fig. 2.4, and Fig. 2.9. In each case, one would be justified in saying that the observations are random samples from some distribution and that the mean of that distribution doesn't change significantly with time. That is, one can visualize an underlying process ξ_t that doesn't change: $\xi_t = a$, where a is the "true value" which we shall never know. The observations x_t include some random noise $x_t = \xi_t + \epsilon_t$. Section III will develop methods of estimating what the numerical value of the average a is, and Section V will discuss the parameters of the distribution of the noise samples ϵ_t.

We don't know what the true value of the average is—we may not even be sure that an average is the correct description of the observations. But we can estimate a value for the average from recent observations. In this book we shall use a "hat" over a symbol for any variable to indicate an estimated value, such as $\hat{a}$. To emphasize that the estimate is based on data through time T we can write $\hat{a}_T$. [Later on, when we need the subscript to distinguish among several parameters, we shall use the notation $\hat{a}(T)$.]

The forecast of the mean of the distribution for future samples will then be represented by

$$\hat{x}_{T+\tau} = \hat{a}_T$$

That is, an observation to be obtained τ sampling intervals in the future will be a sample from a distribution that has a mean equal to our present estimate of the average. Section IV is concerned with such forecasts.

There are many novel, but essential, concepts in this development. The first is the notion of a "true" process ξ underlying the observations. Although we can never know what this true process is, assumptions regarding its form are basic for the form of the model. The observations of the process x include noise samples. It is always assumed that the expected value of the noise is zero; almost always that it has constant variance; usually that the distribution is gaussian; and often that successive samples have no serial correlation. The effects of including or relaxing these assumptions is discussed in Section V.

A most important concept is the model of the process, in this case just a constant. The second concept which we shall meet time and time again is the estimate of the coefficient in that model from a finite set of data $\hat{a}_T$. Finally, there is the forecast of the mean of the distribution from which future observations will be drawn.

There are six key words here: *process, noise, observation, model, estimate,* and *forecast*. If they are new to you in this context, go over the material

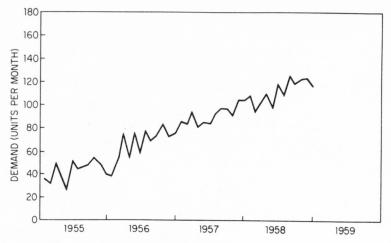

Fig. 4.1 The demand for thermostats.

in this chapter carefully until you understand them clearly. They are the foundation on which this book rests.

LINEAR MODELS. Now look at Fig. 4.1, which shows the demand by months for a thermostat stocked by the Warmdot Corporation. For a long time, this item has been capturing a steadily increasing share of the market. There is a significant secular trend to the demand, which should be recognized in forecasting.

In a case like this, one might use as a model of the process

$$\xi_t = a + bt$$

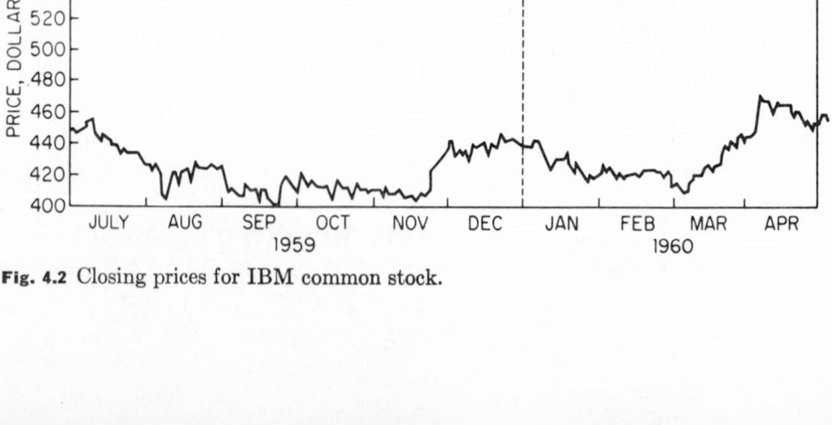

Fig. 4.2 Closing prices for IBM common stock.

where a is the average level of demand at a point where the time t is counted as zero. The other coefficient b is the trend, or rate at which the demand is increasing. If time is measured in months, and x as units per month, then b will be measured in units/month/month.

Again, we do not know the true values a and b, but must estimate them from the data in the recent past. At time T, our estimates would be represented by $\hat{a}_T$ and $\hat{b}_T$. As we get more and more data, the estimates of these two coefficients may change slightly, even though the process was correctly described by the model. The true coefficient values may be going through a slow random walk.

You may also encounter a set of data like Fig. 4.2, which shows the daily closing prices for IBM common stock on the New York Stock Exchange. (The raw data are given in Table C.5, if you want to experiment with them.) From August, 1959, through February, 1960, one might say that the price was very stable, so that a constant model might have been quite adequate for forecasting prices a few days ahead. The average in September through November, 1959 is lower than the average in December, but for short spans of time an average describes the prices quite well.

Beginning in March, 1960, there is an upward trend that carries through until the middle of June (with some minor swings). In that period of time, a linear model would be a much better representation of the price changes than a constant model. The point is that, for short enough spans of time, straight lines are pretty good representations of price movement. In different time segments, the lines are different, however, and that is why we must reestimate the values of the coefficients $\hat{a}_T$ and $\hat{b}_T$.

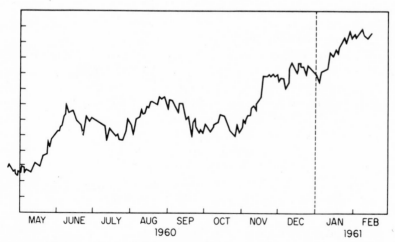

Fig. 4.2 Closing prices for IBM common stock.

This model of price movements in the stock market is reasonable. The specialist manages his trading so that there is a steady change in price—upward when the demand exceeds the supply and downward when the condition is reversed.

Once values have been estimated for these coefficients that represent the proper line right now, the mean of the distribution from which future observations will be taken is forecast as

$$\hat{x}_{T+\tau} = \hat{a}_T + \hat{b}_T\tau$$

This forecast depends only on relative time τ and therefore implies that $\hat{a}_T = \hat{a}_{T-1} + \hat{b}_{T-1}$. It might be noted in passing that *Statistical Forecasting for Inventory Control* considered only linear models.

POLYNOMIAL MODELS. If a car is accelerating at a constant rate, its velocity is changing linearly, and the position is changing as a quadratic function of time. If the acceleration were changing linearly, then the position would be described by a cubic function of time. We noted in Fig. 4.2 that the rate of change of IBM stock prices sometimes changed. Hence if we wanted a better approximation to the price movement, over somewhat longer spans of time, it might be appropriate to use a more elaborate model, for example,

$$\xi_t = a + bt + \tfrac{1}{2}ct^2$$

If the quadratic coefficient c is positive, the trend of prices is changing from downward to upward, whereas if it is negative, that is a sign of passing from an upward movement to a downward one.

In general, one can use any degree polynomial that is required to represent the process by adding terms in t^3, t^4, and so on, up to t^N. The highest exponent in the model determines the degree of the polynomial. The preceding equation is a second-degree polynomial, whereas a constant model is a special case: a zero-degree polynomial.

The number of coefficients which must be estimated is always one more than the degree of the polynomial. In general, we shall speak of the number of coefficients as the *degrees of freedom* in the model. In the transcendental models, the number of degrees of freedom is simply the number of coefficients to be estimated from the data. It is perhaps unfortunate that we also speak of the degree of a polynomial, which is one less than the number of coefficients. So when you see the word *degree* pause and reflect what it is the degree of—there's a difference.

In practice, one seldom encounters the need for polynomial models with more than three degrees of freedom, that is, quadratic models. In studying the velocity of a missile in the reentry phase, several more degrees of freedom are required to represent the change in acceleration with drag and altitude. The model chosen should represent the sequence of observations for some reasonable span of time. A constant may be an adequate representation over a very short span, a linear model over longer spans, and a quadratic model over still longer spans. The number of observations in the span covered by the model should be several times the number of degrees of freedom. If we ask that the quadratic model span only three observations at a time, it can always be made to pass exactly through the three points, which is likely to give very poor forecasts since it doesn't allow for averaging out the random errors. In Chapter 10, we shall discuss the proper choice of "a sufficiently long span of time," as it is affected by the number of degrees of freedom in the model.

If one chooses a quadratic model to represent the process, then the next step is to estimate the coefficients $\hat{a}_T$, $\hat{b}_T$ and $\hat{c}_T$ after obtaining the observation $x_T = \xi_T + \epsilon_T$. The forecast for τ periods into the future, made as of time T, will then be

$$x_{T+\tau} = \hat{a}_T + \hat{b}_T\tau + \tfrac{1}{2}\hat{c}_T\tau^2$$

Exercise. Express $\hat{a}_T$, $\hat{b}_T$ and $\hat{c}_T$ in terms of $\hat{a}_{T-1}$, $\hat{b}_{T-1}$, and $\hat{c}_{T-1}$ for this process.

What degree of polynomial is correct? If there are physical models, such as motion under constant acceleration, then there is no problem in selecting the proper model. When the function is being used as an adequate description of a time series, with no physical justification, the answer is not so clear-cut. If you are quite sure that the level doesn't change significantly with time, a constant will be sufficient. If there is a steady growth, then a linear model is indicated. If the rate of growth can change, then a quadratic model, and so on.

If the process underlying the observations is exactly represented by a polynomial of degree n, then it is possible to find that degree by successive differences. Compute

$$\Delta_t\xi = \xi_t - \xi_{t-1}$$

then the second difference

$$\Delta_t^2\xi = \Delta_t\xi - \Delta_{t-1}\xi = \xi_t - 2\xi_{t-1} + \xi_{t-2}$$

and so on, for successively higher differences. The difference Δ^{n+1} will be identically zero, if the polynomial is of degree n.

Unfortunately, one never has data on the process itself, but only noisy observations $x_t = \xi_t + \epsilon_t$. If the process ξ is a polynomial of degree n, the $(n + 1)$st differences of the data $\Delta^{n+1}x$ will *average* zero. The variances of the differences will grow as the sum of squares of the binomial coefficients. Thus if the noise ϵ has variance σ^2 the values $\Delta^{n+1}x$ will have variance $\sigma^2 [2(n + 1)]!/[(n + 1)!]^2$. This variance will be larger than σ^2 for $n + 1 \geqslant 5$.

The problem is even further complicated because, in most cases of real interest, the coefficients in the underlying process are not literally constant, but undergo a slow random walk in time. The change is small enough so that, at any one point in time, the current estimates prove a satisfactory forecast. When one analyzes a long historical record, like the IBM common stock prices in Table C.5, it is very apparent that the coefficient values appropriate in one year are quite different from those in another year.

The following trick can be used in practice: say you think that there is a significant linear trend with time, but that the trend won't change much. Then tentatively entertain a quadratic model, which allows for changes in the trend if they're present. (Note that one doesn't *assume* that the process is described by a quadratic model, one tentatively entertains the notion.) In Chapter 19, we shall show how to test whether the coefficient of the quadratic term is significantly different from zero. If it isn't, then the assumption of the linear model was justified.

There is no magic way of guessing at the correct model for a time series. Plot up several series and look at them. Are there significant trends or changes in trend? Is a constant an adequate model over the span of time for which a forecast is required? Too much haste in assuming what model describes the process is a common source of difficulty in trying to use statistical forecasting methods.

Transcendental Models

EXPONENTIAL MODELS. An exponential function will describe a process where the rate of growth is proportional to the state of growth, like compound interest. The change in value from one observation to the next can be expressed as a constant percentage of the current value. The American population has grown steadily since the first census in 1790 at an exponential rate. When the census figures (Table C.6) are plotted on semilogarithmic paper (Fig. 4.3), they tend to fall approximately along a straight line. Until about 1870, the population grew about 33 percent in ten years. Since then, the rate is more like 15 percent in ten years.

In 1954, Arthur D. Little, Inc., carried out a study for Aeronautical Radio, Inc., which operates the Federal communications licenses for all the domestic airlines. Part of the assignment called for a forecast of air traffic volumes through 1965. Table C.7 is a record of the revenue passenger miles carried by scheduled domestic airlines, from 1937 to 1961. At the time of the study, only the data through 1953 were available. Figure 4.4 shows that on semilog paper the points fall more or less along a straight line, indicating constant exponential growth. A model of the process is

$$\log \xi_t = \log k + t \log a$$

where k is a constant of proportionality, and a is the ratio of traffic in one year to traffic the previous year. The effects of World War II and the

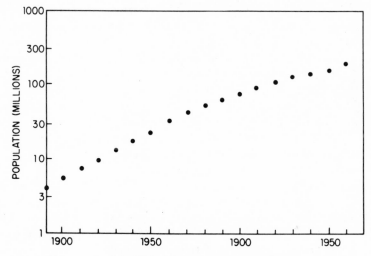

Fig. 4.3 The growth of the United States population.

Korean conflict are simply treated as noise. A more elaborate model would be

$$\log \xi_t = \log h + t \log a + t^2 \log b$$

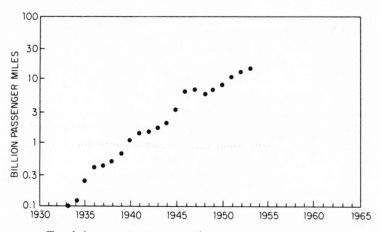

Fig. 4.4 Trends in passenger transportation.

The forecasts based on a simple projection on semilogarithmic paper are compared with the actual figures since then in Table 4.1. At press time, data for 1961 and later had not been published.

Table 4.1   COMPARISON OF ACTUAL DOMESTIC AIRLINE PASSENGER MILES WITH PROJECTION MADE IN 1953 (IN BILLIONS)

Year	Projection	Actual
1954	16.8	16.8
1955	19.2	19.8
1956	21.1	22.4
1957	23.3	25.3
1958	25.5	25.3
1959	28.3	29.3
1960	31.0	30.5
1961	33.8	·
1962	36.9	·
1963	40.0	·

If the process is the simple exponential function

$$\xi_t = ka^t$$

then the ratio of successive values of the process is simply

$$\xi_t/\xi_{t-1} = a$$

The value of this constant could be estimated from the ratios of successive observations x_t/x_{t-1}. Later on, we shall consider exponential models of the general form

$$\xi_t = k_1 \binom{t}{0} a^t + k_2 \binom{t}{1} a^{t-1}b + k_3 \binom{t}{2} a^{t-2}b^2 + \ldots + k_n \binom{t}{n-1} a^{t-n+1}b^{n-1}$$

where

$$\binom{t}{k} = \frac{t!}{(t-k)!k!}$$

is the binomial coefficient of the $(k+1)$st term in the expansion of $(a+b)^t$. Obviously, for such a process, one needs something more powerful than the simple ratio between successive observations.

Exercise. Plot the ratios of successive decennial census figures (see Table C.6). What sort of model in time would you use to describe them?

TRIGONOMETRIC MODELS. When the process to be forecast is periodic, it is appropriate to describe it in terms of sines and cosines. But first let's be quite clear what we mean when we talk about a *periodic function*.

Very simply, it's a function that after a while begins to repeat the same values all over again. The length of time before the sequence starts to repeat is called the *period*. We shall speak of the number of observations in a period, or the period as a multiple of the sampling interval.

The height of the tide may be observed once an hour. Starting at high tide, the heights decrease for six hours, and then start to rise again. Twelve hours later, the heights will start to go through the same sequence again. This is a process with a period of twelve hours, which can be described by a cosine wave.

$$\xi_t = a \cos \frac{2\pi t}{12}$$

where t is measured in hours, starting at high tide, and ξ_t is the departure from average level.

The demand for filters (Fig. 4.5) is regularly high in December and low in June. This demand could also be represented by a cosine wave, as above. In this case, however, the time t is measured in months, starting with $t = 0$ in December. The periodic variation is caused by the normal cycle of weather during the year.

The appearance of Halley's comet is another periodic phenomenon. It returns every 76.02 years (due next in 1986).

The important feature of these processes is that we start with a sequence of observations

$$\{x_t\} = x_1, x_2, x_3, \ldots, x_p$$

Thereafter for $t > p$ we find that each observation is approximately equal to the pth previous observation, $x_t \cong x_{t-p}$. For example, $x_2 \cong x_{p+2} \cong x_{2p+2}$, and so on. In this book, we are concerned with several types of periodic time series. We shall deal, in general, with cases where we know what the period p is and where there are exactly p equally spaced observations per period. Quarterly observations of an annual cycle will have 4 observations per period; 12 observations per period are quite common, since there are twelve hours in a half day, and twelve months in a year. If an annual cycle is observed weekly, there will be 52 observations per period. A weekly cycle may be observed seven times.

It is not always necessary or even desirable to count time from the high point in the cycle. We could allow the origin of time and the mean to be arbitrary by writing the model of the process as

$$\xi_t = a \cos \frac{2\pi}{p} (t - t_0) + c$$

There are now three parameters to estimate from the data, $\hat{a}$, $\hat{c}$, and $\hat{t}_0$. It is more convenient to rewrite this model, in terms of a pair of terms, one for the sine and another for the cosine. By a simple trigonometric identity (Table D.2), we can write the model as

$$\xi_t = A \sin \frac{2\pi t}{p} + B \cos \frac{2\pi t}{p} + C$$

where

$$A = a \sin \frac{2\pi t_0}{p}$$

$$B = a \cos \frac{2\pi t_0}{p}$$

$$C = c$$

We have to estimate the three coefficients $\hat{A}_T$, $\hat{B}_T$, and $\hat{C}_T$. It is always possible to go back to the original model, in which the amplitude is

$$a = \sqrt{A^2 + B^2}$$

and the phase angle is given by

$$t_0 = \frac{p}{2\pi} \arctan \frac{B}{A}$$

It is seldom necessary to go back to this form, however, since the forecasts can also be expressed

$$\hat{x}_{T+\tau} = \hat{A}_T \sin \frac{2\pi \tau}{p} + \hat{B}_T \cos \frac{2\pi \tau}{p} + \hat{C}_T$$

Figure 4.5 is a plot of the first five years of data on the monthly sales of Warmdot Filters (Table C.13). There are apparently $p = 12$ observa-

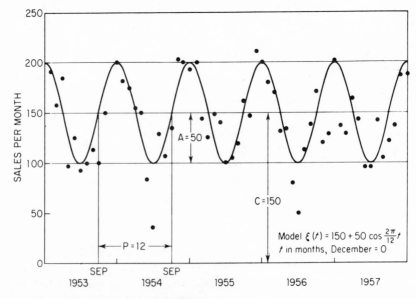

Fig. 4.5 Monthly sales of Warmdot filters.

tions per annual cycle. The sales vary around an average $C = 150$ pieces per month. The amplitude of the variation is $a = 50$ pieces. The sinusoidal variation goes through the average level in September each year and reaches the maximum in December.

Exercise. Write $\hat{A}_T$, $\hat{B}_T$, and $\hat{C}_T$ in terms of $\hat{A}_{T-1}$, $\hat{B}_{T-1}$, and $\hat{C}_{T-1}$ for this forecast model.

A sine wave has a very definite shape, and that shape may not match the shape of the waveform for the process with which you have to deal, even though your process is periodic. In 1822, Fourier showed that any

Table 4.2   VALUES OF COEFFICIENTS

Harmonic k	Coefficient of Sine A_k	Coefficient of Cosine B_k	Amplitude $a_k = \sqrt{A_k^2 + B_k^2}$
1	38.017	−305.494	328
2	−166.660	−110.214	200
3	215.097	−178.593	280
4	−62.290	−85.585	106
5	37.474	−106.745	113
6	63.504	−149.166	162
7	−75.638	−70.708	103
8	−11.055	−84.044	85
9	−4.051	−86.345	87
10	−64.747	−28.892	71
11	−25.577	−64.436	69
12	−32.933	−61.130	70
13	−56.811	−3.125	57
14	−39.211	−38.240	55
15	−51.120	−31.402	60
16	−53.037	7.100	54
17	−46.535	−30.174	55
18	−60.124	1.783	60
19	−43.351	25.396	50
20	−39.607	0.136	40
21	−51.309	13.194	53
22	−35.601	29.787	46
23	42.657	17.923	46
24	−36.791	38.992	59
25	−17.391	32.711	37
26	−29.268	22.724	37
27	−22.157	48.082	53
28	−6.831	38.015	39
29	−14.633	34.524	37
30	0	−32.533	33

reasonable periodic function of time could be well represented by taking a sufficient number of terms in a series

$$\xi_t = C + A_1 \sin \frac{2\pi t}{p} + A_2 \sin \frac{4\pi t}{p} + \ldots + A_k \sin \frac{2k\pi t}{p} + \ldots$$

$$+ B_1 \cos \frac{2\pi t}{p} + B_2 \cos \frac{4\pi t}{p} + \ldots + B_k \cos \frac{2k\pi t}{p} + \ldots$$

When the process is observed at discrete sampling intervals, the highest frequency that can be detected is the Nyquist frequency such that there are two observations per cycle. Thus there are at most p coefficients: $A_1, \ldots, A_{k-1}, B_1, \ldots, B_k, C$, where $k \leqslant p/2$.

The extra terms in this model represent higher harmonics. The difference in tonal quality for different musical instruments is caused by the presence of different proportions of these higher harmonics. A flute playing the note A at a certain loudness sounds different from a violin playing the same note with the same loudness. The difference can be described in terms of the presence of certain harmonics in one case that are not as important in the other.

Table C.8 is a list of 60 observations (in one cycle) of a particular waveform. Table 4.2 gives the 60 coefficients that could, in theory, be determined from this data. (The coefficient of the sine of the highest frequency will always be zero.) The amplitudes of the fundamental and the first two harmonics are quite large. Then the next three harmonics all have about the same amplitude; and the amplitudes of the higher harmonics die out quite rapidly.

Figure 4.6(a) shows the waveform that would result from using just the fundamental frequency. Figure 4.6(b) is the model with the fundamental and two harmonics—the terms that have by far the largest amplitude. This waveform (the whole graph is just one cycle of the pattern) begins to take on a definite shape. Figure 4.6(c) includes six pairs of terms, the fundamental plus five harmonics, and the wave has a very definite shape that does not look anything like a simple wave.

Exercise. Plot the actual data points from Table C.8. What is the waveform?

By taking enough terms of the Fourier series, it is possible to make the model conform as closely as we like to the data. It is useful, however, to bear in mind Occam's razor: *Essentia non sunt multiplicanda praeter necessitatem* (things ought not to be multiplied except out of necessity). That is, if there is a complicated waveform in the data and if it is necessary to forecast this form accurately, then by all means, take a sufficient number of terms in the model. But do not take more terms than are necessary and really significant.

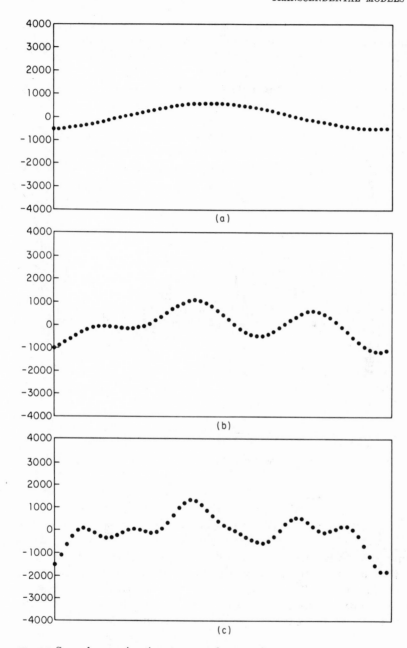

Fig. 4.6 Several approximations to a complex wave form.

This little dictum from the fourteenth century can save an immense amount of work for little return. When we come to estimate the values for the coefficients in the model, at least part of the computing effort rises as the cube of the number of degrees of freedom. In practice, therefore, one usually finds that no more than four or five degrees of freedom can be justified in giving an improvement in forecasting that will pay for the extra effort involved.

It may not always be the best course to select a more elaborate model to represent the data, even when there is some evidence that it might be more appropriate. Figure 4.7 shows the monthly imports by Company B,

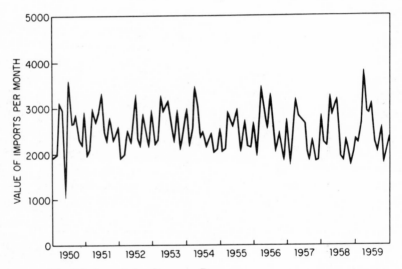

Fig. 4.7 Monthly imports by Company B.

plotted from the data in Table C.9. There seems to be some regularity in the pattern, but it's hard to detect in the plot of the basic data.

We turn for help to the autocorrelation function (Appendix A), plotted in Fig. 4.8. Notice the spike every third period. That says that if the imports in some particular month are above the long-term average level, then the imports in the third month away are more likely to be above average than below. There is apparently some relationship between the levels of imports three months apart, or a three-month period. Based on this evidence, we might try to describe the data with a model like

$$\xi_t = a_0 + a_1 \sin \frac{2\pi t}{12} + a_4 \sin \frac{8\pi t}{12}$$

$$+ b_1 \cos \frac{2\pi t}{12} + b_4 \cos \frac{8\pi t}{12}$$

Here is a case where it is worthwhile to examine the source of the data. These are accounting figures, taken from the company's records. But the accounting months are set up to give exactly thirteen weeks in each quarter, with two months of four weeks each, followed by one with five

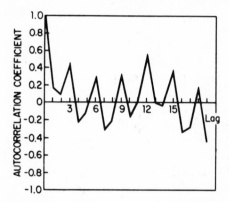

Fig. 4.8 Autocorrelation function for Company B's imports.

weeks. Hence one would expect that the imports in the third month would be 25 percent higher than the level in the intervening two months.

This observation suggests that it may be worth the effort to transform the data before trying to describe it by a model. The simplest transformation

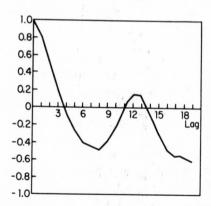

Fig. 4.9 Autocorrelation function for Company B's imports (modified).

would convert all figures to a four-week basis, by taking 80 percent of the imports in the third month of each quarter. When we do, the autocorrelation function (Fig. 4.9) shows a definite sinusoidal tendency. If the level of imports one month is above average, then we can expect it to be below average six months later, and above average again twelve months later. This is pretty clear evidence of a significant annual cycle, and we could use the model

$$\xi_t = a_0 + a_1 \sin \frac{2\pi t}{12} + b_1 \cos \frac{2\pi t}{12}$$

Now there are only three coefficients to be estimated, instead of five.

At the moment, we don't know which is the better approach. In one of the two alternatives available, we would use the accounting data, fitting a model with five degrees of freedom. That requires a certain amount of effort and yields a certain accuracy in describing the process. In the other alternative, we have the extra step of transforming the data, but substantially less work is involved in estimating only three coefficients from the data. We must try both methods and compare the resulting accuracy with the extra labor required.

Trigonometric models should be used only where there is a known underlying cause that gives rise to a periodic phenomenon. At the present state of the art, it is necessary to know how many observations there are per cycle in order to estimate values for the coefficients.

In some economic series there may be an artificially induced cycle that is just as stable as one that is related to hours of the day, or days of the week, or months of the year. For example, in Company G it is the practice to award salesmen's bonuses in July, based on sales through the end of June. The salesmen therefore make an extra effort to get orders during May and June in order to raise their annual total. Hence, the distribution pipeline tends to be quite full of inventory during the summer months. In many states, the distributors who buy Company G's product are subject to a property tax on inventories, assessed at the end of the calendar year. Therefore, during November and December, the distributors tend to cut orders, to bring the inventories down. The result of this sloshing around in the pipeline is a very clear seasonal pattern of demand on the plant—even though it is well known that the consumption of the product shows no seasonal pattern whatsoever.

There may be economic cycles of even longer duration, that are equally stable and dependable for forecasting. In the textile industry there tend to be quite long delays in passing on to the next echelon any changes in consumer demand. There is also a tendency to amplify the magnitude of the changes, because of decisions to build up inventories when demand appears to be good, and vice versa. It is easy to demonstrate that these delays and amplifications can set up oscillations in the apparent demand, especially during the early stages in the manufacture of textiles, such as spinning and weaving. The period of these oscillations is related to the response characteristics of the industry (similar to an RC oscillator in a radio transmitter). The period will change only when the industry changes the methods used in its planning.

When economists observe these cycles, they may tend to use them in forecasting future orders, and that act creates a feedback loop that locks the oscillations into quite a stable frequency.

Composite Models

Sometimes it is necessary to describe a sequence of observations by a model that combines both algebraic and transcendental models. Table C.10 is a summary of the number of passengers carried on scheduled international airlines. Figure 4.10 shows a rising pattern, on the average, that

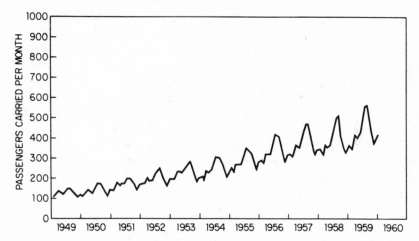

Fig. 4.10 International airline passengers.

might be described by a linear function of time. Superimposed on this basic trend is a very definite seasonal cycle, which would require a pair of trigonometric terms. In addition, we notice that the amplitude of this seasonal pattern is also growing. Therefore, a suitable model of the monthly number of international airline passengers might be

$$\xi_t = a_0 + a_1 t + (a_2 + a_4 t) \sin \frac{2\pi t}{12} + (a_3 + a_5 t) \cos \frac{2\pi t}{12}$$

The seasonal pattern is not exactly a sine wave, so that one might also consider adding one or more further pairs of trigonometric terms in order to represent the necessary higher harmonics in the waveform.

The methods of smoothing, to be discussed in Section III, make it possible to estimate n values of the coefficients a_i, $i = 0, 1, 2, \ldots, n$, in any model that is composed of terms that are the products of algebraic and transcendental functions of time, in any combination required. The computations require the solution of a system of n simultaneous linear equations in n unknowns. The computing time required goes up proportionally to n^3. That is, for each degree of freedom added to the model, the work required in estimating the coefficients will approximately double. In many cases of practical interest, from three to six degrees of freedom have been found to give very satisfactory results, at a reasonable amount of effort. An exceptional case was described by Jones.* The altitude of the 500-mb contour over the North Atlantic is described by 50 spherical harmonics.

The forecasts used for inventory control should be based on quite simple models, for two reasons: First, there are so many items for which forecasts are required that the extra effort for elaborate models rapidly builds up. Second, a good forecast is just as effective for inventory control as an excellent forecast. Data on the demand for any single item are generally so noisy that it requires an immense effort to improve the forecast appreciably. Furthermore, a well-designed inventory control system must be robust in order to work at all. That is, its performance cannot be sensitive to minor refinements in any of its elements.

In contrast, the forecast of total corporate activity may be based on a more elaborate model. The list of different time series for which forecasts are required is quite short: prices, imports, shipments, and total sales. Hence extra effort per series is not multiplied by many series. Furthermore, subtle patterns of change with time in these aggregates are likely to be much more apparent, so that some improvement in forecast can be realized from the use of models with perhaps six degrees of freedom.

Regression Models

The algebraic and transcendental models, and their combinations, by no means exhaust all the models that could be used. There is a very wide class of linear forecast models, in which the process is described by

$$\xi_t = a_1 f_1(t) + \ldots + a_n f_n(t)$$

where the functions $f_i(t)$ can be any arbitrary functions at all. Many of the economic forecasts are based on "leading" series, where the observed series x_t is related to several other time series, represented by $f_i(t)$. Nor are the feasible models restricted to linear combinations of these functions: one could (if he had sufficient reason) use products, quotients, and other combinations of these time series.

---

* R. H. Jones, "Stochastic Processes on a Sphere as Applied to Meteorological 500 mb Forecasts," Symposium on Time Series Analysis, Brown University, June 12, 1962.

I happen to think that, except in certain very special cases, the use of these multiple regression models can be very dangerous. There appears to be no statistical test that will tell whether the model is a good one or not. Yule pointed out in 1926* that if each of two time series has a significant autocorrelation function, then finite samples from the two series are almost certain to show a strong cross correlation. Therefore, it is not enough that in the past your sales have shown a strong correlation with the Dow-Jones Index. Sooner or later, sales will turn in the opposite direction from the index. The better the past correlation, the greater will be your confidence in these forecasts; hence, the greater the fiasco that results when the forecast is misleading.

If you do know a very definite reason why one series is related to another, then you can place your confidence on a continuing relationship, even if the coefficients don't seem to be significant statistically.

A second difficulty is that even if two series are related, one doesn't *know* the independent series long enough in advance to be useful in a forecast.† If one has to predict the independent series, any errors in that prediction will be amplified by the coefficients in the model. If the coefficient isn't large enough to amplify, then that term isn't significant in the model and can be dropped. When the independent functions are mathematical functions of time, like $f_1(t) = t^2$, and $f_2(t) = \sin(2\pi t/12)$, one knows absolutely in advance precisely what any future value of that function will be, with no margin for a prediction error.

A final reason for my reluctance to use multiple regression has to do with the computational techniques involved. In Section III, we shall develop some very efficient and compact routines for estimating the values of coefficients in a time-series model. The efficiency depends on the particular mathematical relationships between the values of the independent functions at one sampling interval and their values at any other sampling interval. It is obviously not possible to find such relationships when the independent functions are arbitrary time series; hence, one loses the compactness of the computing routines. We are specifically interested in real-time computation and therefore computing efficiency is of the essence.

---

* G. U. Yule, "Why Do We Sometimes Get Nonsense Correlations between Time Series," *Journal of the Royal Statistical Society,* Vol. 89 (new series), 61–64.

† An exception is the case of population-related phenomena. The number of people age Y in year T is known quite accurately in year $T - Y$.

5 Probability Models

The usual connotation of the word *forecast* is that of the time-series models discussed in Chapter 4. Such a model, however, does not always preserve the relevant characteristics of the data in a way that is useful as a forecast. In some situations, the pattern of the change in the process with time is more significant than the shape of the probability distribution, and then one uses a time-series model. In other situations, the shape of the probability distribution from which observations are taken is of much more concern than the very gradual shifts in level that may occur. Then one uses a probability model to represent the observations.

The event which we want to forecast is some observation that can be represented by a number: the time when you get home, or the number of "economy rolls" sold by a warehouse in a week. The numbers that will be observed are limited to some range. You never get home before 5:20, and you are always home by 6:30. Or, the warehouse can't sell a negative number of economy rolls in a week (customer returns are not allowed), and no more than 400 rolls have ever been sold in one week.

The probability distribution is a function that describes the chances that an observation will be less than some specified number. The probability that an observation will be less than the lower end of the range is zero. The probability that it will be less than the upper end of the range is one. For any number within the range, the probability is some number between zero and one. The probability function must increase. The probability that an observation will be less than x_1 can be represented by $P(x_1)$. Then, for any other number x_2 such that $x_2 \geqslant x_1$, it must be true that $P(x_2) \geqslant P(x_1)$.

Several standard mathematical functions are frequently used for these probability distributions. Among the more common are the normal distribution, the poisson distribution, the uniform distribution, the exponential distribution, the gamma distribution, and so on. In Section V, we shall deal with some of the properties of these distributions, since they represent quite nicely the probabilities that are met in certain cases.

Any curve that rises monotonically from zero to one can be a probability distribution, and there is no reason to suppose that all such curves will have nice mathematical formulas. And sometimes one encounters a process in which a forecast is required where the probabilities can't be approximated well enough by any of the standard formulas.

Recall the problem discussed on page 55. Your wife can be quite sure that you won't be home before 5:20 and equally sure that you will be home before 6:30. In between those times there is some probability distribution that says "there is a probability $P(t)$ that he will be home before time t, where $P(5:20) = 0$, and $P(6:30) = 1.0$." There may, for example, be a fifty-fifty chance that you get home by 5:40, so that $P(5:40) = 0.5$. By long experience, your wife has built up some sort of estimate of this probability distribution, which might be represented by Fig. 5.1.

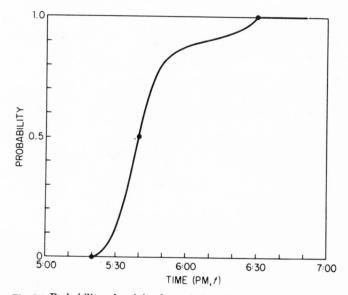

Fig. 5.1 Probability of arriving home before time t.

Now let's take the problem a stage further. This probability distribution changes slowly with time. As new roads are built, your driving time decreases. As there are major construction projects on your, or parallel, routes, the pattern of traffic changes so that what used to be a fast route is now slower. New policemen are assigned to point duty and either accelerate or impede traffic flow. All of these change the driving time. Then as you stay with the company longer, you are either increasingly able to get away early, or more likely to be called into late meetings, which affect your starting time.

These changes are gradual; you don't announce on a Tuesday, "From now on I'll be leaving earlier and driving faster. So my mean time of arrival will be twelve minutes earlier than before." Your wife has to learn, by repetitive observation of actual times of arrival, that the probability distribution has changed.

Here we have a case that illustrates three essential elements for the successful use of probability models: (1) The probability distribution changes with time, but only very gradually. At any one point in time, the present estimate of the distribution is sufficient for forecasting tomorrow's arrival time. (2) Successive observations have no important serial correlation. In our example there may be a significant seasonal pattern, but a knowledge of the time of arrival yesterday is of no particular help in forecasting today's time of arrival. (3) The essential description is contained in a probability distribution (which may have all sorts of weird steps and plateaus). That is, we do not say that a sample is taken from a normal distribution, or a poisson distribution, or a gamma distribution. If we know the form of the distribution, then one or two parameter values describe the entire distribution uniquely. Here we are looking directly at the empirical distribution, not at an approximating family of statistical functions, generated from a few parameter values.

Think for a moment how a forecast will be used. Your wife wants to plan dinner according to when she thinks you'll get home. She wants to be "quite sure" that you will be home by the time dinner is ready. If she planned always to have it at 6:30, you'd always be home in time. But there would be some days when you'd have to wait an hour and ten minutes after you were home before you could eat, so 6:30 is too late. At the risk of some chance that you won't be home in time, your wife plans on an earlier dinner hour, to cut the time you have to wait on the days when you get home early. Perhaps "quite sure" means a probability of 0.95 that you will be home before dinner is ready. If she thinks that there is a 95 percent chance that you'll be home by 5:50, she can plan dinner for that time, and save you up to forty-minutes' wait.

Of course your wife's analysis isn't all that formal. But the manager of

Warehouse 10 has the same sort of problem, in deciding how many economy rolls to have in stock to meet demand. He's never sold as many as 400 rolls in one week, so that if he had 400 rolls in stock he could always satisfy whatever demand there is. But much of the time he'd have a substantial inventory.

If he planned to have a smaller number of rolls in stock, he'd cut the inventory investment at the expense of occasionally not being able to satisfy demand immediately. As a matter of fact (see Table C.11), if he had 60 rolls in stock at all times, he would have had enough to satisfy the demand 95 percent of the time. In only 5 percent of the weeks would he have had to take special measures to satisfy demand.

In both these cases, we see that the use of the forecast is to find a number X such that $P(X) = 0.95$. In other cases, we might want to find a number such that $P(X) = 0.1$, or 0.99, or any other number between zero and one. A forecast of the average time of arrival, or the average sales per week is of interest only if it helps to find a time or a sales level such that there's a 95 percent chance that future observations will be less than that number.

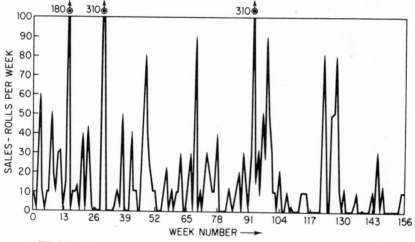

Fig. 5.2 Weekly sales of economy rolls at warehouse 10.

Figure 5.2 shows the data on the weekly sales of economy rolls. There's very little pattern that could usefully be represented by a time-series model. The autocorrelation function for the weekly sales is plotted in Fig. 5.3, and there is no relationship between sales in one week and the sales in any other week. The observations are random samples from some probability distribution, and there's no evidence that that distribution is changing in any significant way with time.

Figure 5.4 is a plot of the probability distribution derived from the data in Table C.11. This distribution would be hard to represent by any of the standard mathematical formulas. Probably the best such representation

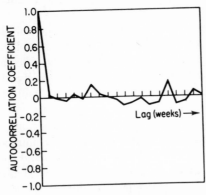

Fig. 5.3 Autocorrelation function for economy roll sales.

would be a 40 percent chance that the warehouse doesn't sell anything in a week, and the other 60 percent described by an exponential distribution. Even this description is not entirely adequate for planning, however, since

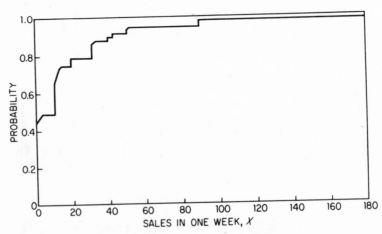

Fig. 5.4 Fraction of weeks in which sales have been $\leqslant X$.

there is a very strong tendency for the orders to be in multiples of 10 and of 30 rolls. The 95 percent point on the exponential distribution model would call for 63 rolls in stock. But the warehouse either has a demand for less than 60, or for at least 80 rolls. There are definite discontinuous jumps;

and if these can be taken into account, the warehouse can save another three rolls in stock.

Exercise. If it were good trade practice to have material in stock 60 percent of the weeks, how many economy rolls would you stock?

When it was appropriate to describe a set of observations by a time series, we set up a model in which there were several functions of time. These functions were combined with a set of coefficients for which the values were to be estimated from the data. We count one degree of freedom for each coefficient to be determined.

In a probability model, we also want to set the problem up so that there is a small set of numbers (parameters) for which the values are to be estimated from the data. These parameters, however, will not be the coefficients in a linear combination of time functions. They will represent probabilities. The next question is, which probabilities will be the most useful?

Since computation of these probabilities will be very simple, we can choose a somewhat larger number of degrees of freedom, perhaps $n = 10$. Divide the range of the variable being observed into n class intervals. That is, pick $n + 1$ class limits x_i, $i = 0, 1, \ldots, n$, in such a way that

$$x_0 < x_1 < x_2 < \ldots < x_n$$

and so that x_0 is the lower end of the range and x_n is the upper end of the range. That is $P(x_0) = 0$ and $P(x_n) = 1.0$.

The kth class interval includes all observations x such that $x_{k-1} < x \leqslant x_k$. (In some applications, it may be desirable to put the equality at the lower end of the class interval.) There are n mutually exclusive and collectively exhaustive events: that an observation will fall in the kth class interval, $k = 1, 2, \ldots, n$. The probabilities that will be computed from the data are the probabilities of these n events. The probability model can be written formally as

$$P(x) = \mathbf{P}$$

where $\mathbf{P}$ is a vector with n components $P(x_1), P(x_2), \ldots, P(x_n)$. These are the probabilities that any observation x will be less than, or equal to, the specified class limit.

In practice, it is simpler to compute estimates for each of the n class intervals, and then to cumulate them to get the required probabilities $\mathbf{P}$. Let $a_1 = P(x_1)$; $a_2 = P(x_2) - P(x_1)$; $a_3 = P(x_3) - P(x_2)$; $\ldots$; and $a_n = P(x_n) - P(x_{n-1})$. These numbers can be conveniently represented as an n-component vector $\mathbf{a}$. Each of the components must be non-negative, and they must sum to one.

Now, of course, the values of **a** are not known, any more than the true values of the coefficients in a time-series model are known. The values will be estimated from the data **â**. The forecast of the probability distribution for future observations is then

$$\hat{P}(x) = \hat{\mathbf{P}}$$

The class limits x_k should not, in general, be picked to divide the entire range equally. If the ninety-fifth percentile of the distribution is the goal of the forecast, then pick the first class limit so that approximately 90 percent of the observations will fall in the first class interval, and 1 percent in each of the others. That is, pick x_1 so that (as well as you can guess in advance) $P(x_1) = 0.90$, and then pick x_2 so that $P(x_2) = 0.91$, and x_3 so that $P(x_3) = 0.92$, and so on. As the data come in, and the estimates of **a** are revised, it won't be true that $\hat{P}(x_6) = 0.95$, but there will be some one of the class limits that is close to the right place.

In the case of the economy rolls, on the basis of the historical data in Table C.11, one might pick the following class limits:

$x_0 = 0$	$P(x_0) = 0$	
$x_1 = 40$	$P(x_1) = 0.90$	$a_1 = 0.90$
$x_2 = 45$	$P(x_2) = 0.91$	$a_2 = 0.01$
$x_3 = 50$	$P(x_3) = 0.93$	$a_3 = 0.02$
$x_4 = 55$	$P(x_4) = 0.94$	$a_4 = 0.01$
$x_5 = 60$	$P(x_5) = 0.95$	$a_5 = 0.01$
$x_6 = 70$	$P(x_6) = 0.96$	$a_6 = 0.01$
$x_7 = 80$	$P(x_7) = 0.97$	$a_7 = 0.01$
$x_8 = 90$	$P(x_8) = 0.98$	$a_8 = 0.01$
$x_9 = 200$	$P(x_9) = 0.99$	$a_9 = 0.01$
$x_{10} = 400$	$P(x_{10}) = 1.00$	$a_{10} = 0.01$

Section III Smoothing Techniques

"It would then be worth accepting as a temporary hypothesis. If the fresh facts which come to our knowledge all fit themselves into the scheme, then our hypothesis may gradually become a solution . . . It is an error to argue in front of your data. You find yourself insensibly twisting them round to fit your theories."

Wisteria Lodge

The process of gasoline consumption in your car can be described by a model of constant gas mileage. You estimate that at present the numerical value of that constant is 20 miles per gallon. You therefore forecast that you can go another 20 miles and burn approximately 1 gallon.

The process controlling an automobile's position under constant acceleration can be described by a quadratic function of time. If the distance is measured in feet from the point where the car started at rest, then a numerical estimate of the coefficient of the quadratic term in the model might be 0.16. A forecast of future positions would then be $0.16t^2$ feet from the starting reference where t is measured in seconds.

The model of the times when you get home is a vector of probabilities **a**, corresponding to certain intervals of time (say each ten minutes from 5:20 to 6:30). Your wife's estimate of the probability that you'll be home between 5:40 and 5:50 may be 0.2. When that estimate is combined with similar estimates for all the other time intervals, her forecast is that there's a 95 percent chance you'll be home by 5:50.

In this section, we shall discuss several smoothing techniques for estimating the numerical values of these coefficients from noisy observations of the process. Smoothing is a process like curve fitting, but there is a distinction that is perhaps more than just a different point of view. In a curve-fitting problem, one has a set of data to which some appropriate curve is to be fitted. The computations are done once, and the curve should fit "equally well" to the entire set of data.

A smoothing problem starts the same way, with good clean data and a reasonable model to represent the process being forecast. The model is fitted to the data; that is, the coefficients in the model are estimated from the data available to date. So far, the problem is a simple curve-fitting problem. The differences are two. (1) The model should fit current data very well, but it is not important that data obtained a long time ago fit so well. (2) The computations are repeated with each new observation. The process is essentially iterative, so that it is important that the computational procedures be fast and simple. These differences stem from the fact that the values of the coefficients in the true process may be changing slowly and at random.

In this section, we shall develop practical techniques for smoothing the observations to date to obtain estimates of the present numerical values of the various coefficients and parameters that appear in the model of the process. The observations of the process include noise: random, unpredictable fluctuations. The smoothing techniques "average" (in a very general sense) past data in order to reduce the average contribution of the random noise to a negligible level. You don't estimate gasoline mileage solely from the data on the last time you filled the tank. You average over several past tankfuls in order to eliminate the effects of the different levels to which the tank is filled and the different driving conditions encountered.

Chapter 6 discusses three criteria for judging the effectiveness of alternative methods of smoothing: accuracy, simplicity of computation, and flexibility to adjust the rate of response of the forecast system. These criteria will have different relative importance in different applications. You may want to investigate other criteria as well.

In Chapter 7, we develop the concepts of simple exponential smoothing for estimating the value of the only coefficient in a constant model. Exponential smoothing is a simple procedure for calculating a weighted moving average in which the heaviest weight is assigned to the most recent data and in which the computations are particularly suited to the characteristics of automatic data-processing equipment. By a suitable selection of the value for the smoothing constant, exponential smoothing can be made to yield estimates of the coefficient that are statistically the same as those derived from any other method of averaging the data. Chapter 8 compares exponential smoothing with several other common moving averages and discusses the problem of selecting an appropriate value of the smoothing constant.

Chapter 9 extends the notion of exponential smoothing to the estimate of all the coefficients in any polynomial model, and the relevant characteristics of such multiple smoothing are analyzed in Chapter 10.

Adaptive smoothing (Chapter 11) is an even further extension of exponential smoothing to the estimates of coefficients in transcendental models, or in models that combine algebraic and transcendental functions. Up to a point, the analysis follows the development of multiple regression. At the fork in the road, we shall follow the path that leads to very simple and compact computations, because of the special characteristics of the mathematical models used.

Chapter 12 continues the development of adaptive smoothing to steady state conditions. The principal result is a set of tables that give the program constants necessary to revise the estimates of coefficients in the light of new data for a wide variety of polynomial and trigonometric models.

The final chapter in this section (Chapter 13) extends exponential smoothing in still another direction to vector smoothing: a process of estimating the current values of the probabilities in a probability model.

At this point, some readers may think that the book would have been better organized by taking up each model and the associated smoothing and forecasting computations in turn, before going on to the next type of model with its associated computations. The present organization is quite deliberate, intended to encourage the reader to think through models as such, then smoothing techniques as such, and finally forecast computations as such. When an entire system of forecasting is presented in one package there is a strong temptation for the designer to adopt one and try to make it work. When one thoughtfully contrasts the available alternatives on each floor of our department store, he is much more likely to select the right combination. Hopefully, the present organization will also suggest new lines of research to develop methods not discussed here.

6 Criteria

A partial bibliography of the literature dealing with forecasting and smoothing techniques (of which many have been proposed) fills many pages at the end of this book. We shall suggest more techniques. Some way of choosing among all these possibilities is needed since no one technique will be universally satisfactory. When making a choice, moreover, you need some criteria by which to judge the relative merits of each alternative.

This chapter discusses three criteria which are frequently important. The relative weight one assigns to each of these three will depend a great deal on the nature of the application. Undoubtedly there are other criteria that will be important. If you do not like a particular method of operating, you must have some reason for your dislike. Try to state formally what that reason is. If you can state it accurately, you may be able to modify the suggested method of operation to satisfy the objection. Section VI will discuss that cycle: suggestion, evaluation, and modification. Repeated tours around that circuit should lead to a very satisfactory result.

Let us start with the following three criteria, which are usually important:

Accuracy
Simplicity of computation
Flexibility to adjust the rate of response

These three criteria have been very important in the development of exponential smoothing and its extensions.

ACCURACY. The need for an accurate estimate of the coefficients in the forecast model is obvious. The ultimate accuracy of the forecast will be greatly influenced by the choice of the data observed about the process and the form of the model chosen to represent the underlying process. The observations should be as near the true process as possible; the noise should have zero mean, small variance, and serial independence among successive samples. The model must be an accurate representation of the true underlying process. In this section, we are concerned with the accuracy of estimating coefficient values; Section V goes more deeply into the analysis of the accuracy of the resulting forecasts. An accurate estimate of the coefficients in the wrong model may lead to poor forecasts.

There are several possible measures of accuracy. Chebyshev developed techniques of fitting a line (or higher-order polynomial) to a set of noisy data in such a way as to minimize the maximum difference between any observation and the value that would be forecast by the model at that time.* In an inventory control system, a good forecast would be one that maximized the service rendered for a given average inventory investment. That is, very large errors in the forecast could be tolerated if they always occurred when the inventory was large: accuracy is required only near the time when one has a real choice in deciding whether or not to order more stock. There is a great deal of work being done on maximum likelihood estimation.

In this book, we shall use a least-squares criterion of accuracy. The values of the coefficients are computed in such a way as to minimize the sum of the squares of the residuals between the observations and the values forecast by the model. The square of this difference is discounted in time away from the most recent observation. The difference between the current observation and the model is weighted at full value. An observation obtained t periods ago is weighted by β^t where β is some appropriate fraction less than one. Therefore, observations obtained a long time ago are weighted very little in the current computation of the coefficients. If one takes $\beta = 1$, then all observations are weighted equally, and the coefficients are estimated just as they would be in a conventional curve-fitting problem.

Exercise. Show that the average of a set of numbers does minimize the sum of the squares of the differences between the data and the resulting constant. Under

---

* F. J. Scheid, "The Under-Over-Under Theorem," *American Mathematical Monthly*, Vol. 68, No. 9 (November, 1961), 862–71. (Incidentally, this article is an excellent example of simple, accurate writing in an entertaining style on a complicated mathematical subject.)

what error criterion would one use the median or the mode, rather than the mean, as the estimate of a single constant?

If you can state the real criterion of accuracy that is important in your control system, you can always find some mathematician who can carry out the necessary derivations. Don't be misled into believing that discounted least squares is the only possible criterion. The correct solution to the wrong problem won't help you much.

SIMPLICITY OF COMPUTATION. The people at Cape Canaveral have to track only one missile shot at a time, to forecast its future course (such as the impact point, and other data for the range safety officer). The cost of computing equipment is very small compared with the total cost of a missile shot, so they can afford to use very elaborate computing techniques, if they can get better results. At the Smithsonian Astrophysical Laboratory where they are tracking satellites, there are only (as of this writing*) 27 satellites for which the orbits are being computed. The data are basically the three coordinates of each observation and their time derivatives. Still there are less than 180 time series to be processed, and elaborate computations can be afforded if they result in greater accuracy.

The SAGE air defense system, however, may some day be required to track many hundreds of targets, and a few microseconds per observation may begin to be significantly different from a few milliseconds per observation, because there are so many more observations.

In an inventory control system, it may be necessary to recompute forecasts for tens or even hundreds of thousands of items every month. One-tenth second consumed unnecessarily for each of 100,000 items amounts to approximately three hours. Three extra hours of computer time a month may be expensive. In some companies, serious consideration has been given to getting a larger computer. Even if you don't incur the direct cost of a larger computer, there may be the indirect cost of not being able to use the computer for some other function in the company.

Clearly then, simplicity of computation has different importance in different applications. The larger the number of different time series for which forecasts are routinely recomputed, the more important it is that each computation be simple and fast.

Simplicity for automatic data-processing equipment is not quite the same as computational simplicity for a person. A computer can generally perform any of the arithmetic operations quickly and easily. Even so, division and square roots should be avoided, especially on some of the slower and simpler machines. A computer takes significant time to read in

* *The New York Times*, 8 Oct., 1961.

the file on which data from previous forecasts are recorded. Even when the previous forecast data are recorded in internal memory, significant time is required to look up each piece of information. If the computations can be based on fewer words of information about the history of the observations, the computation will be faster. Not only is the reading speed per record increased, but there is more room in the memory for program instructions.

In applications involving a large number of different forecasts, a short file of historical data is worth striving for. In this book, we shall try to base the forecasts on as few words of information as possible, so that there will be more room in the record for other information required by the control system for which the forecasts are being generated. Most systems designers seem to want a few more card columns for something.

When a forecast system is being designed for hand computation, a different measure of simplicity is required. Multiplication and division take appreciably longer than addition and subtraction, and many clerks cannot be relied on to get accurate answers. Square roots are not to be considered at all. Hence, a clerical system should stress simplicity of the arithmetic. On the other hand, there is generally no penalty for using a long record of past data in a manual system. A computer can erase a previous result when it's no longer needed and write the new result in the same place. The new result in a manual record is written on the next line, so that the previous data are still available if they will be useful. There is one operation that a person can perform quite well, which is rather difficult for a computer. A clerk can scan a list of figures and find the next-to-the-largest number in the last twenty quite easily. In Chapter 18, we shall discuss some special techniques that capitalize on this ability.

FLEXIBILITY TO ADJUST RATE OF RESPONSE. It is fundamental to the whole development of our theme in this book that we have to deal with noisy data. One way of looking at the smoothing process is as a means of filtering the noise out of the observations in order to recover an estimate of the underlying process.

Here is a new observation. It's different from what we expected it to be. The difference may be purely noise, or it may be the beginning of a new pattern. Every issue of *The Wall Street Journal* or of *Business Week* contains statements like, "The cost of living went up 0.1 percent last month," or "Steel production turned down in the last quarter." "IBM common stock prices have been rising recently. Today the closing price was down $3."

Are these changes significant of a change in the process that governs the cost of living, steel production, or the price of a security? Or are they noisy fluctuations around the same old process?

When the current observation is different from what we had expected there are two considerations. If the difference is a purely random fluctuation, then the forecast should smooth out the fluctuation, and the coefficients in the model should be estimated on the basis of quite a lot of past data. But if this difference is significant of a new pattern, then the past data are irrelevant. The coefficients should be estimated only from data that are relevant to the current process.

On the basis of a great deal of external information, you may predict that this is (or is not) a significant change in pattern. In Chapter 16, we shall show how a significant change can be detected automatically by internal evidence soon after it has taken place. (Sorry, I can't compete in the league that professes to be able to spot turning points before they happen. I can, of course, use its predictions as one of the pieces of data employed in computing the forecast.)

In this book, we are concerned with forecasts of processes where the true values of the coefficients can change from time to time. The introduction of a new product, or a promotional campaign, may change the demand for a manufactured product. A gust of wind may change the course of an aircraft, or the pilot may decide to maneuver. An epidemic may radically affect the demand for drugs. In such cases, it is utter nonsense to try to find a model that fits the time series both before and after the change. Stability of estimates in the face of random fluctuations must be sacrificed in favor of rapid response to the new conditions. We expect the process underlying the observations to go through a slow random walk. The coefficients in the true process change by very small, random increments. That expectation leads to the notion of discounting old data. Occasionally there may be a radical jump in one or more of the true coefficients; it may be necessary to reset initial conditions; in any event, old data should be discounted more rapidly at the time of such a jump.

To the extent that such radical changes are possible in the data, some provision must be incorporated for easily adjusting the number of past observations that are effective in current computations. When a long series of observations comes from the same process, it is best to estimate the coefficients by averaging over a great deal of data. Whenever there is a significant change in the pattern, computations should be based on only the most recent observations.

Exercise. Discuss the relative weights on these three criteria for (1) the sales forecast used to set company budgets; (2) an inventory control system; (3) rally handicapping; (4) weather forecasting; and (5) missile tracking.

Several other criteria will be discussed in this book. One system of forecasting may be desirable in the long run, but another may be used as an interim step from the present methods to the ultimate if it "makes more sense" to the people involved so that they will accept the innovation more readily. Another obvious point is that, if the observations $x_t = \xi_t$ (with no noise), the smoothing process should compute the values for the coefficients in ξ exactly.

A production control process can be designed to plan the correct quantities whether sales continue at a steady rate or start to increase linearly.* Such a system will respond perfectly to changes in the pattern of demand, but will fluctuate in the presence of noise.

* R. A. Howard, "Control Processes," in *Notes on Operations Research 1959* (Cambridge, Mass.: Technology Press, M.I.T., 1959).

7 Exponential Smoothing

In this chapter, we shall consider only a process where a constant model is to be entertained. For one reason or another, we are willing to believe that the underlying process is locally constant $\xi_t = a$. The observations include random noise

$$x_t = a + \epsilon_t$$

where the noise samples $\{\epsilon_t\}$ have an average value of zero. It is quite possible that in different parts of the sequence of observations, widely separated from each other, the value of the single coefficient a will change. But in any local segment, a single value gives a reasonably good model of the process.

We would now like to estimate the current value of that coefficient by some sort of an average. Since the value can change gradually with time, the average computed at any time should place more weight on current observations than on those obtained a long time ago. The moving average is in common use for just that reason; hence we shall start by discussing the moving average as an estimate of the coefficient in a constant model. Then we shall proceed by an intuitive argument to develop the basic principles of exponential smoothing, as an alternative estimate of the coefficient.

Moving Averages

Let us start with six successive observations of the process, say: $x_1 = 18$, $x_2 = 23$, $x_3 = 22$, $x_4 = 17$, $x_5 = 25$, and $x_6 = 15$. The average of these numbers is $M_6 = 20.0$. A reasonable estimate of the coefficient is that average

$$\hat{a}_6 = M_6 = 20.0$$

Since the errors average to zero, the forecast for any future observation is

$$\hat{x}_{6+\tau} = 20.0$$

Remember that any variable with a hat over it is merely an estimate, based on some data, of its value. Thus,

$$M_t = \frac{x_t + x_{t-1} + \ldots + x_{t-N+1}}{N}$$

is the actual average of the N most recent observations, computed at time t. It is a fact. Its value is useful as an estimate of the coefficient $\hat{a}_t$, but as we shall see later, it is not the only possible numerical value that could be used for that estimate.

Now let us move ahead one period in time; we find that the seventh observation is $x_7 = 22$. Now the average is $M_7 = 20\frac{2}{3}$, if we stick to the process of averaging only the most recent $N = 6$ observations. The arithmetic could be arranged in a number of ways. The obvious one, of course, is to add the most recent six observations and divide the sum by 6. Another way is to add $\frac{1}{6}$ of the new observation and subtract $\frac{1}{6}$ of the observation N period ago from the previous value of the average.

$$M_t = M_{t-1} + \frac{x_t - x_{t-N}}{N}$$

For example, suppose the next observation is $x_8 = 18$.

$$M_8 = \frac{18 + 22 + 15 + 25 + 17 + 22}{6} = \frac{119}{6} = 19.8333$$

Alternatively,

$$M_8 = \frac{62}{3} + \frac{18 - 23}{6} = \frac{62}{3} - \frac{5}{6} = 19.8333$$

With this sequence of observations, the successive estimates of the coefficient would be

$$\hat{a}_6 = 20.0, \quad \hat{a}_7 = 20.667, \quad \hat{a}_8 = 19.833, \ldots$$

The process of computing a moving average is quite simple and straightforward. It is accurate: the average minimizes the sum of squares of the differences between the most recent N observations and the estimate of the coefficient in the model. It is simple for automatic data-processing equipment or for manual computation. It is, however, difficult to change the rate of response in this system.

The rate of response is controlled by the choice of the number N of observations to be averaged. If N is large, the estimates will be very stable. Suppose that the observations do, in fact, come from a constant process, where a has a true value, and where the noise samples $\{\epsilon_t\}$ are random samples from some distribution with zero mean and variance σ_ϵ^2. Then the average is an unbiased estimate of the coefficient a, and the variance of the successive estimates is $\sigma_M^2 = \sigma_\epsilon^2/N$. But if the process is one which generates data as random noise superimposed on one constant level a_1 for a while, and then suddenly jumps to a new level a_2, it will take N observations for the moving average to yield estimates relevant to this new level.

When the process is actually constant, it would be helpful to use a large value of N, to get accurate estimates of the mean. When the process is changing, it would be helpful to have small values of N for rapid response. It is usually difficult to change the number of observations averaged; such a change may involve redesign of the files, and some reprogramming.

We shall discuss the choice of N in Chapter 8, as a compromise between these conflicting objectives.

Exercise. Set up a copy of Work Sheet No. 1, with lines for 52 successive observations. Enter the installation rates from Table C.3, as the data. Compute the ten-month moving averages, and plot them with the original data on a graph. Save the results. Later exercises will extend this example.

Exponential Smoothing

In some data-processing installations, it is a disadvantage to have to carry all the past data necessary to compute the moving average. For example, the Trendline Corporation computes a 200-day moving average of stock prices, which means that they must carry records of the actual prices in each of the past 200 days for each of some 1600 stocks traded on the New York Stock Exchange. A lot of data. Let's see if we cen't shorten the files a little.

One way would be to carry just the total to date of all observations and the number of observations there had been. The ratio of these two figures is another average, computed from quite short files. It is the best average when the process doesn't change. It is the worst average, however, when there are significant changes in the true process. In most business problems, the moving average is preferable.

Work Sheet No. 1   MOVING AVERAGES

DATA: Installation Rates, Table C.3
MODEL: Constant $x_t = a + \epsilon_t$
SMOOTHING: Moving average, $N = 10$

Date	Data	Lagged Data	Average
t	x_t	x_{t-10}	$M_t = M_{t-1} + \dfrac{x_t - x_{t-10}}{10}$
1	0.390	....	....
2	0.323	....	....
3	0.371	....	....
4	0.326	....	....
5	0.358	....	....
6	0.448	....	....
7	0.444	....	....
8	0.382	....	....
9	0.276	....	....
10	0.326	(Sum = 3.644)	0.3644
11	0.204	0.390	0.3458
12	0.436	0.323	0.3571
13	0.305	0.371	0.3505
14	0.338	0.326	0.3517
15	0.362	0.358	0.3521
.	.	.	.
.	.	.	.
.	.	.	.

Let's try another tack. Suppose that after the eighth observation in our previous example there were some catastrophe in the data-processing center, which destroyed all historical information, but left a record of the average $M_8 = 19\frac{5}{8}$. This has certainly shortened the files. Now the next observation is $x_9 = 21$. We want to revise our estimate of the average in the light of this new information.

If we knew what x_3 had been, the new average would be

$$M_9 = M_8 + \frac{x_9 - x_3}{6}$$

but we no longer know what x_3 was. Our best estimate is that it was equal to the average of all the data; that is, $\hat{x}_3 = M_8 = 19\frac{5}{8}$. Now the new estimate of the average is

$$\hat{M}_9 = M_8 + \frac{x_9 - M_8}{6} = \frac{1}{6}x_9 + \left(1 - \frac{1}{6}\right)M_8$$

We must put the hat over $\hat{M}_9$ because it isn't the same computation as the way we defined the moving average M_t; it's merely an estimate. This process, however, is a perfectly definite operation on a set of observations, so let us use the notation S (for smoothing) in place of the M (for moving average).

If this process were carried out on each successive observation, the definition of the smoothed function of the observations is

$$S_t(x) = \alpha x_t + (1 - \alpha)S_{t-1}(x)$$

where the smoothing constant α is like, but not exactly equal to, the fraction $1/N$ in a moving average. If we were to carry on our example with $\alpha = \frac{1}{6}$, the answer would be

$$S_9 = \frac{21}{6} + \frac{5}{6} \times \frac{119}{6} = \frac{721}{36} = 20.03$$

This operation performed on any sequence of observations is called *exponential smoothing*. The new smoothed value is equal to the previous smoothed value plus a fraction α of the difference between the new observation and the previous smoothed value. We can substitute for the previous smoothed value the equation that says how it was obtained in terms of a still earlier smoothed value.

$$\begin{aligned}
S_t(x) &= \alpha x_t + (1 - \alpha)[\alpha x_{t-1} + (1 - \alpha)S_{t-2}(x)] \\
&= \alpha x_t + \alpha(1 - \alpha)x_{t-1} + (1 - \alpha)^2[\alpha x_{t-2} + (1 - \alpha)S_{t-3}(x)] \\
&= \alpha x_t + \alpha(1 - \alpha)x_{t-1} + \alpha(1 - \alpha)^2 x_{t-2} + \dots \\
&\qquad\qquad + \alpha(1 - \alpha)^n x_{t-n} + \dots + (1 - \alpha)^t x_0 \\
&= \alpha \sum_{k=0}^{t-1} (1 - \alpha)^k x_{t-k} + (1 - \alpha)^t x_0
\end{aligned}$$

The function $S_t(x)$ is a linear combination of all past observations. The weight given to previous observations decreases geometrically with age. If the smoothing constant is $\alpha = 0.3$, then the current observation has weight 0.3. The previous observations have weights 0.21, 0.147, 0.1029, and so on. Figure 7.1 compares the weight given past data for a moving average ($N = 6$), and exponential smoothing ($\alpha = 0.3$).

The expected value of this function of the observations is

$$\mathcal{E}[S(x)] = \alpha \sum_0^\infty \beta^k \mathcal{E}[x_{t-k}]$$

$$= \mathcal{E}[x]\alpha \sum_0^\infty \beta^k = \frac{\alpha}{1 - \beta} \mathcal{E}[x] = \mathcal{E}[x]$$

where, for convenience, we let $\beta = (1 - \alpha)$. Since the expectation of the function is equal to the expectation of the data, we are justified in calling it an *average*. Now we have a new way of estimating the value of the coefficient in a constant model.

$$\hat{a}_t = S_t(x)$$

Exponential smoothing is accurate. In Chapter 9, we shall prove that the function $S(x)$ minimizes the weighted sum of squared residuals. The computations are simple, requiring even less arithmetic than a moving average, and the file of historical information has been shortened from

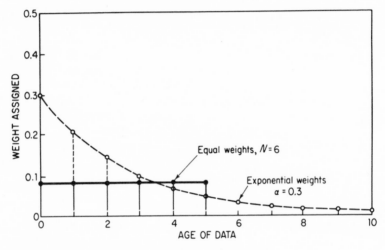

Fig. 7.1 Two ways of weighting data in a moving average.

$N - 1$ past observations to only the one word $S_{t-1}(x)$. Finally, exponential smoothing is quite flexible. When the smoothing constant is small, the function $S(x)$ behaves like the average of a great deal of past data, and therefore the variance of the estimate of the coefficient is small. When the smoothing constant is large, $S(x)$ will respond rapidly to changes in pattern. No reprogramming or change in file layout is required to adjust the speed of response. Much of Chapter 8 is concerned with the effects of alternative choices for the value of the smoothing constant.

INITIAL CONDITIONS. Exponential smoothing always requires a previous value of the smoothing function. When the process is started, there must be some value that can be used as the previous value S_{t-1}. If there are past data at the time one starts to use exponential smoothing, then the best initial value would be a simple average of the most recent N observations: $S_{t-1} = M_{t-1}$ initially.

Frequently there will be no past data to average: smoothing starts with the first observation. In this case, a prediction of the average is required. The prediction may be what the process is intended to do—as in the intended velocity of a missile or the intended sales rate of a new product. In other cases, the prediction can be based on similarity with other processes that have been observed for some time, as in the case of a new item added to an inventory.

After k observations, the weight given to the initial condition is β^k. If you have a great deal of confidence in the prediction of initial conditions, use a small value of the smoothing constant, $\alpha \sim 0$. If you have very little confidence in your initial prediction, use a larger value, so that the initial conditions will quickly be discounted. This argument is just the same as the argument about flexibility to respond to a change in the process. If you think that the real process is just like your prediction, you don't want the estimate to change. If you think that there is a change between your prediction and the real process, then you want rapid response.

Exercise. Set up a copy of Work Sheet No. 2, with the same data (Table C.3, installation rates) as before. Carry out the exponential smoothing computations with a smoothing constant $\alpha = 0.2$. For initial conditions use $M_{10} = 0.3644$. Compare the results with the moving averages of the same data. Save the results for later exercises.

Work Sheet No. 2   EXPONENTIAL SMOOTHING

DATA: Installation Rates, Table C.3
MODEL: Constant, $X_t = a + \epsilon_t$
SMOOTHING: Exponential Smoothing; $\alpha = 0.2$

$$S_{10}(x) = 0.3644$$

Date	Data	Smoothed Data
t	x_t	$S_t(x) = 0.2x_t + 0.8S_{t-1}(x)$
10	....	0.3644
11	0.204	0.3323
12	0.436	0.3530
13	0.305	0.3434
14	0.338	0.3423
15	0.362	0.3462
.	.	.
.	.	.
.	.	.

Exponential smoothing is a quite common sort of averaging. In the field of systems engineering, this is the simplest case of proportional control. The estimate is corrected with each new observation in proportion to the difference between the previous estimate and the new observation. Some manufacturers set a new production plan each month. They consider the inventory they have now and the inventory they would like to have in the future. This inventory difference, together with a forecast of shipments, determines the ideal rate of production to be followed in the next month. But it's not desirable to change production rates abruptly, so the actual plan is equal to the present production rate plus a fraction of the difference between the current production rate and the ideal rate. This computation is exactly that of exponential smoothing.

Psychologists who have studied the detailed process by which a person learns have come up with a similar model. One's understanding at any time is equal to his previous understanding plus some fraction of the difference between a new experience and his previous understanding.

Bradford at General Electric* has hypothesized a model in which sales in the current year will be like sales last year plus a proportional correction for the difference between advertising rates and previous sales.

Continuous Observations

In this book, we are concerned only with discrete time series, where the data are discrete observations. It may be of some interest, however, to mention the continuous analogy of discrete exponential smoothing, which may be used (for example, in continuous target tracking in a fire-control system) when the data are continuous, or in simulating a discrete system on an analog computer.

The basic smoothing operation may be written

$$y(t) = \alpha x(t) + (1 - \alpha)y(t - 1)$$

or
$$\frac{y(t) - y(t - \Delta t)}{\Delta t} = \gamma[x(t) - y(t - \Delta(t))]$$

On passing to the limit $\Delta t \to 0$

$$\frac{dy}{dt} = \gamma[x(t) - y(t)]$$

To solve the differential equation, let $y = uv$. It is easily shown that if

$$u(t) = e^{-\gamma t}$$

then the variables are separable, and we get

---

* G. A. Bradford, "What GE is Doing to Evaluate the Effect on Sales of Its Industrial and Consumer Advertising," Advertising Research Foundation, *OR in Advertising*, New York, 1961.

$$v(t) = \int \gamma e^{\gamma\tau} x(\tau)\, d\tau + C$$

Thus
$$y(T) = \gamma \int_0^T e^{-\gamma(T-\tau)} x(\tau)\, d\tau + Ce^{-\gamma T}$$

This equation is the continuous analog of

$$S_T(x) = \alpha \sum_{j=0}^{T-1} (1 - \alpha)^j x_{T-j} + (1 - \alpha)^T x_0$$

which has been previously noted for the discrete case. If the data are bounded, the discrete sum converges for $0 \leqslant \alpha \leqslant 1$, whereas the continuous integral converges for $0 < \gamma < \infty$. Thus, the smoothing constant γ is not the same as α.

Current data ($\tau = T$) are weighted by α, and the older the data are ($\tau < T$), the smaller the weight assigned. Note that in the continuous case the weights do, in fact, decline exponentially, thus justifying the name applied to the smoothing technique. A purist would call the discrete case *geometric smoothing*.

It remains to discuss the arbitrary constant. We can take the origin of time $t = 0$ as the time when the smoothing process started, with the initial condition $y(0)$. Hence, the particular solution is

$$y(T) = \gamma \int_0^T e^{-\gamma(T-\tau)} x(\tau)\, d\tau + y(0)e^{-\gamma t}$$

If the process goes on sufficiently long, then the effect of the initial conditions becomes negligible.

If $x(t)$ is a stochastic variable with mean μ, then we can obtain the mean of $y(t)$, which is

$$\mathcal{E}y(t) = \lim_{t \to \infty} \gamma\mu \int_0^t e^{-\gamma(t-\tau)}\, d\tau = \mu$$

The autocovariance of the output is

$$R_{yy}(\tau) = \mathcal{E}y(T)y(T - \tau)$$
$$= \gamma^2 \lim_{T \to \infty} \int_0^T e^{-\gamma(T-t)} x(t)\, dt \int_0^{T-\tau} e^{-\gamma(T-\tau-\eta)} x(\eta)\, d\eta$$

Consider the input to be $x_t = 0 + \epsilon_t$, where $\mathcal{E}(\epsilon) = 0$, $\mathcal{E}(\epsilon^2) = \sigma_\epsilon^2$, and $R_{\epsilon\epsilon}(\tau) = 0$ for $\tau \neq 0$. Then the variance of the output is

$$R_{yy}(0) = \gamma^2 \lim_{T \to \infty} \int_0^T e^{-2\gamma(T-t)} \sigma_\epsilon^2\, dt = \frac{\gamma\sigma_\epsilon^2}{2}$$

For extensions of this continuous analogy, see C. R. Glassey and R. H. Morris, "The Dynamics and Statistics of Exponential Smoothing Operations," *Operations Research*.

8 Choosing the Smoothing Constant

Exponential smoothing produces an average in which past observations are geometrically discounted according to their age. A moving average weights the N most recent observations each $1/N$, and all earlier observations have weight zero. Other weighting schemes are also plausible. Any linear combination of past observations, where the sum of the weights is one, produces an average. It is not even necessary that the weights all be positive. (In Chapter 21 we shall derive the optimum linear filter for a stationary time series, and in that case some of the weights may very well be negative.)

All that the systems engineer needs to know about an averaging process can be determined from the weights given to past observations. In this chapter, we shall discuss the average age of the data taken into account, the variance of the estimates, and the accuracy of the forecasts for both the simple moving average and exponential smoothing. We shall also discuss the response of the averages to standard test signals, such as the impulse, the step, the ramp, and a sine wave.

These discussions seek to furnish some basis for selecting the smoothing constant, or the averaging interval. In general, the smoothing constant α will be some number between 0.01 and 0.3, or the number of observations taken in a moving average will range from 6 to 200. The results will not be very sensitive to the exact choice of these parameters, but it is good to understand the conditions under which the value should be at one end of the range or the other.

The details of the analysis will get somewhat technical. Some readers may want to think of the smoothing constant as $\alpha = 0.1$ and skip to the next chapter on first reading. Later, however, it will be worth the effort necessary to understand the arguments given here.

If you carry out a sequence of trials on some set of actual data and find that you want to use a smoothing constant that is higher than 0.3, check the validity of using a constant model. There may be a significant autocorrelation, in which case the methods of Chapter 21 should be explored. Plot the data on a graph. Frequently, a significant trend, or seasonal pattern, will apparently lead to the desirability of a high smoothing constant, whereas the real solution to the problem is a different model of the process. The later chapters of the section deal with the methods of estimating coefficient values for processes which cannot be satisfactorily represented by a simple constant.

The problem of choosing a value for either α or N can be thought of in terms of the rubber stamp of operations research (Fig. 3.1). The rate of response to a changing pattern improves with higher smoothing constants, or with smaller values of N. But this virtue is mitigated by a decreasing ability to smooth out random fluctuations.

AVERAGE AGE OF THE DATA. The age of the current observation is 0; the age of the previous observation is now 1; and the one before that is now of age 2, and so on. In a moving average scheme, each of the N most recent observations is weighted equally by $1/N$, and all prior observations are weighted zero. Let us define the *average age* of the data used in a moving average as

$$\bar{k} = \frac{0 + 1 + 2 + \ldots + N - 1}{N} = \frac{N - 1}{2}$$

The average age is the age of each piece of data used in the average, weighted as the data of that age would be weighted.

In the exponential smoothing process, the weight given data k periods ago is $\alpha\beta^k$, where $\beta = 1 - \alpha$. Hence, the average of the age data is

$$\bar{k} = 0\alpha + 1\alpha\beta + 2\alpha\beta^2 + \ldots$$

$$= \alpha \sum_{k=0}^{\infty} k\beta^k$$

$$= \frac{\beta}{\alpha}$$

One way to define an exponential smoothing system that is equivalent to an N-period moving average is to say that the smoothing constant is selected to give the same average age of the data.

$$\frac{1 - \alpha}{\alpha} = \frac{N - 1}{2} \quad \text{or} \quad \alpha = \frac{2}{N + 1}$$

Table 8.1 lists values of the smoothing constant that are equivalent to several familiar moving averages. If you have some basis for being satisfied with moving averages computed for a definite number of periods, then Table 8.1 can be used to find the smoothing constant that will give the same results.

Table 8.1   SMOOTHING CONSTANTS AND EQUIVALENT MOVING AVERAGES

$$\alpha = \frac{2}{N + 1}, \quad \beta = 1 - \alpha$$

Number of Observations in a Moving Average N	Variance of Estimate $\dfrac{\sigma_a^2}{\sigma_\epsilon^2} = \dfrac{1}{N}$	Smoothing Constant α
3	0.333	0.500
4	0.250	0.400
5	0.200	0.333
5.67	0.177	0.300
6	0.167	0.286
9	0.111	0.200
12	0.083	0.154
18	0.056	0.105
19	0.053	0.100
24	0.042	0.080
39	0.026	0.050
52	0.019	0.038
199	0.005	0.010

NOTE: this equivalence is in terms of a process for which it is valid to assume a model

$$\xi_t = a, \quad x_t = \xi_t + \epsilon_t$$

where the ϵ_t are random noise samples, with zero mean. Sometimes a moving average of twelve months is used to eliminate seasonal cycles. Exponential smoothing of monthly data with a smoothing constant $\alpha = 0.154$ will not eliminate seasonal variation.

Some weight is given to all past observations in exponential smoothing. The total weight given to the N most recent observations is

$$\alpha \sum_{j=0}^{N-1} \beta^j = 1 - \beta^N$$

Since $\beta = (N - 1)/(N + 1)$, $\beta^N = (N - 1)^N/(N + 1)^N$ which approaches $1/e^2 = 0.135335$ for $N > 10$. Hence about 87 per cent of the weight is given the most recent N observations.

VARIANCE OF THE ESTIMATE. The process we are considering is assumed to be described sufficiently well by the model $\epsilon_t = a$, so that the observed data are $x_t = a + \epsilon_t$ where a is a constant, and the noise samples ϵ_t have mean zero, and variance σ_ϵ^2. Since the observations are noisy, there will be some variation in successive estimates of the mean, which can be represented by σ_a^2.

Let us consider the general process in which some number y_t is produced as a linear combination of previous observations x_t.

$$y_t = \sum_{k=0}^{\infty} w_k x_{t-k}$$

where the w_k are the weights. We shall show that if the observations are serially independent with variance σ_x^2 then the variance of the output is

$$\sigma_y^2 = \sigma_x^2 \sum_{k=0}^{\infty} w_k^2$$

For any sequence of numbers we can define the autocorrelation function (see Appendix A).

$$R_{xx}(\tau) = \lim_{T \to \infty} \frac{1}{2T + 1} \sum_{t=-T}^{T} x_t x_{t+\tau}$$

Sometimes we shall use a bar to represent the time average

$$R_{xx}(\tau) = \overline{x_t x_{t+\tau}}$$

We shall begin by deriving the autocorrelation function of the values of y_t in terms of the autocorrelation of the observations.

$$R_{yy}(\tau) = \overline{y_t y}_{t+\tau} = \overline{\sum_{j=0}^{\infty} w_j x_{t-j} \sum_{k=0}^{\infty} w_k x_{t+\tau-k}}$$

$$= \sum_{j=0}^{\infty} \sum_{k=0}^{\infty} w_j w_k \overline{x_{t-j} x_{t+\tau-k}}$$

$$= \sum_{j=0}^{\infty} \sum_{k=0}^{\infty} w_j w_k R_{xx}(\tau - k + j)$$

Hence, in particular, the variance of these values is

$$R_{yy}(0) = \sigma_y^2 = \sum_{j=0}^{\infty} \sum_{k=0}^{\infty} w_j w_k R_{xx}(j - k)$$

If the observations have no serial correlation, then $R_{xx}(0) = \sigma_x^2$ and

$R_{xx}(\tau) = 0$ for $\tau \neq 0$. Therefore, for random data the variance of any linear combination is proportional to the sum of the squares of the weights

$$\sigma_y^2 = \sigma_x^2 \sum_{k=0}^{\infty} w_k^2$$

Exercise. Show that even if the noise in the observations is uncorrelated, the estimates of the average are correlated.

For a moving average $w_0 = w_1 = \ldots = w_{N-1} = 1/N$ and $w_k = 0$ for $k \geqslant N$. Hence the variance of these averages is

$$\sigma_y^2 = \sigma_\epsilon^2 \sum_{j=0}^{N-1} \frac{1}{N^2} = \frac{\sigma_\epsilon^2}{N}$$

In the exponential smoothing scheme, the weights are $w_k = \alpha\beta^k$. The variance of the estimates is therefore

$$\sigma_y^2 = \sigma_\epsilon^2 \alpha^2 \sum_{j=0}^{\infty} \beta^{2j} = \frac{\alpha^2 \sigma_\epsilon^2}{1 - \beta^2} = \frac{\alpha}{2 - \alpha} \sigma_\epsilon^2$$

Note that the equivalence $\alpha = 2/(N + 1)$ also implies equivalence in the variance σ_y^2 between moving average or exponential smoothing. The common variance reduction is also given in Table 8.1.

Exercise. Suppose one obtains a weighted moving average with the weights 0.4, 0.3, 0.2, 0.1 applied respectively to current observations and successively older data, with all data four or more periods old receiving zero weight. What is the average age of the data? What is the variance of the averages? What value of the smoothing constant would you select to produce equivalent results? Howard's article referred to in Chapter 6 suggests weight 2 for current data, -1 for the previous observation, and 0 for all earlier. What is the significance of the average age?

EFFECT OF CORRELATED DATA. Sometimes there is serial correlation in the noise samples included in the observations of the process. Typically, the effect of such correlation is an increase in the variance of the estimate of the mean. For example, suppose that the noise samples have an exponential autocorrelation

$$R_{\epsilon\epsilon}(\tau) = e^{-\lambda|\tau|}\sigma_\epsilon^2$$

Then the autocorrelation of the averages computed by exponential smoothing will be

$$R_{yy}(\tau) = \left(\frac{\alpha\sigma_\epsilon^2}{2 - \alpha}\right)\left(\frac{(1 - \beta^2)e^{-\lambda\tau} + \beta^{\tau+1}(e^{-\lambda} - e^{\lambda})}{(1 - \beta e^\lambda)(1 - \beta e^{-\lambda})}\right)$$

The variance of the exponential smoothed values is

$$R_{yy}(0) = \sigma_y^2 = \left(\frac{\alpha\sigma_\epsilon^2}{2 - \alpha}\right)\left(\frac{1 + \beta e^{-\lambda}}{1 - \beta e^{-\lambda}}\right)$$

Figure 8.1 shows the standard deviation σ_y of the estimates of the mean, as a function of the smoothing constant used in exponential smoothing. The solid line represents random data with no serial correlation. The dotted line is for the case of correlated data with $e^{-\lambda} = 0.9$. With this

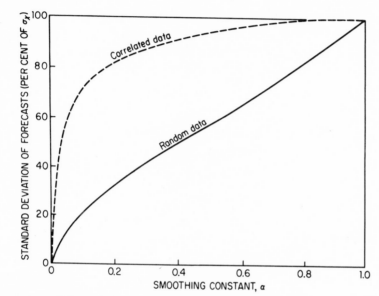

Fig. 8.1 Effect of the smoothing constant on forecast stability.

kind of correlation, one would use a much smaller smoothing constant to get the same smoothing effect, compared with the choice appropriate for random data.

Response to Standard Signals

So far we have discussed the variance of the estimates of the mean of a sequence of observations. The variance is a natural sort of measure of the stability in the face of random fluctuations. If this were the only criterion, one would select a very small smoothing constant. In fact, if the initial conditions assumed for the exponential smoothing were the correct estimate of the mean of the observations for all future time, then $\alpha = 0$ would be very good. That is, don't pay any attention to the data at all, just live with the initial prediction.

Not everyone, however, is so fortunate as to be able to set the correct initial conditions, so the smoothing constant should have some small value, to allow for the change from initial conditions to the actual average of the data as observed.

Now let us turn our attention to the way that the moving average and exponential smoothing respond to several typical standard input signals and to the effect of a choice of the smoothing constant or the number of periods on that response. The first and most important test signal is the impulse.

Any discrete, linear, time-invariant system can be completely described by its impulse response (see Appendix B). An impulse is an input signal $x_t = \delta(t)$, or

$$x_0 = 1 \quad x_t = 0 \quad t \neq 0$$

The impulse response h_t is a description of the output of the system t periods after an impulse at the input. (For a physically realizable system, $h_t = 0$ for $t < 0$; that is, a real system can't respond before the stimulus occurs.)

Since the response to a unit impulse t periods later is h_t, the response of the linear system to an arbitrary signal x_t is

$$y_t = \sum_{n=-\infty}^{\infty} x_n h_{t-n}$$

Therefore, a linear function of past data

$$y_t = \sum_{k=0}^{\infty} w_k x_{t-k}$$

means that the impulse response is the same as the weights applied to past data:

$$h_k = w_k$$

For exponential smoothing, therefore, $h_k = \alpha\beta^k$. For a moving average,

$$h_k = \frac{1}{N} \quad 0 \leqslant k < N \quad \text{and} \quad h_k = 0 \quad k \geqslant N$$

The impulse response is a function of time that says what the output of the system will be t periods after a unit impulse is given at the input. Thus we can talk either about the weights given past data in the averaging process or about the impulse response. The impulse responses are plotted in Fig. 7.1 for exponential smoothing and for a moving average.

Appendix B develops the use of the z-transform as a convenient tool for the analysis of the response of linear, discrete, time-invariant systems to any other input, once the impulse response is known. In place of the convolution $y_t = x_t * h_t$, we can use simple multiplication of transforms, $Y(z) = X(z) \cdot H(z)$, where $H(z)$ is the z-transform of the impulse response. Because of the central role of the impulse response, its transform has the special name *transfer function*.

STEP RESPONSE. A permanent change in the level of the process being observed can be represented by a step function. Suppose that the correct model of the process is

$$\xi_t = a_1 \quad \text{for } t < t_1 \quad \text{and} \quad \xi_t = a_2 \quad \text{for } t \geqslant t_1$$

Since the smoothing processes we have discussed are linear, we can find everything about the response to this kind of a change by studying the response to a unit step at time $t = 0$. The unit step is the function

$$x_t = 0 \quad \text{for } t < 0$$
$$= 1 \quad \text{for } t \geqslant 0$$

The response of exponential smoothing to the unit step is given in Table 8.2. These results are derived in Appendix B. As the time t becomes very large, the term β^{t+1} becomes insignificant, and the estimated value is equal to the input signal.

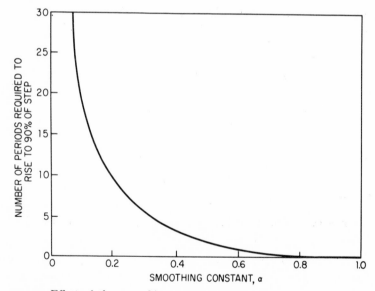

Fig. 8.2 Effect of the smoothing constant on the time required to respond to a step input.

Exponential smoothing (in distinction to the moving average) never exactly reaches the step until infinite time has gone by. The response will equal 90 percent of the step in finite time, and we might use that time to characterize the response to a step. If in n periods the exponential smoothing is to reach the fraction f of the height of a step input, then

$$f = 1 - \beta^{n+1}$$

which can be solved to yield

$$n = \frac{\log (1 - f)}{\log \beta} - 1$$

For $f = 0.9$, the result is simply

$$n = \frac{1}{\log (1/\beta)} - 1$$

which is shown in Fig. 8.2 as a function of the smoothing constant $\alpha = 1 - \beta$.

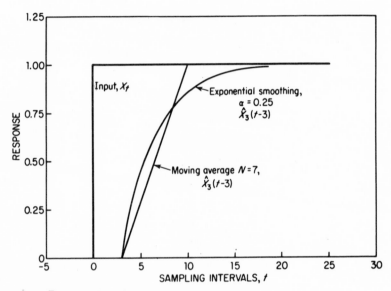

Fig. 8.3 Response to a step.

Figure 8.3 is a graphical representation of the response of exponential smoothing to a unit step input.

RAMP RESPONSE. If the process were to start increasing so that the correct model is

$$\xi_t = a \qquad \text{for } t < t_1$$
$$= a + b(t - t_1) \qquad \text{for } t \geqslant t_1$$

then exponential smoothing will gradually develop a bias, which, in the steady state, is equal to β/α times the magnitude of the trend b.

Exercise. What is the response of a moving average to the same data?

The result shown in Table 8.2 is obtained, by linearity, from the response of the smoothing system to a ramp function

$$x_t = 0 \qquad t < 0$$
$$= t \qquad t \geqslant 0$$

PARABOLA RESPONSE. Table 8.2 also gives the response of exponential smoothing to a quadratic input signal. As might be expected, the exponential smoothing falls farther and farther behind the signal. In the case of both the ramp and the quadratic signals, the degree of the lag can be made quite small if the smoothing constant is chosen to be near one. But when the smoothing constant is near unity, there is no smoothing, and the estimates of the average are nearly equal to the most recent observation. Therefore, if trials with real data show the desirability of a high smoothing constant, it will be well to check and be sure that the constant model is an adequate representation of the process.

Table 8.2 RESPONSES OF THE SINGLE SMOOTHING OPERATOR S
TO STANDARD INPUTS

Input		Response	Steady State Error $x_\infty - y_\infty$
Impulse	$x_t = \delta(t)$	$y_t = \alpha\beta^t$	0
Step	$x_t = 1$	$y_t = 1 - \beta^{t+1}$	0
Ramp	$x_t = t$	$y_t = t - \dfrac{\beta}{\alpha}(1 - \beta^t)$	$\dfrac{\beta}{\alpha}$
Parabola	$x_t = t^2$	$y_t = t^2 - \dfrac{2\beta t}{\alpha} + \dfrac{\beta(1 + \beta)}{\alpha^2}(1 - \beta^t)$	$\dfrac{2\beta t}{\alpha} - \dfrac{\beta(1 + \beta)}{\alpha^2}$

Exercise. Set up another copy of Work Sheet 2. Use the data on Warmdot thermostat sales, Table C.12. Use a smoothing constant $\alpha = 0.1$, initial conditions $S_0(x) = 196.6$ (the average of the first quarter). Do you see any difficulty in smoothing these data? Plot the data and the estimate of the coefficient on a graph. Save the results for later exercises.

RESPONSE TO A SINE WAVE. Exponential smoothing has been developed strictly for a process that can be represented satisfactorily by a constant model. There are many cases of interest where the data are inherently periodic, and for which other methods must be used (see Chapter 11).

It may be of interest, however, to explore the consequence of trying to smooth a sine wave with exponential smoothing in order to be alert to the symptoms of such misapplication.

It is shown in Appendix B that the response to $x_t = \sin(2\pi t/12)$ is

$$y_t = \frac{\alpha}{1 - \sqrt{3}\,\beta + \beta^2}\left[\frac{\beta^{t+1}}{2} + \sin\frac{2\pi t}{12} - \beta\sin\frac{2\pi(t+1)}{12}\right]$$

$$= \frac{\alpha\beta^{t+1}}{2(1 - \sqrt{3}\,\beta + \beta^2)} + \frac{\alpha}{\sqrt{1 - \sqrt{3}\,\beta + \beta^2}}\sin\frac{2\pi}{12}(t - \theta)$$

where the phase angle θ is given by

$$\tan\theta = \frac{\beta}{\sqrt{3}\,\beta - 2}$$

Thus, we find that the response of exponential smoothing to a sine wave is itself a sine wave of the same period (plus a transient term) but with an amplitude and relative phase angle that depend on the smoothing

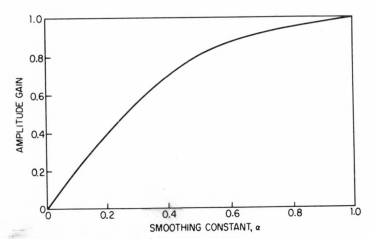

Fig. 8.4 Response to a unit sine wave.

constant α. The amplitude of the steady-state response is plotted in Fig. 8.4 and the phase angle in Fig. 8.5.

Figure 8.6 shows the response graphically for a smoothing constant $\alpha = 0.4$.

As a forecast of a sine wave, exponential smoothing is very unsatisfactory: the forecast rises while the signal falls, and vice versa.

Optimum Smoothing Constant

It is conceptually possible, with the information developed so far in this chapter, to find "the best" value of the smoothing constant. Recall

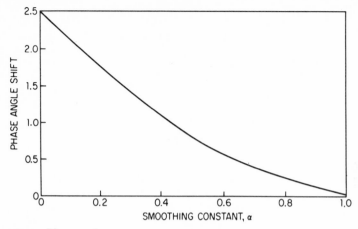

Fig. 8.5 Phase angle.

the rubber stamp of operations research (Fig. 3.1). The forecasts are less stable for larger values of the smoothing constant, but the speed of response to a step input increases. Suppose that, in some units, each percentage point increase in the fluctuations in the forecasts costs $100. Suppose further that each additional period required for the forecast to respond to 90 percent of the step input costs $0.25. Then the curves in Fig. 8.1 and Fig. 8.2 could be superimposed as in Fig. 8.7. The total "cost" is the sum of the two curves, and the best smoothing constant is somewhere between 0.05 and 0.1—the total cost is quite insensitive in that region.

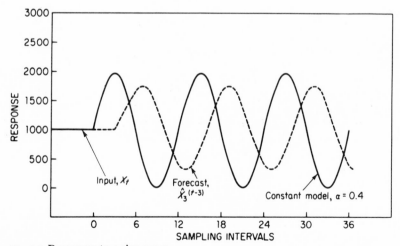

Fig. 8.6 Responses to a sine wave.

Obviously one would have obtained the same result if the costs had been $1.00 and $0.0025 respectively; it is only the ratio of the importance of fast response to stable forecasts that matters. The smoothing constant that minimizes total cost can be determined as a function of that ratio. Figure 8.8 shows that, for one assumption about the form of the "cost" equation, the smoothing constant is approximately proportional to the square root of the ratio of these costs. The total costs don't change much

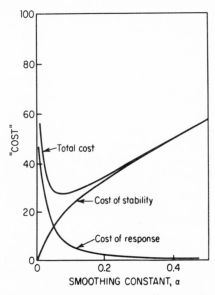

Fig. 8.7 The rubber stamp for the smoothing constant.

for a 2:1 change in the smoothing constant relative to the "optimum." Therefore, the smoothing constant is insensitive to a 10:1 range of uncertainty in the relative values of response versus stability.

ACCURACY OF FORECASTS. If the forecasts are to be stable and are to smooth out random fluctuations, we have shown that one should use a small smoothing constant, or a large number of observations in the average. On the other hand, when one wants rapid response to a real change in the pattern of the observations, then a larger value of the smoothing constant is appropriate. Table 8.1 should be helpful in deciding how long to use the higher smoothing constant, when a change is detected, before returning to the original value.

Another very important criterion is the accuracy of the forecasts. Therefore let us consider the errors generated when forecasting by exponential smoothing to estimate the coefficient in a constant model. Since the forecast is

$$\hat{x}_{t+\tau} = \hat{a}_t = S_t(x)$$

the error in forecasting τ periods ahead with exponential smoothing is

$$e_t(\tau) = x_t - \alpha \sum_{n=0}^{\infty} \beta^n x_{t-\tau-n}$$

Rather than go to the immense labor of carrying through all the algebra

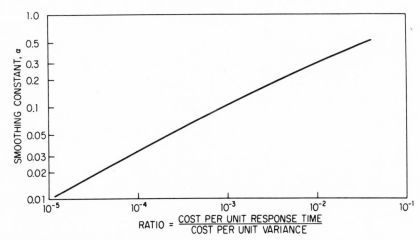

Fig. 8.8 "Least cost" smoothing constant.

to get the complete correlation function for the errors, we shall be content with obtaining the mean square error (MSE).

$$\text{MSE} = \mathcal{E}[e^2(\tau)] = \overline{x_t^2} - 2\alpha \sum_{n=0}^{\infty} \beta^n \, \overline{x_t x_{t-\tau-n}}$$

$$+ \alpha^2 \sum_{n=0}^{\infty} \sum_{m=0}^{\infty} \beta^{n+m} \, \overline{x_{t-\tau-m} x_{t-\tau-n}}$$

$$= \sigma_x^2 - 2\alpha \sum_{n=0}^{\infty} \beta^n R_{xx}(\tau + n) + \alpha^2 \sum_{n=0}^{\infty} \sum_{m=0}^{\infty} \beta^{n+m} R_{xx}(m - n)$$

Change the indices of summation to $k = m - n$, $-\infty < k < \infty$, to obtain

$$\text{MSE} = \frac{2}{2 - \alpha} \sigma_x^2 - 2\alpha \sum_{n=0}^{\infty} \beta^n R_{xx}(\tau + n) + \frac{2\alpha}{2 - \alpha} \sum_{k=1}^{\infty} \beta^k R_{xx}(k)$$

When the inputs are random, neither of the latter two terms contributes anything and the result is simply

$$\text{MSE} = \frac{2\sigma_x^2}{2 - \alpha}$$

Figure 8.9 shows that when the inputs are random, the most accurate forecast is obtained with $\alpha = 0$. This result, of course, assumes in effect that one knew accurately what the mean of the series was going to be and selected the initial value S_0 accordingly. In practice, however, it means that once the system has run long enough to "settle down," a low smoothing constant will produce both greater accuracy and greater stability, *so long as the noise in the observations is random and the process is constant.*

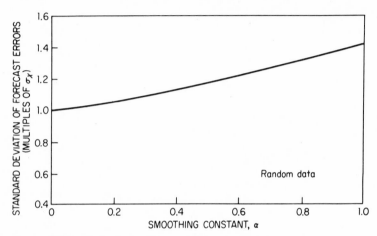

Fig. 8.9 Effect of the smoothing constant on forecast accuracy.

ACCURACY OF THE FORECASTS WITH CORRELATED INPUTS. Now we come to the interesting case—except that the results don't turn out to be very exciting. If the input data are correlated, then it is actually possible to find a value of the smoothing constant that minimizes the mean square error (MSE). The data must be *very* correlated, and the lead time has to be quite short; even then, the "optimum" smoothing constant (for accuracy) is so high that the forecasts will be essentially the same as the previous observations.

Well, one can't have everything.

We shall assume an exponential correlation function

$$R_{xx}(\tau) = \sigma_x^2 e^{-\lambda|\tau|}$$

for the input data, so that we can obtain a closed form for the mean square error.

$$\text{MSE} = \frac{2\sigma_x^2}{(1 + \beta)(1 - \beta e^{-\lambda})} \left[1 - e^{-\lambda\tau} - \beta^2(e^{-\lambda} - e^{-\lambda\tau})\right]$$

It will help in differentiating this expression to let

$$A = 1 - e^{-\lambda \tau}$$
$$B = e^{-\lambda} - e^{-\lambda \tau}$$
$$C = e^{-\lambda}$$

so that
$$\frac{\text{MSE}}{2\sigma_x^2} = \frac{A - \beta^2 B}{(1 + \beta)(1 - C\beta)}$$

Then
$$\frac{d}{d\beta}\left(\frac{\text{MSE}}{2\sigma_x^2}\right) = \frac{A(C - 1) + 2\beta(AC - B) + \beta^2(B)(C - 1)}{(1 + \beta)^2(1 - C\beta)}$$

The denominator is strictly positive for $0 < \beta < 1$. The numerator N, on resubstitution, reduces to

$$N = -(1 - e^{-\lambda})[(1 - e^{-\lambda \tau}) - 2\beta e^{-\lambda \tau} + \beta^2(e^{-\lambda} - e^{-\lambda \tau})]$$

At one end of the range $\beta = 0$ and the numerator is negative, so that the MSE will decrease for an increase in β. At the other extreme $\beta = 1$ and the numerator is positive for short lead times, such that $e^{-\lambda \tau} < (1 + e^{-\lambda})/4$. Hence for these lead times (up to $\tau = 7$ for $e^{-\lambda} = 0.9$), there is a proper minimum MSE for some $0 < \beta < 1$.

The minimum occurs when the derivative is zero (that is, $N = 0$) which is

$$\beta = \frac{e^{-\lambda \tau} - \sqrt{e^{-\lambda \tau}(1 + e^{-\lambda})} - e^{-\lambda}}{e^{-\lambda} - e^{-\lambda \tau}}$$

(This form is indeterminate for $\tau = 1$.)

Figure 8.10 is a plot that shows the MSE for all values of the smoothing

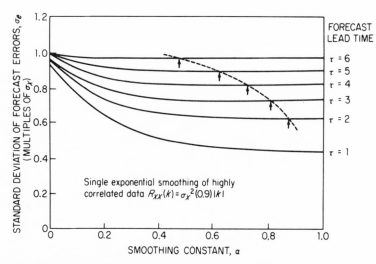

Fig. 8.10 Effect of the smoothing constant on forecast accuracy.

constant. A dotted line shows the locus of the solution that minimizes this error.

One may conclude that if the data are very highly correlated, if the accuracy of forecasting one period ahead is very important, and if considerable variation can be tolerated in the forecasts themselves, don't smooth: use the most recent observation as the forecast of the next one.

Meyer* has considered explicitly the nature of the slow random walk through which the process goes. Specifically he takes the case where the process at time t is a linear combination of n past values of the process plus a small increment chosen at random from a normal distribution with mean zero and variance σ_η^2.

$$\xi_t = \sum_{i=1}^{n} \gamma_i \xi_{t-i} + \eta_t$$

Such a process is observed in the presence of noise which is represented by random samples from a normal distribution with zero mean and variance σ_ϵ^2

$$x_t = \xi_t + \epsilon_t$$

He then shows that the optimum linear filter for forecasting such a process is exponential smoothing, and that in the steady state the smoothing constant approaches as a limit the ratio of the standard deviation of the random increments to the standard deviation of the noise samples.

$$\alpha \simeq \frac{\sigma_\eta}{\sigma_\epsilon}$$

---

* R. F. Meyer, "An Adaptive Method of Routine Short-term Forecasting," International Federation of Operational Research Societies, Oslo, July, 1963. See also D. R. Cox, "Prediction by Exponentially Weighted Moving Averages and Related Methods," *Jour. Roy. Stat. Soc.* (Series B) 23, No. 2 (1961), 414–22; and J. F. Muth, "Optimal Properties of Exponentially Weighted Forecasts," *Jour. Amer. Stat. Assoc.*, 55, No. 290 (June, 1960), 299–306.

9 Multiple Smoothing for Higher-order Polynomials

We have spent quite a bit of time analyzing exponential smoothing and moving averages. These are the simplest techniques of smoothing and are suitable for estimating the current value of the single coefficient in the model of a locally constant process. The analysis in Chapter 8 of the factors that influence the choice of the smoothing constant (or the number of periods of data that are averaged) is basic to the concept of making a satisfactory compromise between stability of the forecasts and the speed of response to changes in the model that represents the data. With that background, we can now proceed to develop the smoothing techniques for estimating the coefficients in other models.

The first extension of a simple constant model is the addition of a linear term, where the process is changing steadily at a rate that must be reflected in the model

$$\xi_t = a + bt$$

and there are two coefficients to be estimated. We shall develop a compact procedure for fitting a straight line to the most recent N points by least squares. This is the extension of a moving average to the linear model. Then we shall consider the analogous extension of exponential smoothing to obtain estimates of the two coefficients in the linear model. The exponential smoothing computations are simpler than the conventional least squares, and only two words of historical information are required, rather than the past $N - 1$ observations. The double smoothing procedures also retain the flexibility to modify the balance between smooth forecasts and rapid response when necessary.

Finally we shall prove the fundamental theorem of exponential smoothing, which makes it possible to estimate the $n + 1$ coefficients in an nth-order polynomial model

$$\xi_t = a_0 + a_1 t + \frac{1}{2} a_2 t^2 + \ldots + \frac{1}{n!} a_n t^n$$

The computations require the storage of only one word of historical information per degree of freedom in the model. Since it is rare that any model more elaborate than a quadratic is required, three stored statistics can give all the information about past observations required to compute the three coefficients in the model.

Least Squares

Many processes can be adequately described by a linear function of time $\xi_t = a + bt$. The observations of this process included noise so that

$$x_t = \xi_t + \epsilon_t = a + bt + \epsilon_t$$

where ϵ_t is the tth sample from a probability distribution with zero mean. In Chapter 7, we concentrated on a process that could be described locally by a constant; the value of that constant may change very slowly with time and hence the estimates of its value were based only on recent observations. When there is a systematic change in the process that should be reflected in the model, more terms must be included. We still expect that the values of these coefficients will change slowly, and unpredictably, with time, so that the estimates of these values will be based on recent observations: $x_T, x_{T-1}, \ldots$ There are a great many possible techniques for estimating the coefficients $\hat{a}_T$ and $\hat{b}_T$. Let us first consider simple linear regression on N observations, sometimes called the *least squares method* (see Appendix A). The values of the coefficients are to be computed so that the sum of the squares of the residuals between the data $x_T, \ldots, x_{T-N+1}$ and the model $\hat{x}_{T+\tau} = \hat{a}_T + \hat{b}_T \tau$

$$\sum_{t=0}^{-N+1} (\hat{a} + \hat{b}t - x_{T+t})^2$$

is a minimum. The minimization requires the solution of a pair of simultaneous equations

$$aN + b \sum t = \sum x$$

$$a \sum t + b \sum t^2 = \sum tx$$

Change the origin of time so that $t' = t - (N - 1)/2$; then $\Sigma\, t' = 0$ and $\Sigma\, t'^2 = N(N^2 - 1)/12$. The estimates of the two coefficients is simply

$$\hat{a}_T = M_T = \frac{x_T + x_{T-1} + \ldots + x_{T-N+1}}{N}$$

$$\hat{b}_T = W_T = \frac{12}{N(N^2 - 1)}\left[\frac{N-1}{2}\,x_T + \frac{N-3}{2}\,x_{T-1} + \ldots - \frac{N+1}{2}\,x_{T-N+1}\right]$$

Chapter 7 showed how the moving average M_t could be obtained from the previous value

$$M_t = M_{t-1} + \frac{x_t - x_{t-N}}{N}$$

NOTE: the moving average is the least squares estimate for the midpoint of the averaging interval; that is, $(N - 1)/2$ observations ago.

The weighted moving average W_t can be obtained recursively as

$$W_t = W_{t-1} + \frac{12}{N(N^2 - 1)}\left[\frac{N-1}{2}\,x_t + \frac{N+1}{2}\,x_{t-N} - NM_{t-1}\right]$$

Suppose, for example, that $N = 7$ were chosen as the appropriate number of past observations to be considered in estimating these two coefficients. (Actually, seven observations in general would be far too few, unless there were almost no noise in the data.)

The first seven observations used in the example in Chapter 7 were $x_1 = 18$; $x_2 = 23$; $x_3 = 22$; $x_4 = 17$; $x_5 = 25$; $x_6 = 15$; and $x_7 = 22$. The average of these observations is $M_7 = \frac{142}{7} = 20\frac{2}{7}$. The weighted average of these same observations is

$$W_7 = \frac{1}{28}\,(3 \times 22 + 2 \times 15 + 1 \times 25 + 0 \times 17$$
$$- 1 \times 22 - 2 \times 23 - 3 \times 18)$$
$$= -\frac{1}{28}$$

The forecasts made as of the seventh observation would be

$$x_{T+\tau} = \hat{x}_{t'+(N-1)/2+\tau} = \hat{a}_T + \left(\frac{N-1}{2} + \tau\right)\hat{b}_T$$
$$= \frac{142}{7} + (3 + \tau)\left(-\frac{1}{28}\right) = \frac{573}{28} - \frac{\tau}{28}$$

With the next observation $x_8 = 18$, the moving average becomes

$$M_8 = \frac{142}{7} + \frac{18 - 18}{7} = \frac{142}{7}$$

The weighted moving average becomes

$$W_8 = -\frac{1}{28} + \frac{1}{28}\left(3 \times 18 + 4 \times 18 - 7 \times \frac{142}{7}\right) = -\frac{17}{28}$$

Exercise. Make up a copy of Work Sheet No. 3. Use the data from Table C.12 on the weekly sales of Warmdot Thermostats, and compute the thirteen-week moving least squares estimates of the coefficients in a linear fit. Save the results for later exercises. Repeat the trials with the noisefree data in Table C.13 to see that the coefficients are correctly estimated.

Work Sheet No. 3 LEAST SQUARES

DATA: Warmdot Thermostat Weekly Sales, Table C.12
MODEL: Linear, $x_t = a + bt + \epsilon_t$
SMOOTHING: Least Squares, $N = 13$

$$M_t = M_{t-1} + \frac{x_t - x_{t-13}}{13}$$

$$W_t = W_{t-1} + \frac{6x_t + 7x_{t-13} - 13M_{t-1}}{182}$$

Date	Data	Lagged Data	Moving Average	Weighted Average
t	x_t	x_{t-13}	M_t	W_t
1	206	·	·	·
2	245	·	·	·
3	185	·	·	·
4	169	·	·	·
5	162	·	·	·
6	177	·	·	·
7	207	·	·	·
8	216	·	·	·
9	193	·	·	·
10	230	·	·	·
11	212	·	·	·
12	192	·	·	·
13	162	(Sum = 2556)	196.6	−0.75
14	189	206	195.3	−0.64
15	244	245	195.2	+2.88
·	·	·	·	·
·	·	·	·	·
·	·	·	·	·

Modification for Hand Calculations

These computations could be carried out quite easily on any sort of automatic data-processing equipment. The indicated division could be eliminated for those machines that do not have a divide feature, since the numerator is a constant that depends on N, the number of observations used. The sum of three products required to revise the weighted average W_t is not a task that would ordinarily be assigned to a clerk in a manual system. The procedures can be modified to get the same sort of results easily by hand computation.

Suppose for the moment that a linear process could be observed exactly with no noise, say

$$x_t = a + bt$$

We saw above that the moving average M_t lags the observations

$$M_t = x_t - \tfrac{1}{2}(N - 1)b = a - \tfrac{1}{2}(N - 1)b + bt$$

If we plot them on a graph, the moving averages computed in successive periods would fall along a straight line, parallel to the line through the observed data (Fig. 9.1).

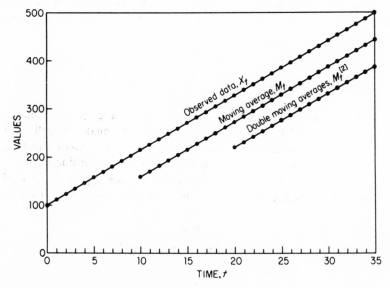

Fig. 9.1 Noisefree data with a moving average and a double moving average.

Now compute a moving average of the moving averages

$$M_t^{[2]} = \frac{M_t + M_{t-1} + \ldots + M_{t-N+1}}{N}$$

By the same argument, these "double moving averages" would also fall along a straight line parallel to the lines through x_t and M_t, as in Fig. 9.1. Since $M_t^{[2]} = M_t = \tfrac{1}{2}(N - 1)b = a - (N - 1)b + bt$, simple addition yields

$$x_t = a + bt = 2M_t - M_t^{[2]}$$

$$b = \frac{2}{N-1}(M_t - M_t^{[2]})$$

The estimates of the two coefficients in the forecast equation

$$\hat{x}_{T+\tau} = \hat{x}_T + \hat{b}_T \tau$$

can therefore be reduced to simple addition and subtraction of moving averages, which can be carried out efficiently by hand.

Exercise. Set up a copy of Work Sheet No. 4, and repeat the previous exercise with the data from Table C.12, using ten-period moving averages to estimate the coefficients $\hat{a}_t$ and $\hat{b}_t$. What are the disadvantages of this method for automatic data-processing equipment?

A moving average of $N = p$ observations is very useful for eliminating seasonal variation. Repeat Work Sheet 4 (or 3) for the airline passenger data in Table C.10, where there are $p = 12$ observations per cycle.

Double Exponential Smoothing

Now let us see how the ideas of exponential smoothing can be extended to provide estimates of the two coefficients in a linear model. Recall from Chapter 8 that the steady state response of exponential smoothing to a ramp $x_t = t$ has a constant lag of β/α, where α is the smoothing constant and $\beta = 1 - \alpha$ (Table 8.2), which corresponds to the lag of $(N-1)/2$ in the case of the moving average. Therefore, if the observations exactly follow the law

$$x_t = a + bt$$

then the exponentially smoothed data will be given by

$$S_t(x) = \alpha x_t + \beta S_{t-1}(x)$$

$$= a - b\frac{\beta}{\alpha} + bt$$

(after the initial transient β^{t+1}/α has become negligible). If the successive values $S_t(x)$ were plotted on a graph with the data x_t, the smoothed values would fall on a line parallel to the line through the data, where the constant distance between the lines depends only on the coefficient of the linear term and on the value of the smoothing constant.

Recall the definition of a double moving average. In the same way, we can define *double exponential smoothing*

$$S_t^{[2]}(x) = \alpha S_t(x) + (1 - \alpha)S_{t-1}^{[2]}(x)$$

Work Sheet No. 4 MANUAL LEAST SQUARES COMPUTATIONS

DATA: Warmdot Thermostat Weekly Sales, Table C.12
MODEL: Linear $x_t = a + bt + \epsilon_t$
SMOOTHING: Double Moving Average, $N = 10$
FORECAST: $\hat{x}_{t+\tau} = \hat{x}_t + \hat{b}_t \tau$

$$M_t = M_{t-1} + \frac{x_t - x_{t-10}}{10}$$

$$M_t^{[2]} = M_{t-1}^{[2]} + \frac{M_t - M_{t-10}}{10}$$

$$\hat{x}_t = 2M_t - M_t^{[2]}$$

$$\hat{b}_t = \frac{2}{9}(M_t - M_t^{[2]})$$

Date	Data	Moving Average	Double Average	Coefficients	
t	x_t	M_t	$M_t^{[2]}$	$\hat{x}_t$	$\hat{b}_t$
1	206				
2	245				
3	185				
4	169				
5	162				
6	177				
7	207				
8	216				
9	193				
10	230	199.0			
11	212	199.6			
12	192	194.3			
13	162	192.0			
14	189	194.0			
15	244	202.2			
16	209	205.4			
17	207	205.4			
18	211	204.9			
19	210	206.6	200.34	212.86	1.39
20	173	200.9	200.53	201.27	0.08
21	194	199.1	200.48	197.72	−0.31
22	234	203.3	201.38	205.22	0.43
23	156	202.7	202.45	202.95	0.06
24	206	204.4	203.49	205.31	0.20
25	188	198.8	203.15	194.45	−0.97
26	162	194.1	202.02	186.18	−1.76

as the result of applying exponential smoothing to the results of smoothing the original data. The notation $S_t^{[2]}(x)$ means double smoothing, not the square of exponential smoothing. It will help enforce the distinction if you read the symbol as "ess two" rather than "ess squared."

By the same argument, the double smoothed values will (after the transient dies out) lie along a straight line parallel to the line through the smoothed data $S_t(x)$. The distance between these two lines will be $\beta b/\alpha$. If the linear coefficient b is negative, then the smoothed lines will lie above the data, rather than below.

The distance between the line of the smoothed data and the line through the observations will be equal to the distance between the lines through the smoothed data and the double smoothed data. Therefore a current estimate of the value of a point on the line through the data can be obtained from the two smoothed values

$$\hat{x}_t = S_t(x) + (S_t(x) - S_t^{[2]}(x)) = 2S_t(x) - S_t^{[2]}(x)$$

Since the distance between these lines depends on the coefficient of the linear term and on the smoothing constant, we can estimate its value from

$$\hat{b}_t = \frac{\alpha}{\beta} [S_t(x) - S_t^{[2]}(x)]$$

(These results will be proved rigorously later on.) Forecasts of future observations would therefore be

$$\hat{x}_{T+\tau} = \hat{x}_T + \hat{b}_T \tau$$

NOTE: exponential smoothing as described here will not eliminate periodic variation in the way that a moving average with $N = p$ will. In Chapters 11 and 12 we shall generalize the methods of exponential smoothing to include such periodic processes.

Exercise. Set up a copy of Work Sheet No. 5 and estimate the values of the two constants required for a forecast with a linear model, using the Warmdot Thermostat data from Table C.12. It can be assumed that the linear coefficient initially is zero, so that $S_{13}(x) = S_{13}^{[2]}(x) = 196.6$, the average of the sales in the first quarter.

INITIAL CONDITIONS. Exponential smoothing is quite simple, even compared with the least squares computations when rearranged for ease of hand calculation. Two initial conditions must be supplied, however, for $S_{t-1}(x)$ and for $S_{t-1}^{[2]}(x)$. The simplest way of getting these initial conditions is from an estimate of the two coefficients $\hat{a}_0$ and $\hat{b}_0$. If there are past data that can be analyzed, these estimates can be obtained by the least squares calculations described above. For a new time series, the coefficients should be predicted, either by analogy with other similar time series,

Work Sheet No. 5 DOUBLE EXPONENTIAL SMOOTHING

DATA: Warmdot Thermostat Weekly Sales Table C.12
MODEL: Linear $x_t = a + bt$
SMOOTHING: Double Exponential Smoothing, $\alpha = 0.1$

$$S_t(x) = \alpha x_t + \beta S_{t-1}(x)$$

$$S_t^{[2]}(x) = \alpha S_t(x) + \beta S_{t-1}^{[2]}(x)$$

COEFFICIENTS: $\hat{a}_t = 2S_t(x) - S_t^{[2]}(x)$

$$\hat{b}_t = \frac{0.1}{0.9} \left[S_t(x) - S_t^{[2]}(x) \right]$$

FORECAST: $\hat{x}_{t+\tau} = \hat{a}_t + \hat{b}_t \tau$

Date	Data	Smoothed Data	Double Smoothed Data	Coefficients	
t	x_t	$S_t(x)$	$S_t^{[2]}(x)$	$\hat{a}_t$	$\hat{b}_t$
13		196.6	196.6	196.6	0
14	189	195.8	196.5	195.1	−0.08
15	244	200.6	196.9	204.3	0.41
16	209	201.4	197.4	205.4	0.44
17	207	202.0	197.9	206.1	0.45
18	211	202.9	198.4	207.4	0.50
·	·	·	·	·	·
·	·	·	·	·	·
·	·	·	·	·	·
·	·	·	·	·	·

or according to your intentions for the model that will describe future observations.

In one way or another, there will be some initial estimate of what these coefficients are likely to be in the model. The equations for estimating the coefficients in terms of smoothed values can be solved to yield the initial smoothed values in terms of estimates of the coefficients.

$$\hat{S}_0(x) = \hat{a}_0 - \frac{\beta}{\alpha} \hat{b}_0$$

$$\hat{S}_0^{[2]}(x) = \hat{a}_0 - 2\frac{\beta}{\alpha} \hat{b}_0$$

For example, suppose one expected the data to be described by the model

$$x_t = 500 + 10t$$

The estimates of the coefficients are $\hat{a}_0 = 500$ and $\hat{b}_0 = 10$. Since the calculations are simple, let us choose a smoothing constant $\alpha = 0.1$, so that

$\beta = 0.9$ and $\beta/\alpha = 9$. Therefore the initial conditions for the two smoothed values would be

$$S_0(x) = 500 - 9 \times 10 = 410$$

$$S_0^{[2]}(x) = 500 - 2 \times 9 \times 10 = 320$$

Exercise. Use the noisefree data in Table C.13 to see how double exponential smoothing calculates the correct values of the coefficients in a linear model.

Fundamental Theorem of Exponential Smoothing

The development to this point has been plausible rather than rigorous. Let us now proceed to a rigorous proof that multiple exponential smoothing can be used to provide an estimate of the values of the coefficients in a polynomial model of the data.

Suppose the model chosen to represent the sequence of observations is an nth-degree polynomial

$$\xi_t = a_0 + a_1 t + \frac{a_2}{2} t^2 + \ldots + \frac{a_n}{n!} t^n$$

The forecast of future observations is most conveniently expressed by a Taylor series* expansion around the tth observation.

$$\hat{x}_{t+\tau} = \hat{x}_t^{(0)} + \tau \hat{x}_t^{(1)} + \frac{\tau^2}{2} \hat{x}_t^{(2)} + \ldots + \frac{\tau^n}{n!} \hat{x}_t^{(n)}$$

where $x_t^{(k)}$ is the kth derivative evaluated at time t (taken to represent the current observation), and $\hat{x}_t^{(k)}$ is an estimate of its value.

$$x_t^{(k)} = \frac{d^k x}{dt^k}\bigg|_t$$

Thus we can write

$$\hat{x}_{t+\tau} = \sum_{k=0}^{n} \frac{\tau^k \hat{x}_t^{(k)}}{k!} = \sum_{k=0}^{n} \frac{\tau^k a_k}{k!}$$

for the forecast in terms of the current estimates of the derivatives of the model. These derivatives are the coefficients we require.

The discussion in Chapter 7 developed exponential smoothing for estimating the single coefficient in a constant model

$$\hat{a}_t = S_t(x) = \alpha x_t + (1 - \alpha) S_{t-1}(x)$$

Earlier in this chapter we suggested the notion of double smoothing for estimating the two coefficients in a linear model. For generality we shall

---

* Brook Taylor, *Methodus Incrementorum* (London: 1715).

call the exponential smoothing of Chapter 7 *single smoothing*, represented by $S_t^{[1]}(x)$. Then double smoothing is defined as the following function

$$S_t^{[2]}(x) = \alpha S_t^{[1]}(x) + (1 - \alpha)S_{t-1}^{[2]}(x)$$

In a similar way we shall define *multiple smoothing of order k* by

$$S_t^{[k]}(x) = \alpha S_t^{[k-1]}(x) + (1 - \alpha)S_{t-1}^{[k]}(x)$$

That is, kth-order smoothing is just simple exponential smoothing applied to the results of $(k - 1)$st-order smoothing as the data.

The fundamental theorem of exponential smoothing* proves that it is possible to estimate the $(n + 1)$ coefficients (derivatives) in an nth-order polynomial model by linear combinations of the first $(n + 1)$ orders of exponential smoothing.

THE FUNDAMENTAL THEOREM OF EXPONENTIAL SMOOTHING. If the observations x_t are represented by the model

$$x_{t+\tau} = \sum_{k=0}^{n} \frac{\tau^n x_t^{(k)}}{k!}$$

then

$$S_t^{[p]}(x) = \sum_{k=0}^{n} (-1)^k \frac{x_t^{(n)}}{k!} \frac{\alpha p}{(p - 1)!} \sum_{j=0}^{\infty} j^k \beta^j \frac{(p - 1 + j)!}{j!}$$

Thus there are $n + 1$ simultaneous equations giving the smoothed values $S_t^{(k)}(x)$ in terms of linear combinations of the derivatives $x_t^{(n)}$. These equations can be solved to give the values of the derivatives as linear combinations of the smoothed data.

Proof: Think of the infinite sequence of observations as a vector **x**, with components x_t for $t = -\infty, \ldots, -1, 0, 1, \ldots, \infty$. We can define a vector **S** with components

$$S_t = \begin{cases} 0 & (t < 0) \\ \alpha\beta^t & (t \geqslant 0) \end{cases}$$

Then exponential smoothing can be represented by the convolution of two vectors **x** * **S** which has components

$$(\mathbf{x} * \mathbf{S})_t = S_t(x) = \sum_{j=0}^{\infty} x_{t-j}S_j = \alpha \sum_{j=0}^{\infty} \beta^n x_{t-j}$$

Since the convolution operation is associative, multiple smoothing of order k is equivalent to the convolution $\mathbf{x} * \mathbf{S}^{(p)}$ where $\mathbf{S}^{(p)}$ has components†

---

* The proof given here was first published by R. G. Brown and R. F. Meyer, *Operations Research*, 9, No. 5 (September–October, 1961), 673–87.

† See proof by induction in Lemma 2, Brown and Meyer, *op. cit.*

$$(S^{[p]})_t = \begin{cases} 0 & (t < 0) \\ \alpha^p \beta^t \dfrac{(p - 1 + t)!}{t!(p - 1)!} & (t \geqslant 0) \end{cases}$$

Therefore,
$$S_t^{[p]}(x) = \sum_{j=0}^{\infty} x_{t-j} \frac{\alpha^p \beta^j (p - 1 + j)!}{j!(p - 1)!}$$

but
$$x_{t-j} = \sum_{k=0}^{n} (-1)^k \frac{x_t^{(k)}}{k!} j^k$$

Hence the theorem is proved.

The fundamental theorem gives the first five smoothed statistics as

$$S_t(x) = \sum_{k=0}^{n} (-1)^k \frac{x_t^{(k)}}{k!} \alpha \sum_{j=0}^{\infty} j^k \beta^j$$

$$S_t^{[2]}(x) = \sum_{k=0}^{n} (-1)^k \frac{x_t^{(k)}}{k!} \alpha^2 \sum_{j=0}^{\infty} j^k(j + 1)\beta^j$$

$$S_t^{[3]}(x) = \sum_{k=0}^{n} (-1)^k \frac{x_t^{(k)}}{k!} \frac{\alpha^3}{2} \sum_{j=0}^{\infty} j^k(j + 1)(j + 2)\beta^j$$

$$S_t^{[4]}(x) = \sum_{k=0}^{n} (-1)^k \frac{x_t^{(k)}}{k!} \frac{\alpha^4}{6} \sum_{j=0}^{\infty} j^k(j + 1)(j + 2)(j + 3)\beta^j$$

$$S_t^{[5]}(x) = \sum_{k=0}^{n} (-1)^k \frac{x_t^{(k)}}{k!} \frac{\alpha^5}{24} \sum_{j=0}^{\infty} j^k(j + 1)(j + 2)(j + 3)(j + 4)\beta^j$$

Look at the structure of these equations. The pth order of smoothing is given as an alternating sum of the n coefficients in the Taylor series $x_t^{(k)}/k!$. The coefficients of these derivatives are infinite sums involving the smoothing constant. The infinite sums can be written in closed form with the aid of Table 9.1. The linear equations for the smoothed statistics can be written in a compact form using matrix notation.

Let $\mathbf{S}_t$ be a vector
$$\begin{bmatrix} S_t(x) \\ S_t^{[2]}(x) \\ \cdot \\ \cdot \\ \cdot \\ S_t^{[p]}(x) \end{bmatrix}$$

(which is not the same as the vector $\mathbf{S}$ defined in the proof of the fundamental theorem) and let $\mathbf{a}$ be a vector

$$\mathbf{a} = \begin{bmatrix} a_0^{(t)} \\ a_1^{(t)} \\ \cdot \\ \cdot \\ \cdot \\ a_n^{(t)} \end{bmatrix} = \begin{bmatrix} x_t^{(0)}/0! \\ x_t^{(1)}/1! \\ \cdot \\ \cdot \\ \cdot \\ x_t^{(n)}/n! \end{bmatrix}$$

of the coefficients in the Taylor expansion. Then the result of the fundamental theorem can be expressed as

$$\mathbf{S}_t = M\mathbf{a}$$

where M is an $n \times p$ matrix with elements involving infinite sums of powers of the smoothing constant.

$$M_{ik} = \frac{\alpha^i}{(i-1)!} \sum_{j=0}^{\infty} j^k \beta^j \frac{(i-1+j)!}{j!}$$

Table 9.1 SUMS $\sum_{j=0}^{\infty} j^n \beta^j$ USEFUL IN ANALYZING EXPONENTIAL SMOOTHING*

n	Form	Sum
0	$\sum \beta^j$	$\dfrac{1}{1-\beta}$
1	$\sum j\beta^j$	$\dfrac{\beta}{(1-\beta)^2}$
2	$\sum j^2\beta^j$	$\dfrac{\beta(1+\beta)}{(1-\beta)^3}$
3	$\sum j^3\beta^j$	$\dfrac{\beta(1+4\beta+\beta^2)}{(1-\beta)^4}$
4	$\sum j^4\beta^j$	$\dfrac{\beta(1+11\beta+11\beta^2+\beta^3)}{(1-\beta)^5}$
5	$\sum j^5\beta^j$	$\dfrac{\beta(1+26\beta+66\beta^2+26\beta^3+\beta^4)}{(1-\beta)^6}$
6	$\sum j^6\beta^j$	$\dfrac{\beta(1+57\beta+302\beta^2+302\beta^3+57\beta^4+\beta^5)}{(1-\beta)^7}$

* See D. Zeitlin, "Two Methods for the Evaluation of $\sum_{k=0}^{\infty} k^\mu x^k$," *American Mathematical Monthly*, Vol. 68, No. 10 (December, 1961), 986–89.

The matrix M for $n = 5$, $p = 5$ is

$$M = \begin{bmatrix} 1 & \dfrac{-\beta}{\alpha} & \dfrac{\beta(1+\beta)}{2\alpha^2} & \dfrac{-\beta(1+4\beta+\beta^2)}{6\alpha^3} & \dfrac{\beta(1+11\beta+11\beta^2+\beta^3)}{24\alpha^4} \\[2ex] 1 & \dfrac{-2\beta}{\alpha} & \dfrac{2\beta(1+2\beta)}{2\alpha^2} & \dfrac{-2\beta(1+7\beta+4\beta^2)}{6\alpha^3} & \dfrac{2\beta(1+18\beta+33\beta^2+8\beta^3)}{24\alpha^4} \\[2ex] 1 & \dfrac{-3\beta}{\alpha} & \dfrac{3\beta(1+3\beta)}{2\alpha^2} & \dfrac{-3\beta(1+10\beta+9\beta^2)}{6\alpha^3} & \dfrac{3\beta(1+25\beta+67\beta^2+27\beta^3)}{24\alpha^4} \\[2ex] 1 & \dfrac{-4\beta}{\alpha} & \dfrac{4\beta(1+4\beta)}{2\alpha^2} & \dfrac{-4\beta(1+13\beta+16\beta^2)}{6\alpha^3} & \dfrac{4\beta(1+32\beta+113\beta^2+64\beta^3)}{24\alpha^4} \\[2ex] 1 & \dfrac{-5\beta}{\alpha} & \dfrac{5\beta(1+5\beta)}{2\alpha^2} & \dfrac{-5\beta(1+16\beta+25\beta^2)}{6\alpha^3} & \dfrac{5\beta(1+39\beta+171\beta^2+125\beta^3)}{24\alpha^4} \end{bmatrix}$$

If the process being observed can be represented by a polynomial of degree n, then all derivatives of order $n + 1$ and higher will be identically zero. Correspondingly, the differences of successive discrete observations will average zero for the $(n + 1)$st differences. The variance of the differences will increase with the order of the difference because of the variance of the noise in the observations.

Suppose, for example, that a process can be adequately represented by a quadratic function of time. That means that derivatives $x^{(3)}$ and higher are all zero. Three smoothed statistics are necessary and sufficient to revise the estimates of these derivatives with each new observation. The three smoothed statistics can be expressed in terms of the three non-zero derivatives by a 3×3 matrix obtained by taking the first three rows and the first three columns of the matrix M.

$$S_t(x) = x_t^{(0)} - \frac{\beta}{\alpha} x_t^{(1)} + \frac{\beta(2 - \alpha)}{2\alpha^2} x_t^{(2)}$$

$$S_t^{[2]}(x) = x_t^{(0)} - \frac{2\beta}{\alpha} x_t^{(1)} + \frac{2\beta(3 - 2\alpha)}{2\alpha^2} x_t^{(2)}$$

$$S_t^{[3]}(x) = x_t^{(0)} - \frac{3\beta}{\alpha} x_t^{(1)} + \frac{3\beta(4 - 3\alpha)}{2\alpha^2} x_t^{(2)}$$

In this form the equations can be used to estimate initial conditions for the smoothed statistics in terms of predictions (or other estimates) of the derivatives.

For example, suppose that there was some basis for assuming that the data would be reasonably well described by

$$\xi_t = 500 + 10t + \tfrac{1}{2}(0.4)t^2$$

The initial estimates of the derivatives are

$$\hat{x}^{(0)} = 500$$

$$\hat{x}^{(1)} = 10$$

$$\hat{x}^{(2)} = 0.4$$

Now if one intends to smooth the data with a smoothing constant $\alpha = 0.05$ ($\beta = 0.95$), the initial estimates of the smoothed statistics would be

$$\hat{S}_0(x) = 500 - \frac{0.95}{0.05}(10) + \frac{(0.95)(1.95)}{2(0.05)^2}(0.4) = 458.2$$

$$\hat{S}_0^{[2]}(x) = 500 - \frac{2(0.95)}{0.05}(10) + \frac{(2)(0.95)(2.90)}{2(0.05)^2}(0.4) = 560.8$$

$$\hat{S}_0^{[3]}(x) = 500 - \frac{3(0.95)}{0.05}(10) + \frac{(3)(0.95)(3.85)}{2(0.05)^2}(0.4) = 807.8$$

The $n + 1$ simultaneous linear equations in $n + 1$ derivatives can be solved for these derivatives in terms of the $n + 1$ smoothed statistics.

$$\mathbf{a} = \hat{S}_t M^{-1}$$

where M^{-1} is the inverse of the corresponding square submatrix. For our example of a quadratic polynomial $(n = 2)$,

$$\hat{x}_t^{(0)} = 3S_t(x) - 3S_t^{[2]}(x) + S_t^{[3]}(x)$$

$$\hat{x}_t^{(1)} = \frac{\alpha}{2\beta}\left[(6 - 5\alpha)S_t(x) - 2(5 - 4\alpha)S_t^{[2]}(x) + (4 - 3\alpha)S_t^{[3]}(x)\right]$$

$$\hat{x}_t^{(2)} = \frac{\alpha^2}{\beta^2}\left[S_t(x) - 2S_t^{[2]}(x) + S_t^{[3]}(x)\right]$$

Exercise. Set up a copy of Work Sheet No. 6. Use the noisefree data from Table C.13. Calculate the first three orders of smoothing, and the coefficients. The initial conditions are given in the text.

Work Sheet No. 6   TRIPLE EXPONENTIAL SMOOTHING

DATA: Noisefree Data, Table C.13
MODEL: Quadratic, $\xi_t = a + bt + \frac{1}{2}ct^2$, $\hat{x}_{T+\tau} = \hat{x}_T^{(0)} + \tau\hat{x}_T^{(1)} + \frac{1}{2}\tau^2\hat{x}_T^{(2)}$
SMOOTHING: Triple Smoothing, $\alpha = 0.05$

$$S_t(x) = \alpha x_t + (1 - \alpha)S_{t-1}(x)$$
$$S_t^{[2]}(x) = \alpha S_t(x) + (1 - \alpha)S_{t-1}^{[2]}(x)$$
$$S_t^{[3]}(x) = \alpha S_t^{[2]}(x) + (1 - \alpha)S_{t-1}^{[3]}(x)$$

COEFFICIENTS: $\hat{x}_t^{(0)} = 3S_t(x) - 3S_t^{[2]}(x) + S_t^{[3]}(x)$

$$\hat{x}_t^{(1)} = 0.15927S_t(x) - 0.26591S_t^{[2]}(x) + 0.10664S_t^{[3]}(x)$$

$$x_t^{(2)} = \frac{[S_t(x) - 2S_t^{[2]}(x) + S_t^{[3]}(x)]}{361}$$

Date	Data	Smoothed Values			Coefficients		
t	x_t	$S_t(x)$	$S_t^{[2]}(x)$	$S_t^{[3]}(x)$	$\hat{x}_t^{(0)}$	$\hat{x}_t^{(1)}$	$\hat{x}_t^{(2)}$
0	500.0	458.2	560.8	807.8	500.0	10.0	0.4
1	510.2	460.8	555.8	795.2	510.2	10.4	0.4
2	520.8	463.8	551.2	783.0	520.8	10.8	0.4
3	531.8	467.2	547.0	771.2	531.8	11.2	0.4
4	543.2	471.0	543.2	759.8	543.2	11.6	0.4
.	.	.	.	.	.	.	.
.	.	.	.	.	.	.	.
.	.	.	.	.	.	.	.

The merit of multiple smoothing, of course, is not merely that one can recover the exact coefficients of the model when there is no noise in the data. Suppose the observations can be described by

$$x_t = a + bt + ct^2 + \ldots + gt^n + \epsilon_t$$
$$= \xi_t + \epsilon_t$$

including noise samples $\{\epsilon_t\}$.

Since smoothing is a linear operation

$$S(x) = S(\xi) + S(\epsilon)$$

But smoothing was shown above to yield the expected value of the data so that $\mathcal{E}S(\epsilon) = 0$, and hence $\mathcal{E}S(x) = S(\xi)$.

D'Esopo* has proved that for any sequence of observations, the polynomial P (of degree n) obtained by multiple exponential smoothing is the solution that minimizes the discounted square error criterion

$$\alpha \sum_{i=0}^{\infty} \beta^i (x_{t-i} - P_{t-i})^2$$

Exercise. Set up another copy of Work Sheet No. 6 and estimate the coefficients in a quadratic forecast model for the IBM stock prices (Table C.5). Use the first 20 points to estimate initial conditions. Use a smoothing constant $\alpha = 0.1$. (Figure 9.2 is a graphical plot of the results.)

The purpose of smoothing the data is to obtain recursive revisions to the initial estimates of the coefficients $\{a_i\}$ in a model such as

$$x_t = a_0 + a_1 t + \frac{1}{2} a_2 t^2 + \ldots + \frac{1}{n!} a_n t^n$$

We have stressed the smoothed statistics $S_t^{[j]}(x)$ and shown how the values of the coefficients can be estimated as linear combinations of these statistics at any time. It is, of course, necessary to have initial estimates of the coefficient values to set the initial values of the smoothed statistics.

We can shift the emphasis from the smoothed statistics to the coefficients themselves.

Suppose the model involves only the constant a_0 so that the observations are

$$x_t = a_0 + \epsilon_t$$

We have seen that

$$\hat{a}_0(t) = S_t(x) = \alpha x_t + \beta S_{t-1}(x) = x_t + \beta[S_{t-1}(x) - x_t]$$

---

* D. A. D'Esopo, "A Note on Forecasting by the Exponential Smoothing Operator," *Operations Research*, Vol. 9, No. 5, 686–87. See also **Chapter 11.**

The estimate of the next observation under this model is

$$\hat{x}_{t+1} = \hat{a}_0(t) = S_t(x)$$

Now let us substitute among these expressions to obtain

$$\hat{a}_0(t) = x_t + \beta[\hat{x}_t - x_t]$$

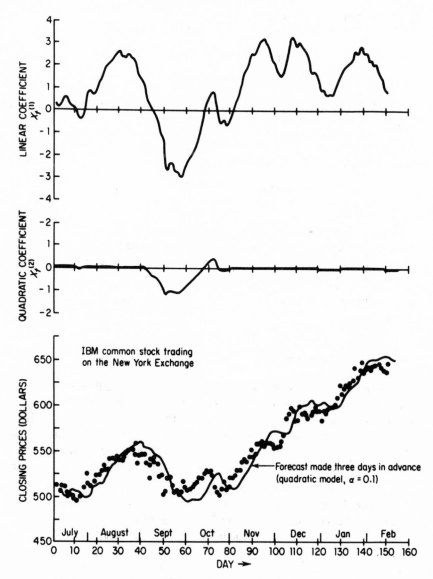

Fig. 9.2 Estimates of the coefficients in a quadratic forecast model of the IBM closing prices.

The new value of the coefficient is equal to the new observation plus a correction proportional to the forecast error, where we understand $\hat{x}_t$ to be the previous estimate of the new observation $\hat{x}_t = S_{t-1}(x)$.

If the model is linear in time,

$$x_t = a_0 + a_1 t$$

we can obtain the following result

$$\hat{a}_0(t) = x_t + \beta^2 [\hat{x}_t - x_t]$$

and

$$\hat{a}_1(t) = \hat{a}_1(t-1) - \alpha^2 [\hat{x}_t - x_t]$$

where

$$\hat{x}_t = \hat{a}_0(t-1) + \hat{a}_1(t-1)$$

For the quadratic model,

$$x_t = a_0 + a_1 t + \tfrac{1}{2} a_2 t^2$$

the analogous results are

$$\hat{a}_0(t) = x_t + \beta^3 [\hat{x}_t - x_t]$$

$$\hat{a}_1(t) = \hat{a}_1(t-1) + \hat{a}_2(t-1) - \frac{3\alpha^2}{2}(2-\alpha)[\hat{x}_t - x_t]$$

$$\hat{a}_2(t) = \hat{a}_2(t-1) - \alpha^3 [\hat{x}_t - x_t]$$

where the expected observation is $\hat{x}_t = \hat{a}_0(t-1) + \hat{a}_1(t-1) + \dfrac{\hat{a}_2}{2}(t-1)$.

Exercise. Set up a copy of Work Sheet No. 7. Use the same initial estimates of the coefficients used before (page 138) for the IBM stock prices in Table C.5.

Proof for Triple Smoothing

Since the last case is not necessarily obvious, we shall sketch out the proof below. (The reader can work out the case of double smoothing for himself.) In each case, the constant term in the model is the current observation plus a correction term proportional to the error in forecasting one period ahead. We can anticipate a result of Chapter 10 to note the apparent correspondence between β for single smoothing, β^2 for double smoothing, and β^3 for triple smoothing.

(1) Express the current values of the smoothed statistics in terms of the current observed data and previous values of the smoothed statistics, by substituting the definitions of multiple smoothing.

$$S_t^{[1]} = \alpha x_t + \beta S_{t-1}^{[1]}$$

$$S_t^{[2]} = \alpha^2 x_t + \alpha\beta S_{t-1}^{[1]} + \beta S_{t-1}^{[2]}$$

$$S_t^{[3]} = \alpha^3 x_t + \alpha^2 \beta S_{t-1}^{[1]} + \alpha\beta S_{t-1}^{[2]} + \beta S_{t-1}^{[3]}$$

Work Sheet No. 7 TRIPLE COEFFICIENT SMOOTHING

DATA: Daily Closing Prices of IBM Stock (Table C.5)

MODEL: Quadratic, $x_t = a_0 + a_1 t + \frac{1}{2} a_2 t^2$

SMOOTHING: $\alpha = 0.1, \beta = 0.9, \beta^3 = 0.729, \dfrac{3\alpha^2}{2}(2 - \alpha) = 0.0285, \alpha^3 = 0.001$

COEFFICIENTS: $\hat{a}_0(t) = x_t + \beta^3(\hat{x}_t - x_t)$

$$\hat{a}_1(t) = \hat{a}_1(t - 1) + \hat{a}_2(t - 1) - \frac{3\alpha^2}{2}(2 - \alpha)(\hat{x}_t - x_t)$$

$$\hat{a}_2(t) = \hat{a}_2(t) - \alpha^3(\hat{x}_t - x_t)$$

FORECAST: $\hat{x}_t = \hat{a}_1(t - 1) + \hat{a}_2(t - 1) + \frac{1}{2}\hat{a}_3(t - 1)$

Date	Data		Coefficients		Forecast	Error
t	x_t	$\hat{a}_0(t)$	$\hat{a}_1(t)$	$\hat{a}_2(t)$	$\hat{x}_t$	$\hat{x}_t - x_t$
Start	...	513	0.842	0		
Aug 8	523	515.83	1.12	0.01	513.84	−9.84
9	527	519.67	1.41	0.02	516.95	−10.05
10	533				521.08	
11	528					
12	529					
Aug 15	538					
16	539					
17	541					
18	543					
19	541					

(2) Express the coefficients in terms of the smoothed statistics,

$$\hat{a}_0(t) = 3S_t^{[1]} - 3S_t^{[2]} + S_t^{[3]}$$

$$\hat{a}_1(t) = \frac{\alpha}{2\beta^2}\left[(6 - 5\alpha)S_t^{[1]} - 2(5 - 4\alpha)S_t^{[2]} + (4 - 3\alpha)S_t^{[3]}\right]$$

$$\hat{a}_2(t) = \frac{\alpha^2}{\beta 2}\left[S_t^{[1]} - 2S_t^{[2]} + S_t^{[3]}\right]$$

(3) Now substitute (1) into (2)

$$\hat{a}_0(t) = (1 - \beta^3)x_t + \beta(3 - 3\alpha + \alpha^2)S_{t-1}^{[1]} + \beta(\alpha - 3)S_{t-1}^{[2]} + \beta S_{t-1}^{[3]}$$

$$\hat{a}_1(t) = \frac{\alpha}{2\beta^2}\left[3\alpha(2 - \alpha)\beta^2 x_t + 3\beta^3(2 - \alpha)S_{t-1}^{[1]}\right.$$
$$+ \beta(-10 + 12\alpha - 3\alpha^2)S_{t-1}^{[2]}$$
$$\left. + \beta(4 - 3\alpha)S_{t-1}^{[3]}\right]$$

$$\hat{a}_2(t) = \frac{\alpha^2}{\beta^2}\left[\alpha\beta^2 x_t + \beta^3 S_{t-1}^{[1]} + \beta(\alpha - 2)S_{t-1}^{[2]} + \beta S_{t-1}^{[3]}\right]$$

(4) Write the smoothed statistics in terms of the coefficients, from the fundamental theorem.

$$S_t^{[1]} = a_0 - \frac{\beta}{\alpha} a_1 + \frac{(2 - \alpha)}{2\alpha^2} a_2$$

$$S_t^{[2]} = a_0 - \frac{2\beta}{\alpha} a_1 + \frac{2\beta(3 - 2\alpha)}{2\alpha^2} a_2$$

$$S_t^{[3]} = a_0 - \frac{3\beta}{\alpha} a_1 + \frac{3\beta(4 - 3\alpha)}{2\alpha^2} a_2$$

(5) Now substitute (4) into (3) to obtain the stated results.

There are two possible ways of organizing the computations. In one, the smoothed statistics $S_t^{[p]}(x)$ are revised with each new observation by a very simple recursion relation

$$S_t^p(x) = \alpha S_t^{p-1}(x) + \beta S_{t-1}^p(x)$$

Then the coefficients in the forecast equation

$$\hat{x}_{T+\tau} = \hat{x}_T^{(0)} + \tau x_T^{(1)} + \frac{1}{2} \tau^2 x_T^{(2)} + \ldots + \frac{1}{n!} \tau^n x_T^{(n)}$$

can be calculated as a linear combination of the smoothed statistics. The coefficients of τ^k in this linear combination are complicated expressions involving the smoothing constant, but they are fixed program constants for any one application.

The other method of computation is to store the n coefficients $\hat{x}_T^{(n)}$ from observation to observation, and to revise them directly in the light of the new information. The recursion relationships are more complicated in that they involve the complete set of coefficients from the previous time, but again the constants for any one application are fixed and can be treated as program constants. This second method does have the advantage that the numbers in the record are the coefficients used in forecasting and therefore have more of a physical meaning to anyone who must consult the record, perhaps to predict a revision of one or more of these coefficient values.

Summary of Multiple Smoothing

The various formulas developed in Chapters 7 and 9 in respect to polynomial models are summarized below for convenience. In order to emphasize the lead time τ for which the forecast is calculated, we shall use the notation $\hat{x}_\tau(T)$ in place of the previous $\hat{x}_{T+\tau}$ for a computation made with data through time T. For symmetry, we shall also use $x(T)$ as the current observation in place of x_T. In each case there is a process ξ that can be represented by a polynomial

$$\xi(t) = \sum_{i=0}^{n} \frac{a_i}{i!} t^i$$

which is observed in the presence of noise

$$x(t) = \xi(t) + \epsilon(t)$$

1. *Constant Model:* $n = 0$

    Process: $\xi(t) = a_0$

    (a) Smoothed statistic: $S_t(x) = \alpha x(t) + \beta S_{t-1}(x)$

     Estimate of coefficient: $\hat{a}_0(T) = S_T(x)$

     Initial condition: $S_0(x) = a_0(0)$

     Forecast: $\hat{x}_r(T) = \hat{a}_0(T) = S_T(x)$

    (b) Smoothed coefficient: $a_0(t) = x(t) + \beta[\hat{x}_1(t-1) - x(t)]$

     Forecast: $\hat{x}_r(T) = a_0(T)$

2. *Linear Model:* $n = 1$

    Process: $\xi(t) = a_0 + a_1 t$

    (a) Smoothed statistics: $S_t(x) = \alpha x(t) + \beta S_{t-1}(x)$

    $$S_t^{[2]}(x) = \alpha S_t(x) + \beta S_{t-1}^{[2]}(x)$$

    Estimate of coefficients:

    $$\hat{a}_0(T) = 2S_T(x) - S_T^{[2]}(x)$$

    $$\hat{a}_1(T) = \frac{\alpha}{\beta}[S_T(x) - S_t^{[2]}(x)]$$

    Initial conditions:

    $$S_0(x) = a_0(0) - \frac{\beta}{\alpha} a_1(0)$$

    $$S_0^{[2]}(x) = a_0(0) - \frac{2\beta}{\alpha} a_1(0)$$

    Forecast: $\hat{x}_r(T) = \hat{a}_0(T) + \tau \hat{a}_1(T)$

    $$= \left(2 + \frac{\alpha\tau}{\beta}\right) S_T(x) - \left(1 + \frac{\alpha\tau}{\beta}\right) S_T^{[2]}(x)$$

    (b) Smoothed coefficients:

    $$a_0(t) = x(t) + \beta^2[\hat{x}_1(t-1) - x(t)]$$
    $$a_1(t) = a_1(t-1) - \alpha^2[\hat{x}_1(t-1) - x(t)]$$

    Forecast: $\hat{x}_r(T) = \hat{a}_0(T) + \tau \hat{a}_1(T)$

3. *Quadratic Model: $n = 2$*

Process: $\xi(t) = a_0 + a_1 t + \frac{1}{2} a_2 t^2$

(a) Smoothed statistics:

$$S_t(x) = \alpha x(t) + \beta S_{t-1}(x)$$
$$S_t^{[2]}(x) = \alpha S_t(x) + \beta S_{t-1}^{[2]}(x)$$
$$S_t^{[3]}(x) = \alpha S_t^{[2]}(x) + \beta S_{t-1}^{[3]}(x)$$

Estimate of coefficients:

$$\hat{a}_0(t) = 3S_t(x) - 3S_t^{[2]}(x) + S_t^{[3]}(x)$$

$$\hat{a}_1(t) = \frac{\alpha}{2\beta} \left[(6 - 5\alpha)S_t(x) - 2(5 - 4\alpha)S_t^{[2]}(x) + (4 - 3\alpha)S_t^{[3]}(x) \right]$$

$$\hat{a}_2(t) = \frac{\alpha^2}{\beta^2} \left[S_t(x) - 2S_t^{[2]}(x) + S_t^{[3]}(x) \right]$$

Initial conditions:

$$S_0(x) = a_0(0) - \frac{\beta}{\alpha} a_1(0) + \frac{\beta(2 - \alpha)}{2\alpha^2} \frac{a_2(0)}{2}$$

$$S_0^{[2]}(x) = a_0(0) - \frac{2\beta}{\alpha} a_1(0) + \frac{2\beta(3 - 2\alpha)}{2\alpha^2} \frac{a_2(0)}{2}$$

$$S_0^{[3]}(x) = a_0(0) - \frac{3\beta}{\alpha} a_2(0) + \frac{3\beta(4 - 3\alpha)}{2\alpha^2} \frac{a_2(0)}{2}$$

Forecast:

$$\hat{x}_\tau(T) = \hat{a}_0 + \tau \hat{a}_1(T) + \frac{1}{2}\tau^2 \hat{a}_2(T)$$

$$= [6\beta^2 + (6 - 5\alpha)\alpha\tau + \alpha^2\tau^2] \frac{S_T(x)}{2\beta^2}$$

$$- [6\beta^2 + 2(5 - 4\alpha)\alpha\tau + 2\alpha^2\tau^2] \frac{S_t^{[2]}(x)}{2\beta^2}$$

$$+ [2\beta^2 + (4 - 3\alpha)\alpha\tau + \alpha^2\tau^2] \frac{S_t^{[3]}(x)}{2\beta^2}$$

(b) Smoothed coefficients:

$$a_0(t) = x(t) + \beta^3[\hat{x}_1(t - 1) - x(t)]$$

$$a_1(t) = a_1(t - 1) + a_2(t - 1) - \frac{3\alpha^2}{2}(2 - \alpha)[\hat{x}_1(t - 1) - x(t)]$$

$$a_2(t) = a_2(t - 1) - \alpha^3[\hat{x}_1(t - 1) - x(t)]$$

Forecast:

$$\hat{x}_\tau(T) = \hat{a}_0(T) + \tau\hat{a}_1(T) + \frac{1}{2}\tau^2\hat{a}_2(T)$$

10 Analysis of Characteristics

Multiple exponential smoothing is a linear, discrete, time-invariant system and can therefore be completely described by its impulse response (see Appendix B). In Chapter 8, we discussed the impulse response for single exponential smoothing and used it to determine the statistical behavior in smoothing random or correlated data and the dynamic behavior in responding to a change in pattern. Understanding these two characteristics was helpful in reaching a practical compromise in selecting a value for the smoothing constant α.

In this chapter we shall go through a similar analysis for multiple smoothing systems in order to get the impulse response and then the response to other standard inputs. From this information, we can develop the notion of an equivalent smoothing constant so that conclusions drawn for single exponential smoothing can be extended to smoothing of any order.

Some readers may want to skip to Chapter 11, referring back to sections of this chapter as they are required in support of later work.

IMPULSE RESPONSES FOR THE EXPONENTIAL SMOOTHING OPERATORS. The response for single exponential smoothing is (Table 8.2)

$$h(t) = \alpha(1 - \alpha)^t = \alpha\beta^t$$

where $\beta = 1 - \alpha$. The transform of the impulse response, or transfer function (Table B.1) is

$$H_1(z) = \frac{\alpha}{1 - \beta z}$$

The double smoothing operator $S^{[2]}$ gives the same result as applying single smoothing to the output of a single smoothing system. Therefore its transfer function is

$$H_2(z) = \frac{\alpha^2}{(1 - \beta z)^2}$$

Similarly, for the triple smoothing operator, the transfer function is

$$H_3(z) = \frac{\alpha^3}{(1 - \beta z)^3}$$

These transfer functions correspond to exponential decay impulse responses (Table 10.1). Recall that the impulse response after t observations is the weight given data t observations old in the smoothing process.

Table 10.1   IMPULSE RESPONSES AND TRANSFER FUNCTIONS
FOR EXPONENTIAL SMOOTHING OPERATORS

Operator	Impulse Response, $h(t)$	Transfer Function, $H(z)$
Single, S	$\alpha\beta^t$	$\dfrac{\alpha}{1 - \beta z}$
Double, $S^{[2]}$	$\alpha^2(t + 1)\beta^t$	$\dfrac{\alpha^2}{(1 - \beta z)^2}$
Triple, $S^{[3]}$	$\alpha^3 \dfrac{(t + 1)(t + 2)}{2}\beta^t$	$\dfrac{\alpha^3}{(1 - \beta z)^3}$

Equivalent Smoothing Constant

Suppose that the input signal has been $x_t = 0$ for a long enough time that all the smoothed values of the data are also identically zero. Then at time $t = 0$ there is a unit signal $x_0 = 1$. This may be just an impulse, the beginning of a step, or the beginning of any other time function.

The single smoothed value of the data will rise to a height α in response to this input. It is easy to see that the response of the double smoothed value is α^2 and that, in general, the response of the kth order of smoothing will be α^k.

The order of smoothing used is based on the choice of the degree of the polynomial model that is to represent the data. By virtue of the fundamental theorem, and the initial response to a unit signal, the estimate of the constant term $\hat{a}_0(t)$ is given by

$$\hat{a}_0(t) = 1 - (1 - \alpha)^k$$

for a model that is a polynomial of degree $k + 1$. In a great many respects, it will prove to be convenient to define an *equivalent value of the smoothing*

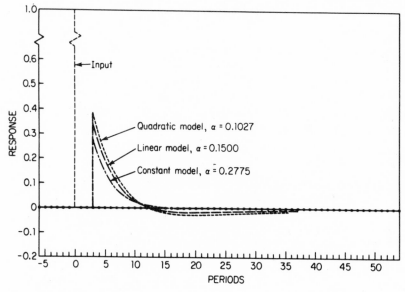

Fig. 10.1 Impulse responses.

constant for higher-order smoothing in such a way that the estimates of the constant term are the same. That is, suppose α_1 is used in single smoothing, to estimate the only coefficient there is in a linear model. Then for a linear model, the equivalent value of the smoothing constant for double smoothing would be α_2 that

$$(1 - \alpha_2)^2 = 1 - \alpha_1 \quad \text{or} \quad \beta_2^2 = \beta_1$$

In general, for pth-order smoothing, the *equivalent value of the smoothing constant* would be β_p such that

$$(1 - \alpha_p)^p = 1 - \alpha_1 \quad \text{or} \quad \beta_p^p = \beta_1^1$$

This definition of equivalence is consistent with (and related to) another equivalence. In Chapter 9, we derived the recursive estimates of the constant term $a_0(t)$ in any polynomial model as

$$a_0(t) = x(t) + \beta^p[\hat{x}_1(t - 1) - x(t)]$$

where $\hat{x}_1(t - 1)$ is the observation that was to be expected at time t according to the information available through time $t - 1$. Hence the equivalent smoothing constant gives the same correction to the constant term for a given difference between the expected and actual observations.

Some common values of the smoothing constant are compared in Table 10.2. Figure 10.2 shows how the value of the smoothing constant decreases

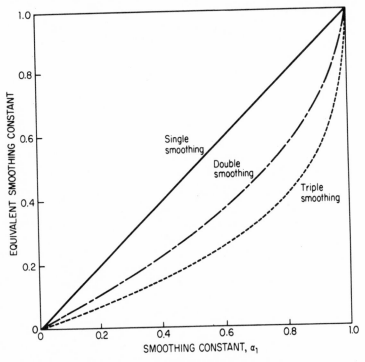

Fig. 10.2 Equivalent value of the smoothing constant.

for higher orders of smoothing. Recall that the smoothing constant controls the number of past observations that have any effect on the forecast. A small value includes many observations; for larger values of the smoothing constant, only recent information is included. With the higher-order models, there are more coefficients to be estimated. It is good statistical practice to estimate coefficients from noisy data using several times as many points as there are degrees of freedom in the model. The equivalence defined above automatically increases the number of past observations that are considered in estimating more coefficients.

Earlier in this section, we discussed the flexibility of changing the smoothing constant to give, on the one hand, stable forecasts in the presence of noise superimposed on a stable process, and on the other,

Table 10.2 EQUIVALENT VALUES OF THE SMOOTHING CONSTANT α

Constant Model (Single Smoothing)	Linear Model (Double Smoothing)	Quadratic Model (Triple Smoothing)
0.01	0.005	0.003
0.03	0.015	0.010
0.05	0.025	0.017
0.10	0.051	0.035
0.15	0.078	0.053
0.20	0.106	0.072
0.25	0.134	0.091
0.30	0.163	0.112

forecasts that respond rapidly when the value of any of the coefficients in the process appears to have changed radically. Theoretically, the optimum value of the smoothing constant can be computed from the variance of the noise in the observations and the variance of the small random changes in

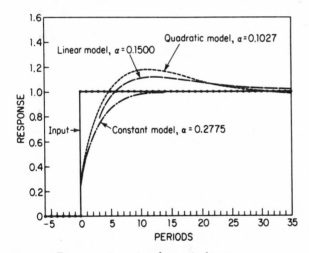

Fig. 10.3 Responses to a step, forecasts $\hat{x}_3$.

the true coefficients that describe the process. In practice, it is quite suitable to select two values of the smoothing constant, one for stable conditions and the other, higher value for conditions of rapid change. The value $\alpha_1 = 0.05$ is frequently suitable for very stable processes, in which case $\alpha_1 = 0.10$ would be used whenever there is an indication of rapid change (see Chapter 16). Forecasts of demand on an industrial inventory frequently employ $\alpha_1 = 0.1$ for the stable case and $\alpha_1 = 0.25$ for the times when a more rapid response is required. We shall use these three values in Chapter 12 in preparing tables of the program constants required for several alternative models of the process.

Figure 10.3 shows the responses to a step, using equivalent values of the smoothing constant. Note that the initial responses are all identical. Thereafter, the quadratic model rises much more steeply than the others.

Transient Responses to Polynomial Signals

From the impulse response for any discrete, linear, time-invariant system, one can obtain the response to other functions either by convolution in the time domain or by multiplication of transform. Since exponential smoothing has been developed primarily to forecast time series that can be adequately represented by polynomial functions of time, we shall next proceed to develop the transient response of the three exponential smoothing operators to a step, a ramp, and a parabola. Any polynomial input (up to second degree) can be represented as a linear combination of these standard signals; hence, the response will be the same linear combination of the standard responses.

For example, suppose the process is represented by the model

$$\xi_t = a + bt + ct^2$$

Now let the response of an exponential smoothing system to a step ($x_t = 1$), a ramp ($x_t = t$), and a parabola ($x_t = t^2$), be y_{1t}, y_{2t}, and y_{3t}, respectively. Then the response to the observed data will be

$$y_t = ay_{1t} + by_{2t} + cy_{3t}$$

Tables 10.3 and 10.4* summarize, for the double and triple smoothing

Table 10.3 RESPONSES OF THE DOUBLE SMOOTHING OPERATOR $S^{[2]}$ TO STANDARD INPUTS

Input	x_t	Response y_t	Steady State Error $x_\infty - y_\infty$
Impulse	$\delta(t)$	$\alpha^2(t+1)\beta^t$	0
Step	1	$1 - [1 + (t+1)\alpha]\beta^{t+1}$	0
Ramp	t	$t - \dfrac{2\beta}{\alpha} + \left(\dfrac{2}{\alpha} + t\right)\beta^{t+1}$	$\dfrac{2\beta}{\alpha}$
Parabola	t^2	$t^2 - \dfrac{2\beta}{\alpha}\left(t - \dfrac{1}{\alpha}\right) - \left(t(1+\beta) + \dfrac{2}{\alpha}\right)\dfrac{\beta^{t+1}}{\alpha}$	$\dfrac{4\beta t}{\alpha} - \dfrac{2\beta}{\alpha^2}$

* I am indebted to Mr. Gordon J. Crook for carrying through and checking the tedious algebra needed to prepare these tables.

Table 10.4 RESPONSES OF THE TRIPLE SMOOTHING OPERATOR $S^{[3]}$
TO STANDARD INPUTS

Input	x_t	Response y_t	Steady State Error $x_\infty - y_\infty$
Impulse	$\delta(t)$	$\dfrac{\alpha^3(t+1)(t+2)}{2}\beta^t$	0
Step	1	$1 - \left[1 + \alpha^2\dfrac{(t+1)(t+2)}{2} + \alpha(t+1)\beta^{t+1}\right]\beta^{t+2}$	0
Ramp	t	$t - \dfrac{3\beta}{\alpha} + \left[\dfrac{3}{\alpha} + 2t + \dfrac{\alpha t(t+1)}{2}\right]\beta^{t+1}$	$\dfrac{3\beta}{\alpha}$
Parabola	t^2	$t^3 - \dfrac{3\beta}{\alpha}(2t-1) - \left[\left(\dfrac{3}{\alpha} + \dfrac{t\beta}{2}\right)(t-\alpha) + \dfrac{t\beta}{2}\right]\beta^{t+1}$	$\dfrac{6\beta t}{\alpha} - \dfrac{3\beta}{\alpha}$

operators, respectively, the transient response as a function of time. These
tables also compare the response y_∞ (after all transients of the form β^t have
died out) with the signal x_∞. In some cases there are terms, such as $\beta t/\alpha$,
that will grow arbitrarily large. (Table 8.2 gave similar information for
single smoothing.)

The double-smoothing operator drops back to zero after an impulse, or
settles down to unity for the step. The error in the response to a ramp is
just twice that for the single smoothing operator, so that there is no error in
the estimate

$$\hat{x}_t^{(0)} = 2S_t(x) - S_t^{[2]}(x)$$

The estimate of the current value of the constant term in a quadratic
model is

$$x_t^{(0)} = 3S_t^{(x)} - 3S_t^{[2]}(x) + S_t^{[3]}(x)$$

Therefore there is no steady state error in this estimate for any of the four
standard input signals, or for any linear combination of them.

Tables 8.2, 10.3, and 10.4 contain all of the information necessary to
determine analytically the response of a forecast system to a polynomial
signal. The equations in Chapter 9 define the estimates of the coefficients
in terms of linear combinations of the smoothed functions of the data.
We know the response of any operator to an impulse, and therefore to any
other signal. The response of the forecast is therefore a linear combination
of known responses.

The tables give all the information from which these responses could be
derived. In a complicated system, however, it isn't always practical to do
so. For example, it was shown above that when the data are to be
represented by a quadratic model

$$\xi_t = a + bt + ct^2$$

the estimate of the current value of the first derivative (the slope of the tangent, or the trend of the data) is of the form

$$\hat{x}_t^{(1)} = AS_t(x) + BS_t^{[2]} + CS_t^{[3]}(x)$$

where A, B, and C are functions of α. Call h_s^p the impulse response of the pth degree of smoothing to the sth signal ($s = 1$ for a step, $s = 2$ for a ramp, and $s = 3$ for a parabola). Then the response of the estimate $\hat{x}_t^{(1)}$ to the signal x_t will be

$$y_t = A(ah_1^1 + bh_2^1 + ch_3^1) + B(ah_1^2 + bh_2^2 + ch_3^2) + C(ah_1^3 + bh_2^3 + ch_3^3)$$

which gets rather formidable. Therefore, the following results were obtained by a simulation of the process of forecasting. In each case, the equivalent smoothing constant was used for each of the three orders of smoothing. Note that the equivalence does not extend to precisely equal responses to all signals. The graphs plotted show the forecasts $\hat{x}_3(t - 3)$ estimated from the data available three observations earlier.

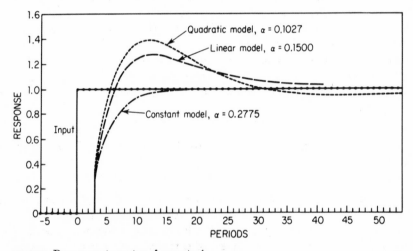

Fig. 10.4 Responses to a step, forecasts $\hat{x}_3$.

Step: Figure 10.4 shows the responses to a step function. The forecast for the third period ahead ultimately settles down to the step, but that the more elaborate models take appreciably longer than single smoothing. This response could be accelerated, of course, by use of a larger value of the smoothing constant with the multiple smoothing. Note that the forecasts from the linear model overshoot and settle back, whereas the quadratic model characteristically overshoots, undershoots, and then settles down. The overshoot is small compared with the height of the step.

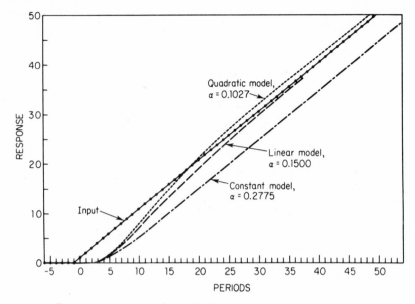

Fig. 10.5 Responses to a ramp, forecasts $\hat{x}_3$.

Ramp: The responses to a ramp input are compared in Fig. 10.5. After the initial transient, forecasts with a constant model stay a constant distance below the signal; forecasts with a linear model ultimately converge with the actual signal; and forecasts with the quadratic model overshoot and then settle down.

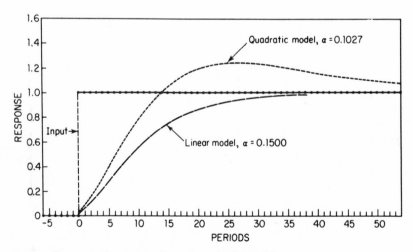

Fig. 10.6 Responses to a ramp—linear term in the model.

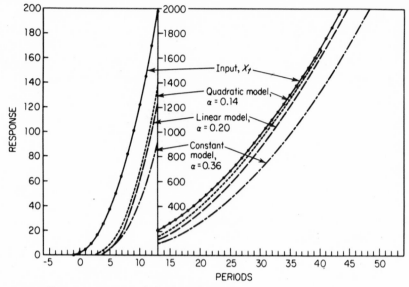

Fig. 10.7 Responses to a parabola, forecasts $\hat{x}_3$.

The derivative of the ramp signal is a step. The derivative of the polynomial model contains b as a constant term. Figure 10.6 shows the response of b for linear and quadratic models: compare with Fig. 10.3.

Parabola: Figure 10.7 shows how the systems respond to a parabola as input.

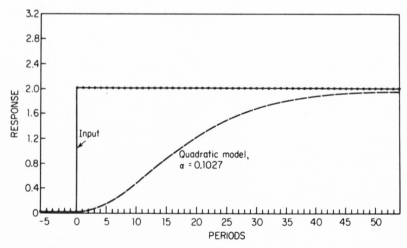

Fig. 10.8 Responses to a parabola, quadratic term in the model.

The forecasts with a simple constant model fall farther and farther behind the signal, whereas the linear model settles down with a constant bias. The quadratic model ultimately converges to give an accurate forecast.

The second derivative of the parabola is a step, to be compared (Fig. 10.8) with the response of the quadratic coefficient in the model. Contrast with Fig. 10.3 and Fig. 10.6.

Distribution of the Estimates of the Coefficients

The current values of the derivatives of the model are to be estimated as coefficients in the forecast equation. When the input data are noisy, these estimates will have a probability distribution. In any of the linear systems we have been considering, the output is the sum of two kinds of response—the response to the process itself and the response to the superimposed noise. Since the systems are linear, in this section we shall consider only a noise input

$$x_t = \epsilon_t$$

where the noise samples have zero mean and variance σ_ϵ^2. We shall assume that the noise samples have no serial correlation

$$R_{\epsilon\epsilon}(\tau) = 0 \qquad \text{for all } \tau \neq 0$$

(See Chapter 21 for a discussion of correlated noise.)

Under these conditions, the output y_t will have mean zero, and a variance that is proportional to the variance of the input, where the constant of proportionality is the sum of the squares of the impulse responses.

$$\sigma_y^2 = \sigma_\epsilon^2 \sum_{n=0}^{\infty} h^2(n)$$

In Chapter 8, it was shown that for a constant model, with single smoothing, the variance of the estimate of that constant was

$$\sigma_{x(0)}^2 = \frac{\alpha}{1 + \beta} \sigma_\epsilon^2$$

When a linear model is used to represent the data, the estimate of the coefficients in the model are

$$\hat{x}_t^{(0)} = 2S_t(x) - S_t^{[2]}(x) \quad \text{and} \quad x_t^{(1)} = \frac{\alpha}{\beta} [S_t(x) - S_t^{[2]}(x)]$$

The impulse responses for these estimates are

$$h_0(t) = \alpha\beta^t(2 - \alpha - \alpha t) \quad \text{and} \quad h_1(t) = \alpha^2\beta^t\left(1 - \frac{\alpha t}{\beta}\right)$$

From the sum of the squares of the impulse response, we find that the variance of the estimates of the coefficient is

$$\sigma^2_{x^{(0)}} = \frac{\alpha(1 + 4\beta + 5\beta^2)}{(1 + \beta)^3} \sigma^2_\epsilon$$

$$\sigma^2_{x^{(1)}} = \frac{2\alpha^3}{(1 + \beta)^3} \sigma^2_\epsilon$$

Since the algebra gets tedious for higher-order polynomials, we defer

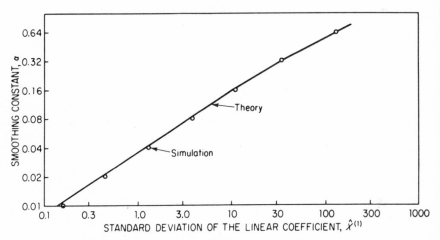

Fig. 10.9 Standard deviation of the estimates for b compared with theory.

analysis of the variance of the estimated coefficients until Chapter 12 when we shall have developed more powerful methods.

Table 10.5 STANDARD DEVIATIONS OF ESTIMATES FOR COEFFICIENT VALUES ($\sigma_\epsilon = 289.4$)

Smoothing Constant	Linear Term $\hat{b}$ Double Smoothing	
	Theory	Simulation
0.01	0.14	0.16
0.02	0.41	0.44
0.04	1.19	1.27
0.08	3.47	3.77
0.16	10.47	11.00
0.32	34.15	34.47
0.64	131.97	130.20

A simulation was run, for several values of the smoothing constant, using 1000 random numbers as input (see Chapter 23 and Table D.12). Theoretically, the numbers should have had mean 499.5 and standard deviation 288.7. Actually, the mean was 506.2 and the standard deviation 289.4. Table 10.5 compares the standard deviation of the estimates of the linear coefficients for the theoretical and computed results. The results are plotted in Fig. 10.9.

11 Adaptive Fitting of Transcendental Functions

Exponential smoothing is a simple and effective technique for estimating the coefficients in a polynomial model. It is not always possible, however, to represent a process adequately by polynomial functions. Often the significant variation, which must be reflected in the model, is periodic: hourly height of tides, daily volume of mail, monthly value of sales, elliptical orbits of ballistic missiles, and so on.

In this chapter, we consider methods of fitting an arbitrary set of functions to the time series; that is, we shall determine values of the coefficients that minimize the weighted sum of square residuals. (These methods are in contrast to techniques common in the literature on economic forecasting that separate the "trend components" from the "seasonal and cyclical components." Such techniques introduce spurious autocorrelation in the residuals.*)

We shall begin with the consideration of a process that can be represented by †

$$\xi(t) = a_1 f_1(t) + a_2 f_2(t) + \ldots + a_n f_n(t)$$

---

* M. G. Kendall, *The Advanced Theory of Statistics* (New York: Hafner, 1951), chap. 29.

† A note on notation. In this chapter, we shall want to use subscripts to distinguish the various functions $f_i(t)$ and their associated coefficients. The dependence on time will

where the functions $f_i(t)$ are any functions of time, subject only to the restriction that the value of the function is known *exactly* both at the time of the current observation and at the time in the future for which the forecast is required. These fitting functions can include: (1) simple mathematical functions of time, such as the algebraic and transcendental functions discussed in Chapter 4; (2) empirical functions, the number of children born seventeen years ago or the number of building contracts let six months ago; or (3) previous observations of the dependent series, such as the sales of the same item twelve months ago.

When the fitting functions are powers of time:

$$f_1(t) = 1, f_2(t) = t, \ldots, f_n(t) = t^{n-1}$$

the discounted multiple regression methods give exactly the same forecasts as those that would have been obtained by the appropriate degree of exponential smoothing.

There are some computational difficulties in carrying out the discounted multiple regression, requiring the solution of n simultaneous linear equations in n unknowns at each sampling interval: equivalent to the repeated inversion of an $n \times n$ matrix. If it is possible to describe the process adequately by a model that includes only the algebraic and transcendental functions discussed in Chapter 4, the calculations can be reduced to the simplicity of exponential smoothing. The development of those methods is covered in the next chapter (Chapter 12).

Discounted Multiple Regression

There is a temptation to say, "Let's assume that the process can be represented by the model

$$\xi(t) = \sum_{i=1}^{n} a_i f_i(t)$$

and that the observations $x(t) = \xi(t) + \epsilon(t)$ where $\{\epsilon(t)\}$ are random samples from a stationary noise process with zero mean." Then one passes quickly on to the question of estimating the values for the coefficients a_i. Too many forecasts go awry from a hasty assumption of the correct model. Therefore let me repeat the stricture of Chapter 4: be very sure that each

---

be represented by parentheses. The observation at time t will be referred to in this chapter as $x(t)$ instead of x_t as in the earlier chapters. The functions in the model of the process may well be continuous functions of time, but the observations $x(t) = \xi(t) + \epsilon(t)$ are still to be obtained at discrete sampling intervals. Later on, when we come to discuss computer programs, still a different notation will be most convenient for the task at hand. There seems to be no instance in real life where one name is a sufficient identification of an object for all purposes. Mathematics is no exception.

of the functions $f_i(t)$ is necessary for the practical forecasting of future observations and that you will know the exact value of each function not only at the time of the current observation of the data, but for the future when the forecast will be required. The methods developed in this section depend on knowing the fitting function values exactly. There are more powerful methods, usually applicable to interpolation rather than extrapolation, which should be used when there is any uncertainty in the values of the independent variables.

Mathematical functions of time, such as t, t^2, sin ωt, and so on, are, of course, known exactly. *Past* values of empirical functions are also known exactly: number of children born, temperature in New York, gross national product, sales department predictions, and so on. The difficulty comes in knowing future values exactly. In general, the only reliable results will be obtained when the fitting function is lagged in time. That is, the number of college students in the year t should depend on (among other things) the number of children born seventeen years earlier, at time $t - 17$. Hence values of that function are known up to sixteen years in the future and could be used as the basis for a forecast. Perhaps the temperature at Easter is significant in affecting sales of women's hats during the summer. But if you want a five-year forecast of sales, it is no good using gross national product in the current year as one of the fitting functions. The best alternative would be to use the National Bureau of Economic Research, Inc., five-year estimate of GNP, made in year $t - 5$ as the fitting function. A similar remark applies to the use of any independent prediction as the basis for a forecast (see Chapter 14.)

Suppose the data show a significant periodic pattern, so that $x(t + p) \simeq x(t)$. For example, in some sales forecasting problems, there is reason to believe that sales in the current week are related to the sales in the same week last year—the *Wall Street Journal* continually reports automobile production and retail sales volumes in terms of a percentage change from the similar period in the previous year. Then one of the functions included in the model could be $f_1(t) = x(t - p)$, the actual observation one cycle earlier.

Note: *Statistical Forecasting for Inventory Control* (Chapter 5) had only this model to suggest as a basis for seasonal forecasting.

Other obvious functions would be $x(T - \tau)$ for all lags τ for which the autocovariance (Appendix A) is significantly different from zero. For example, even when the sequence of observations is not cyclical, it may be appropriate to describe it as autoregressive (more on this point in Chapter 20):

$$\xi(t) = a_1\xi(t - 1) + a_2\xi(t - 2) + \ldots + a_n\xi(t - n)$$

Thus, the fitting functions are prior observations of the same sequence.

This scheme presents some difficulties in forecasting, however. Unless the data have a periodic cycle, the strongest relationship is likely to be apparent between adjacent observations. But for obvious reasons, one cannot use $x(t-1), \ldots, x(t-\tau+1)$ in a forecast τ time periods into the future.

Exercise. What fitting functions would you use if the ratio of current monthly sales to the sales in the same month last year was increasing steadily?

All right. Now if you get into trouble by using inappropriate fitting functions for the independent variables in your forecast model, you have been warned. Let's assume that the data can be represented by the model

$$x(t) = a_1 f_1(t) + a_2 f_2(t) + \ldots + a_n f_n(t) + \epsilon(t)$$
$$= \sum_{i=1}^{n} a_i f_i(t) + \epsilon(t)$$

where the $f_i(t)$ are any known functions of time, mathematical or empirical. Over some local period of time, the coefficients a_i can be treated as constants. The period of time extends into the past far enough to include a sufficient number of observations for estimating a value for each coefficient, and far enough into the future to include the period for which the forecast is required. We do not, however, insist that the time series be stationary in any way. Two sequences of observations of the same process, obtained at widely separated intervals of time, may require different values of one or more of the coefficients. The underlying process $\xi(t)$ can be going through a slow random walk in respect of one or more of the coefficients.

Therefore we want to develop a simple iterative procedure for revising the estimate of the coefficient values with each new observation, and the revision should in some way discount information obtained a long time in the past. One approach would be to use only the most recent N observations as the basis for the estimation of the coefficient value, as in a moving average. Another approach, taking a cue from exponential smoothing, is discounting the data gradually in time. The estimated values of the coefficients $\hat{a}_i(t)$ will therefore depend on the information received to date. The resulting forecast will be

$$\hat{x}(t+\tau) = \hat{a}_1(t)f_1(t+\tau) + \hat{a}_2(t)f_2(t+\tau) + \ldots + \hat{a}_n(t)f_n(t+\tau)$$
$$= \sum_{i=1}^{n} \hat{a}_i(t)f_i(t+\tau)$$

We can evaluate the current model at prior sampling intervals. Let $\hat{x}(T-j)$ stand for the model where the coefficients evaluated with all the data through time T, but the model evaluated at a time j periods earlier.

If the current model (as of time T) were used to describe past data, the residual would be defined as $x(T-j) - \hat{x}(T-j) = e(T-j)$. The usual least squares multiple regression seeks to determine the coefficients $\hat{a}_i(T)$ so that the sum of the squares of these residuals will be a minimum over the finite number of observations T. Least squares is not the only useful criterion: in many applications, one wants to minimize the maximum error. In what follows, we shall determine values for the coefficients so as to minimize the *discounted* sum of squared residuals

$$\sum_{j=1}^{T} \beta^j \left[x(T - j) - \sum_{i=1}^{n} \hat{a}_i(T) f_i(T - j) \right]^2$$

The discount factor β must be positive and less than, or equal to, one. It will generally be taken as $\beta = 1 - \alpha$ where α is the smoothing constant that would be used for n degrees of freedom.

The procedure for estimating these least squares coefficients can be discussed most compactly using matrix notation.* We shall let $\mathbf{x} = (x_1, x_2, \ldots, x_T)$ be a row vector of the T observations available for the computation, and

$$\mathbf{f}(t) = \begin{bmatrix} f_1(t) \\ f_2(t) \\ \cdot \\ \cdot \\ \cdot \\ f_n(t) \end{bmatrix}$$

be a column vector of the n fitting functions.

We shall also let $\mathfrak{F}$ be an $n \times T$ matrix with elements $f_i(t)$, the values of the ith fitting function at time t. The residual is $e(t) = x(t) - \mathbf{a}'\mathbf{f}(t)$ where

---

* Let a column vector $\mathbf{a}$ have components a_i ($i = 1, 2, \ldots, m$), and another column vector $\mathbf{b}$ have components b_j ($j = 1, 2, \ldots, n$). Then $\mathbf{b}'$ is the transpose, a row vector. When $m = n$, the scalar product is defined by

$$\mathbf{b}'\mathbf{a} = \sum_{i=1}^{n} b_i a_i$$

When the multiplication is taken in the other order $\mathbf{a}\mathbf{b}' = M$ where M is an $m \times n$ matrix (m rows and n columns), with elements $M_{ij} = a_i b_j$.

Let N be another matrix, with n rows and p columns. Then the product MN is an $m \times p$ matrix Q with elements

$$Q_{ij} = \sum_{k=1}^{n} M_{ik} N_{kj}$$

In general, matrix multiplication is not defined in the reverse order. A square matrix F, under some conditions, will have an inverse F^{-1}, such that $FF^{-1} = I$, where I is the identity matrix, with ones along the main diagonal and zeros elsewhere. The transpose M' of a matrix M interchanges the rows and columns. If $M' = M$, the matrix is said to be symmetrical.

$$\mathbf{a} = \begin{bmatrix} a_1 \\ a_2 \\ \cdot \\ \cdot \\ \cdot \\ a_n \end{bmatrix}$$

is the vector of coefficients to be determined from the data. The criterion for this determination is to minimize the weighted square residuals

$$\sum_{t=1}^{T} w_t^2 e_2^2$$

The weights are the diagonal elements of a $T \times T$ matrix W, which has zeros everywhere off the diagonal.

It is shown in Appendix A that the set of coefficients that meets this criterion is

$$\mathbf{a}' = \mathbf{x} W' \mathfrak{F} W F^{-1}$$

where F is the $n \times n$ matrix $(\mathfrak{F}W)(\mathfrak{F}W)'$.

The F matrix depends on (1) the total number of observations available T; (2) the set of fitting functions used to describe the process $\{f_i(t)\}\, i = 1, 2, \ldots, n$; and (3) the weighting function w_t^2, which in our case of discounted multiple regression is simply $w_{T-j}^2 = \beta^j$. The element in the ith row and the kth column is

$$F_{ik}(T) = \sum_{j=1}^{T} \beta^j f_i(T - j) f_k(T - j)$$

Since this matrix does not depend on the actual observations, only one such matrix needs to be computed for all time series described by the same set of fitting functions. For example, the sales of each of many items in an inventory might be described by a constant, a linear trend, a periodic component (with p = twelve months per period), and the departmental prediction of total sales volume. At each sampling interval, the one matrix F would have to be revised, which can be done recursively. Initially $F(0) = \mathbf{f}(0)\mathbf{f}'(0)$, or $F_{ik}(0) = f_i(0)f_k(0)$. Thereafter, at each sampling interval the matrix is revised by

$$F(t) = \mathbf{f}(t)\mathbf{f}'(t) + \beta F(t - 1)$$

or

$$F_{ik}(t) = f_i(t)f_k(t) + \beta F_{ik}(t - 1)$$

When the number of observations T is at least as large as the number of degrees of freedom n in the model, the matrix of fitting functions F will have* an inverse F^{-1}. Since the matrix changes at each sampling interval, the inverse must be recomputed after each observation. The inversion is equivalent to solving a system of n simultaneous linear equations in n unknowns. Since the matrix F is symmetrical, a particularly efficient inversion routine can be used (see Chapter 24).

The other part of the computational procedure involves an n-component data vector

$$\mathbf{g}(T) = \begin{bmatrix} g_1(T) \\ g_2(T) \\ \cdot \\ \cdot \\ \cdot \\ g_n(T) \end{bmatrix} = xW'\mathfrak{F}W$$

Since this vector consolidates all the past data, it would be necessary to store the values of the n components for each individual time series, such as each item in the inventory. The ith component of the data vector can be written

$$g_i(T) = \sum_{j=0}^{T-1} \beta^j x(T - j) f_i(T - j)$$

Initially the value of the ith component of the data vector would be the product of the first observation $x(1)$ and the value of the ith fitting function at that time $f_i(1)$. Thereafter, each component of the data vector is revised as new observations are obtained

$$g_i(T) = x(T)f_i(T) + \beta g_i(T - 1)$$

When a sufficient number of observations have been taken, the coefficients can be estimated by

$$\hat{\mathbf{a}}' = \hat{\mathbf{a}}'(T) = \mathbf{g}(T)F^{-1}(T)$$

that is, by multiplying the data vector (for each time series) by the inverse of the matrix of fitting functions. These coefficients minimize the discounted sum of square residuals over past observations. Therefore, if the process underlying the observations continues, a reasonable forecast of future observations is

$$x(T + \tau) = \hat{\mathbf{a}}'(T)\mathbf{f}(T + \tau)$$

$$= \sum_{i=1}^{n} \hat{a}_i(T)f_i(T + \tau)$$

---

* Provided that none of the fitting functions can be described as a linear combination of the rest of the functions. When it can be so arranged, it is highly desirable that the fitting functions be orthogonal, so that

$$\sum_{t=1}^{T} f_i(t)f_k(t) = 0 \qquad \text{for all pairs } (i \neq k)$$

Functions with Fixed Transition Matrix

Now we want to introduce a restriction on the class of fitting functions. The vector of values of these functions at time $t + 1$ must be a linear combination of the values of the same functions at the previous time t. That is, there is a set of coefficients L_{ij} that do not depend on time, such that

$$f_1(t + 1) = L_{11}f_1(t) + L_{12}f_2(t) + \ldots + L_{1n}f_{1n}(t)$$
$$f_2(t + 1) = L_{21}f_1(t) + L_{22}f_2(t) + \ldots + L_{2n}f_{2n}(t)$$
$$\vdots \qquad \vdots \qquad \vdots \qquad \vdots$$
$$f_n(t + 1) = L_{n1}f_1(t) + L_{n2}f_2(t) + \ldots + L_{nn}f_n(t)$$

We shall represent these coefficients by the *transition matrix L*, so that $\mathbf{f}(t + 1) = L\mathbf{f}(t)$. The transition matrix L in general is not symmetrical, but it must have an inverse L^{-1}. The only sets of functions for which such a transition matrix exists are the polynomials, exponentials, and sinusoids discussed in Chapter 4. These functions are the solutions of linear difference equations.

These transition matrices can be written down by inspection from the class of functions used in the model. Associated with the transition matrix, we also need to specify the values of the function at time $t = 0$: $\mathbf{f}(0)$. From one vector and the matrix, we can obtain the function values at any other time $\mathbf{f}(t) = L^t\mathbf{f}(0)$.

POLYNOMIALS. For a polynomial of order n the transition matrix is an $n \times n$ matrix with one's on the diagonal, one's in the first element to the left of the diagonal, and zero's everywhere else. For example, for a linear model, the transition matrix and the vector of initial values are

$$L = \begin{bmatrix} 1 & 0 \\ 1 & 1 \end{bmatrix}, \quad \mathbf{f}(0) = \begin{bmatrix} 1 \\ 0 \end{bmatrix}, \quad \mathbf{f}(t) = \begin{bmatrix} 1 \\ t \end{bmatrix}$$

In a cubic model, the transition matrix and the vector of initial values are

$$L = \begin{bmatrix} 1 & 0 & 0 & 0 \\ 1 & 1 & 0 & 0 \\ 0 & 1 & 1 & 0 \\ 0 & 0 & 1 & 1 \end{bmatrix}, \quad \mathbf{f}(0) = \begin{bmatrix} 1 \\ 0 \\ 0 \\ 0 \end{bmatrix}$$

Polynomial models in terms of the sampling intervals t are particularly general and useful. Any function that has finite derivatives can be represented in the neighborhood of a point by such a polynomial. The coefficients in this Taylor series* expansion involve the derivatives.

---

* See page 132.

Exercise. In the linear model, the fitting functions generated by the above transition matrix are $f_1(t) = 1, f_2(t) = t$. What are the fitting functions generated by the transition matrix for the cubic model? They are *not* simply $f_3(t) = t^2$, and $f_4(t) = t^3$. HINT: Construct $L^2, L^3, \ldots, L^t$, and then multiply $L^t\mathbf{f}(0)$. Recall the binomial coefficient

$$\binom{t}{k} = \frac{t!}{(t-k)!k!}$$

SINUSOIDS. If the fitting functions are trigonometric functions, both the sine and the cosine for each harmonic must be included. (See Chapter 4 for a discussion of the amplitude and phase angle as determined from the coefficients of the sine and the cosine.) If the fitting functions are $f_1(t) = \sin \omega t$, $f_2(t) = \cos \omega t$, then the transition matrix and the vector of initial values are

$$L = \begin{bmatrix} \cos \omega & \sin \omega \\ -\sin \omega & \cos \omega \end{bmatrix}, \quad \mathbf{f}(0) = \begin{bmatrix} 0 \\ 1 \end{bmatrix}$$

The procedure can cope with growing amplitudes or shifting phase angles by including the functions $f_3(t) = t \sin \omega t$ and $f_4(t) = t \cos \omega t$. The transition matrix for these four functions and the associated vector of initial values are

$$L = \begin{bmatrix} \cos \omega & \sin \omega & 0 & 0 \\ -\sin \omega & \cos \omega & 0 & 0 \\ \cos \omega & \sin \omega & \cos \omega & \sin \omega \\ -\sin \omega & \cos \omega & -\sin \omega & \cos \omega \end{bmatrix}, \quad \mathbf{f}(0) = \begin{bmatrix} 0 \\ 1 \\ 0 \\ 1 \end{bmatrix}, \quad \mathbf{f}(t) = \begin{bmatrix} \sin \omega t \\ \cos \omega t \\ t \sin \omega t \\ t \cos \omega t \end{bmatrix}$$

Sinusoidal models are particularly useful for representing periodic functions, since such functions can be represented by a Fourier series.*

EXPONENTIALS. Finally, for an exponential model, where $f(t) = e^{at}$, the transition matrix is simply $L = (e^a)$ and the initial value is $\mathbf{f}(0) = 1$. Sometimes, it is of interest to include a sort of "birth and death" process, with the functions $f_1(t) = e^{at}$ and $f_2(t) = te^{a(t-1)}$. The transition matrix and initial vector are

$$L = \begin{bmatrix} e^a & 0 \\ 1 & e^a \end{bmatrix}, \quad \mathbf{f}(0) = \begin{bmatrix} 1 \\ 0 \end{bmatrix}, \quad \mathbf{f}(t) = \begin{bmatrix} e^{at} \\ te^{at} \end{bmatrix}$$

In general, the transition matrix with $n + 1$ rows and columns

$$L = \begin{bmatrix} a & & & 0 \\ b & & & \\ & & & \\ 0 & b & & a \end{bmatrix}$$

* See page 69.

and the vector

$$\mathbf{f}(0) = \begin{bmatrix} 1 \\ 0 \\ \cdot \\ \cdot \\ \cdot \\ 0 \end{bmatrix}$$

will generate

$$\mathbf{f}(t) = L^t\mathbf{f}(0) = \begin{bmatrix} \binom{t}{0} & a^t \\ \binom{t}{1} & a^{t-1}b \\ \cdot & \\ \cdot & \\ \cdot & \\ \binom{t}{n} & a^{t-n}b^n \end{bmatrix} \qquad \text{(if } t > n)$$

AUTOREGRESSION. Stochastic processes may be included in these models, as well as the deterministic mathematical functions. Suppose that the process is autoregressive, in that

$$\xi(t) = \delta_1\,\xi(t-1) + \delta_2\,\xi(t-2) + \ldots + \delta_n\,\xi(t-n)$$

where the δ_i are known constant coefficients. Then we can define $f_i(t) = \xi(t-i)$, and the transition matrix is of the form

$$L = \begin{bmatrix} \delta_1 & \delta_1 & \delta_3 & \ldots & \delta_{n-1} & \delta_n \\ 1 & 0 & 0 & \ldots & 0 & 0 \\ 0 & 1 & 0 & \ldots & 0 & 0 \\ \cdot & \cdot & \cdot & & \cdot & \cdot \\ 0 & 0 & 0 & \ldots & 1 & 0 \end{bmatrix}, \qquad \mathbf{f}(0) = \begin{bmatrix} \xi(-1) \\ \xi(-2) \\ \cdot \\ \cdot \\ \xi(-n) \end{bmatrix}$$

The polynomials, exponentials, and sinusoids can all be represented in this autoregressive form (see Chapter 21). Conversely, any model of the auto-regressive form can be represented by the solution of a linear difference equation: some combination of polynomials, exponentials, and sinusoids.

COMBINATIONS. When the model is some combination of these various forms, the grand transition matrix can be constructed by stacking up these simple matrices along the main diagonal. For example, consider a case where six degrees of freedom are included.

$$\xi(t) = a_1 + a_2(1.0106)^t + a_3\sin\frac{2\pi t}{12} + a_4\cos\frac{2\pi t}{12}$$

$$+ a_5 t\sin\frac{2\pi t}{12} + a_6 t\cos\frac{2\pi t}{12}$$

The grand transition matrix is

$$
L = \begin{bmatrix}
1 & 0 & 0 & 0 & 0 & 0 \\
0 & 1.0106 & 0 & 0 & 0 & 0 \\
0 & 0 & \sqrt{3}/2 & 1/2 & 0 & 0 \\
0 & 0 & -1/2 & \sqrt{3}/2 & 0 & 0 \\
0 & 0 & \sqrt{3}/2 & 1/2 & \sqrt{3}/2 & 1/2 \\
0 & 0 & -1/2 & \sqrt{3}/2 & -1/2 & \sqrt{3}/2
\end{bmatrix}
$$

Note that it is composed of three little matrices, one for the constant (polynomial), one for the exponential, and one for the trigonometric functions with growing amplitude. These small matrices are combined so that their diagonal elements lie along the diagonal of the grand matrix. Zeros are entered to fill out the rows and columns.

Exercise. Construct the transition matrix for a model that includes a constant, a linear trend, and a birth-and-death exponential growth. What is the vector of initial values?

Adaptive Smoothing*

Now let us return to the problem of estimating the coefficients in a forecast equation. Instead of estimating the coefficients in the model, with a fixed origin in time, we shall estimate the coefficients in a model of similar form, but with time relative to the most recent observation (as we did in Chapter 9, where we estimated current values of the $n + 1$ derivatives of the polynomial).

$$\hat{x}(t + \tau) = \mathbf{f}'(\tau)\hat{\mathbf{a}}(t)$$

Note particularly, that in this form we do not use $\mathbf{f}(t + \tau)$ but count time relative to the present, so that these coefficients will not have the same values they had in discounted multiple regression. We shall use $t + 1 = T$ observations.

Now the error criterion that is to be minimized is

$$\sum_{j=0}^{t} \beta^j [\mathbf{f}'(-j)\mathbf{a}(t) - x(t - j)]^2$$

---

* R. F. Meyer deserves the credit for the original development of these ideas. See "An Adaptive Method for Routine Short-Term Forecasting," International Federation of Operational Research Societies, Oslo, July, 1963.

The basic matrix of fitting functions to $F(t)$, has elements

$$F_{ik}(t) = \sum_{j=0}^{t} \beta^j f_i(-j) f_k(-j)$$

The data vector $\mathbf{g}(t)$ has n components

$$g_i(t) = \sum_{j=0}^{t} \beta^j f_i(-j) x(t-j)$$

The n simultaneous equations that result from setting the partial derivatives of the error criterion equal to zero can be written in matrix form as

$$F(t)\hat{\mathbf{a}}(t) = \mathbf{g}(t)$$

If there have been at least n observations, then the symmetrical matrix $F(t)$ is positive definite and has an inverse. Hence, the coefficients in the forecast equation can be estimated as before by

$$\hat{\mathbf{a}}(t) = F^{-1}(t)\mathbf{g}(t)$$

With each new observation, the data vector $\mathbf{g}(t)$ and the function matrix $F(t)$ must be modified. Because of the change in the origin of time in evaluating the fitting functions, the recursive computations of these collections of information will be different than they were in the case of discounted multiple regression.

The data vector $\mathbf{g}(t)$ can be written as

$$\mathbf{g}(t) = x(t)\mathbf{f}(0) + \sum_{j=1}^{t} \beta^j \mathbf{f}(-j) x(t-j)$$

If successive values of the fitting function vector are generated by a transition matrix L,

then
$$\mathbf{f}(-j) = L^{-1}\mathbf{f}(-j+1)$$

Therefore, $\quad \mathbf{g}(t) = x(t)\mathbf{f}(0) + \sum_{j=1}^{t} \beta^j L^{-1}\mathbf{f}(-j+1) x(t-j)$

Now change the index of summation to $k = j - 1$, and we see that the rule for modifying the data vector in the light of new information is

$$\boxed{\mathbf{g}(t) = x(t)\mathbf{f}(0) + \beta L^{-1}\mathbf{g}(t-1)}$$

This rule is similar to the one for discounted multiple regression, except that, because of the local origin of time, the current observation is weighted by the function vector $\mathbf{f}(0)$ [instead of $\mathbf{f}(t)$], and the inverse of the transition matrix L^{-1} is included in the term for the previous value of the data vector. The coefficients that define the data vector recursively from the current data $x(t)$ and the previous values of the components in the data vector $\mathbf{g}(t-1)$ no longer depend on absolute time and, hence, could be tabulated as program constants.

The matrix of fitting functions $F(t)$ can also be computed recursively

$$F(t) = \sum_{j=0}^{t} \beta^j \mathbf{f}(-j)\mathbf{f}'(-j) = F(t-1) + \beta^t \mathbf{f}(-t)\mathbf{f}'(-t)$$

Here we see the interesting property of this method of counting time. When the fitting functions are trigonometric functions or polynomials, and $\beta < 1$, β^t tends to zero faster than $\mathbf{f}(-t)$ can grow, so that the matrix of fitting functions reaches a steady state value, and its inverse can be computed once and for all. A problem appears only when one of the fitting functions is a decreasing exponential of the form

$$f(t) = e^{-at}$$

The $F(t)$ will need a steady state only if $\beta < e^{-2a}$. That is, when the model includes a falling exponential, past data must be discounted rapidly. With this exception, we reach the state in which

$$\boxed{F(t) = F(t-1)}$$

If the fastest-growing function in the model is t^n, then the number of periods taken for this convergence is approximately

$$T = \frac{7 + 5.1n}{(1 - \beta)^{0.95}}$$

The criterion of convergence is that the largest quantity added to any element of F is less than 10^{-6} times the previous value of that element.

In the steady state, we do not need the time identification of the matrix of fitting functions, but can call it simply F. By the time the steady state is reached, F will obviously have an inverse F^{-1}. Therefore the coefficients in the model can be estimated by

$$\hat{\mathbf{a}}(t) = F^{-1}\mathbf{g}(t)$$

and the forecast of future observations will be given by

$$\begin{aligned}
\hat{x}(t + \tau) &= \hat{\mathbf{a}}'(t)\mathbf{f}(\tau) \\
&= [F^{-1}\mathbf{g}(t)]'\mathbf{f}(\tau) \\
&= \mathbf{g}'(t)F^{-1}\mathbf{f}(\tau) \\
&= \mathbf{g}'(t)\mathbf{c}(\tau)
\end{aligned}$$

where $\mathbf{g}'(t)$ is the transpose of the current data vector and $\mathbf{c}(\tau)$ is a column vector of coefficients that depend only on the values of the fitting functions at time τ, but *not* on absolute time.

When the steady state conditions are to be used,

$$\hat{\mathbf{a}}'(t) = \mathbf{g}'(t)F^{-1}$$

which suggests that the data vector can be given initial conditions from some estimate of the model. For example, suppose at the time the forecasting process is to begin, one had an estimate of these coefficients $\hat{\mathbf{a}}(0)$. Then the data vector should be set up according to

$$\hat{\mathbf{g}}(0) = F\hat{\mathbf{a}}(0)$$

Thereafter, the data vector would be modified with each new observation according to

$$\mathbf{g}(t) = x(t)\mathbf{f}(0) + \beta T^{-1}\mathbf{g}(t - 1)$$

The forecast can then be obtained immediately by

$$\hat{x}(t + \tau) = \mathbf{g}'(t)\mathbf{c}(\tau)$$

where the vector of coefficients $\mathbf{c}(\tau)$ has been precomputed. Thus no matrix inversions are required, and the only calculations are the revisions of the n components of the data vector with the new data, and then a linear combination of these results to produce the revised forecast. The steps are precisely those of multiple exponential smoothing: an iterative revision of n words of historical information in the light of the latest observation. Then a fixed linear combination of the stored statistics yields either the coefficients in the model, or a forecast for any future time. The process is no longer restricted to polynomials, but includes trigonometric functions and exponentials. The computational procedures will be further refined in Chapter 12.

COMPARISON WITH EXPONENTIAL SMOOTHING. In Chapter 9, we developed multiple exponential smoothing to estimate the coefficients in the forecast equation

$$\hat{x}(T + \tau) = \hat{a}_1(T) + \hat{a}_2(T)\tau + \ldots + \hat{a}_n(T)\tau^{n-1}$$
$$= \hat{\mathbf{a}}'(T)\mathbf{f}(\tau)$$

Let us follow through the computations of discounted multiple regression in the particular case where the process can be represented by a linear model

$$\mathbf{f}(t) = \begin{bmatrix} 1 \\ t \end{bmatrix}$$

Since the forecast equation considers time relative to the current observation, the matrix of fitting functions is

$$F(T) = \sum_{j=0}^{T-1} \beta^j \mathbf{f}(-j)\mathbf{f}'(-j)$$
$$= \sum_{j=0}^{T-1} \beta^j \begin{bmatrix} 1 & -j \\ -j & j^2 \end{bmatrix}$$

The sums of the geometric series can be written in closed form so that

$$F(T) = (1 - \beta)^T \begin{bmatrix} \dfrac{1}{\alpha} & \dfrac{\beta}{\alpha^2} \\[2mm] \dfrac{-\beta}{\alpha^2} & \dfrac{\beta(1 + \beta)}{\alpha^3} \end{bmatrix}$$

and the inverse is

$$F^{-1}(T) = \frac{\alpha^4}{\beta(1 - \beta^T)} \begin{bmatrix} \dfrac{\beta(1 + \beta)}{\alpha^3} & \dfrac{\beta}{\alpha^2} \\[2mm] \dfrac{\beta}{\alpha^2} & \dfrac{1}{\alpha} \end{bmatrix}$$

The data vector for the same case is

$$\mathbf{g}(T) = \sum_{j=0}^{T-1} \beta^j x(T - j)\mathbf{f}(-j)$$

$$= \begin{bmatrix} \displaystyle\sum_{j=0}^{T-1} \beta^j x(T - j) \\[3mm] \displaystyle\sum_{j=0}^{T-1} -j\beta^j x(T - j) \end{bmatrix}$$

Recall from Chapter 9 that the smoothing operators can be written

$$S^T(x) = \alpha \sum_{j=0}^{T-1} \beta^j x(T - j) + \beta^T S_0(x)$$

$$S_T^{[2]}(x) = \alpha^2 \sum_{j=0}^{T-1} (j + 1)\beta^j x(T - j) + \beta^T(T + 1)S_0^{[2]}(x)$$

Therefore, we can substitute the expressions containing the smoothed statistics and the initial conditions for the finite sums in $\mathbf{g}(T)$

$$\mathbf{g}(T) = \begin{bmatrix} \dfrac{S_T(x) - \beta^T S_0(x)}{\alpha} \\[3mm] \dfrac{\alpha^3[S_T(x) - \beta^T S_0(x)] + \beta^T(T + 1)S_0^{[2]}(x) - S_T^{[2]}(x)}{\alpha^2} \end{bmatrix}$$

The coefficients in the forecast equation are $a(T) = F^{-1}(T)\mathbf{g}(T)$

$$\mathbf{a}(T) = \frac{1}{(1 - \beta^T)} \begin{bmatrix} 2S_T - S_T^{[2]} - 2\alpha\beta^T S_0 + \beta^T(T + 1)S_0^{[2]} \\[3mm] \dfrac{\alpha}{\beta}(S_T - S_T^{[2]}) - \dfrac{\alpha^2}{\beta}\beta^T S_0 + \dfrac{\alpha^3}{\beta}\beta^T(T + 1)S_0^{[2]} \end{bmatrix}$$

When T is large enough that terms involving β^T are negligible, the forecast coefficients are precisely those of double exponential smoothing

$$a_1(T) = 2S_T - S_T^{[2]}$$

$$a_2(T) = \frac{\alpha}{\beta}\,(S_T - S_T^{[2]})$$

Early in the series, however, the methods of this chapter correctly take account of the transients caused by the finite amount of data.

12 General Exponential Smoothing

In the previous chapter, we showed that, under certain conditions, the matrix of weighted fitting functions $F(t)$ reached a steady state $F = F(\infty)$. The conditions for such convergence are principally two: (1) successive values of the fitting functions can be generated by a fixed transition matrix L; (2) the forecast is based on these functions with the origin of time at the most recent observation. Furthermore, the data vector $\mathbf{g}(t)$ could be defined recursively from the previous values of its n components and the new observation.

These results will now be exploited to minimize the computational effort required in revising the successive estimates of the coefficients

$$\hat{\mathbf{a}}'(T) = (\hat{a}_1(T), \hat{a}_2(T), \ldots, \hat{a}_n(T))$$

used in the forecast equation

$$\hat{x}(T + \tau) = \hat{\mathbf{a}}'(T)\mathbf{f}(\tau)$$

$$= \sum_{i=1}^{n} \hat{a}_i(T)f_i(\tau)$$

The fitting functions used in the forecast equation are any functions that can be generated by $\mathbf{f}(t) = L\mathbf{f}(t - 1)$ and therefore include (1) polynomials, (2) exponentials, (3) sinusoids, and (4) sums and products of such functions. The principal excluded processes are those that require some empirical function (like gross national product or birth rates) to describe them.

Suppose that there were no noise in the observations, so that the data $x(t)$ were exactly equal to that expected from the model of the process. Then, because time in the forecast equation is always counted from the most recent observation, the coefficients would change according to

$$\mathbf{a}'(\epsilon) = \mathbf{a}'(t-1)L$$

The value of the next observation that would conform to the model of the process is given by the forecast equation

$$\hat{x}_1(t-1) = \hat{\mathbf{a}}'(t-1)\mathbf{f}(1) = \hat{\mathbf{a}}'(t-1)L\mathbf{f}(0) = \mathbf{a}'(t)\mathbf{f}(0)$$

In general, of course, there is noise in the observations so that the data do not conform exactly to the model of the process, and therefore the successive estimates of the coefficients in the forecast equation fluctuate around their true values. Each observation will differ from what had been expected as of the previous observation by an error

$$e_1(t) = x(t) - \hat{x}_1(t-1)$$

The principal result of this chapter will be the derivation of an n-component vector

$$\mathbf{h} = \begin{bmatrix} h_1 \\ h_2 \\ \cdot \\ \cdot \\ \cdot \\ h_n \end{bmatrix}$$

of program constants from which the estimates of the forecast coefficients can be revised with each new observation by

$$\boxed{\mathbf{a}(t) = L'\mathbf{a}(t-1) + \mathbf{h}e_1(t)}$$

That is, the coefficients are revised to reflect (1) the change in the origin of time to the end of the next sampling interval and (2) the error in forecasting the next observation. This result will be derived as the set of coefficients that minimizes the sum of discounted squared residuals.

The constants h_i depend only on the particular set of fitting functions, defined by the transition matrix L and the vector of values at some one time, usually $\mathbf{f}(0)$, and on the discount factor β.

$$\mathbf{h} = F^{-1}\mathbf{f}(0)$$

where F is the steady state matrix of weighted fitting functions. Tables of these program constants are provided for a rich variety of models, especially those involving sinusoids with twelve observations per period, for seasonal sales patterns or diurnal variation in tides.

Derivation of General Exponential Smoothing

In Chapter 11, we tackled the problem of discounted multiple regression. A sequence of observations $\{x(t)\} = (x(1), x(2), \ldots, x(T))$ is obtained from some process $\xi(t)$ buried in noise, $x(t) = \xi(t) + \epsilon(t)$. The process can be described locally by

$$\xi(t + \tau) = \hat{\mathbf{a}}'(t)\mathbf{f}(\tau)$$

where we know the fitting functions

$$\mathbf{f}(\tau) = \begin{bmatrix} f_1(\tau) \\ f_2(\tau) \\ \cdot \\ \cdot \\ \cdot \\ f_n(\tau) \end{bmatrix}$$

The job is to estimate the coefficients $\mathbf{a}(t)$, which change by $a(t) = L'a(t-1)$ and further may change by small random amounts as time goes on. Therefore, at any time the squared residuals are discounted, and the coefficients $\mathbf{a}(T)$ are estimated to minimize

$$\sum_{j=0}^{T} \beta^j [x(T-j) - \mathbf{a}'(T)\mathbf{f}(-j)]^2$$

The solution of this problem involves a matrix of weighted fitting functions

$$F(T) = \sum_{j=0}^{T} \beta^j \mathbf{f}(-j)\mathbf{f}'(-j) = F(T-1) + \beta^T \mathbf{f}(-T)\mathbf{f}'(-T)$$

and a data vector

$$\mathbf{g}(T) = \sum_{j=0}^{T} \beta^j x(T-j)\mathbf{f}(-j) = x(T)\mathbf{f}(0) + \beta L^{-1}\mathbf{g}(T-1)$$

where L is the transition matrix that generates successive values of the fitting functions $\mathbf{f}(t) = L\mathbf{f}(t-1)$. The minimum discounted squared residual sum is attained when

$$F(T)\mathbf{a}(T) = \mathbf{g}(T)$$

and since for any reasonable set of fitting functions $F(T)$ has an inverse $F^{-1}(T)$, the coefficients are $\mathbf{a}(T) = F^{-1}(T)\mathbf{g}(T)$.

If the fitting functions do not decay too rapidly

$$(f_i(t) > \beta^{-t/2} \qquad \text{for all } i)$$

then the matrix F reaches a steady state

$$F = F(\infty) = \sum_{j=0}^{\infty} \beta^j \mathbf{f}(-j)\mathbf{f}'(-j)$$

Substitute the minimum steady state solution in the recursive equation for the data vector.

$$F\mathbf{a}(T) = x(T)\mathbf{f}(0) + \beta L^{-1}F\mathbf{a}(T-1)$$

and then premultiply by the inverse F^{-1}

$$\mathbf{a}(T) = x(T)F^{-1}\mathbf{f}(0) + \beta F^{-1}L^{-1}F\mathbf{a}(T-1)$$

Thus the current values of the coefficients are defined in terms of a vector $\mathbf{h}$ of constants that do not depend on time multiplying the current observation and a matrix H that doesn't depend on time either, multiplying the previous vector of coefficients.

$$\mathbf{a}(T) = \mathbf{h}x(T) + H\mathbf{a}(T-1)$$

where
$$\mathbf{h} = F^{-1}\mathbf{f}(0)$$

$$H = \beta F^{-1}L^{-1}F$$

We shall show that

$$H = L' - \mathbf{h}\mathbf{f}'(1)$$

First attack the matrix $L^{-1}F$. Postmultiply the definition of the F matrix by $L'^{-1}L'$

$$L^{-1}FL'^{-1}L' = \sum_{j=0}^{\infty} \beta^j [L^{-1}\mathbf{f}(-j)][L^{-1}\mathbf{f}(-j)]'L'$$

$$= \frac{1}{\beta}[F - \mathbf{f}(0)\mathbf{f}'(0)]L'$$

Hence
$$H = \beta F^{-1}L^{-1}F = [I - F^{-1}\mathbf{f}(0)\mathbf{f}'(0)]L'$$

But we defined the vector $\mathbf{h} = F^{-1}\mathbf{f}(0)$,

so
$$H = L' - \mathbf{h}[L\mathbf{f}(0)]' = L' - \mathbf{h}\mathbf{f}'(1)$$

Now we can write

$$\mathbf{a}(T) = \mathbf{h}x(T) + H\mathbf{a}(T-1)$$

$$= \mathbf{h}x(T) + L'\mathbf{a}(T-1) - \mathbf{h}\mathbf{f}'(1)\mathbf{a}(T-1)$$

And since $\mathbf{f}'(1)\mathbf{a}(T-1) = \hat{x}_1(T-1)$ is the forecast of what the observation at time T will be, as of the data received through time $T-1$,

$$\boxed{\mathbf{a}(T) = L'\mathbf{a}(T-1) + \mathbf{h}[x(T) - \hat{x}_1(T-1)]}$$

This equation demonstrates that the coefficients change at each sampling interval because of (1) the change in the origin of time, and (2) errors in estimating what the next observation will be.

We obtained the same result by a different route for polynomial models in Chapter 9. The revision of coefficients has now been shown generally true for all processes that can be described by functions generated by a transition matrix.

The method is strictly valid only in the steady state. The initial vector of coefficients $\hat{a}(0)$ should be the result of discounted multiple regression on a very large set of historical data from the same process. (See page 170 for an estimate of the number of observations required to reach the steady state.) When it is not practical for any reason to analyze so much history, a prediction $a(0)$ can serve. Obviously, the more accurate the prediction, the better the early forecasts.

After T sampling intervals, the weight given to the initial conditions is proportional to β^T. If you have a great deal of confidence in the initial prediction $\hat{a}(0)$, the value of β can be large (close to unity). If, however, the initial prediction is admittedly at best a guess, then β should be smaller, perhaps equivalent to 0.8^n (for n degrees of freedom) to discount that guess rapidly in favor of actual data about the process.

MODELS. There are ten models, defined by the transition matrix L and the vector of values $f(0)$ for the functions at time $T = 0$, that are encountered most often in describing processes by means of polynomials and sinusoids.

Tables are given for each of these ten models. There are six parts to each table, arranged thus:

Model, $\xi(t)$
Degrees of Freedom, n

1. Transition matrix, L	2. Initial values, $f(0)$, $f(1)$
3. Smoothing vector, $\mathbf{h}$	4. Variance of coefficients
5. Variance of the forecast	6. Standard deviation of the cumulative forecast error

The heading of the table describes the model of the process $\xi(t)$ underlying the observations. The ten models will be discussed more fully. The number of degrees of freedom n is the number of coefficients in the model to be estimated from the data. There are models with from one to nine degrees of freedom.

1.–2. The transition matrix L, together with either of the intial values of the vector of fitting functions $f(0)$ or $f(1)$, defines the model being used. The sinusoidal models can be represented only approximately, since a true sine will involve irrational numbers. That is "$\xi(t) = \sin \omega t$" is merely a convenient representation. The actual model represented by the table is something that can approximate a mathematical sine function only to a finite number of decimals. The distinction is not important unless one were going to extrapolate the model a large number of sampling intervals into the future.

The remainder of the table is based on three specific values of the discount factor β. The low value is equivalent (for one degree of freedom) to $\beta_1 = 0.75$; that is $\beta^n = 0.75$, where n is the number of degrees of freedom in the model. Such a value would be used in the first few sampling intervals if there were little confidence in the initial conditions, or for a process where the values of the true coefficients could change by amounts that are appreciable fractions of the noise included in the observations. The middle value is equivalent (again for one degree of freedom) to 0.90; $\beta^n = 0.90$. This value is a "general utility value," used most commonly. The high value of the discount factor is equivalent to 0.95; $\beta^n = 0.95$ and is used where the coefficients in the true process do not change very much. The tables give the actual values of the discount factors β, together with the smoothing constant to which the values are equivalent. Although it might seem more reasonable to choose a value for the discount factor that is a simple number (for example, 0.97, instead of 0.97468), this factor does not appear explicitly in the routine computations. The essential numbers are the components of the smoothing vector $\mathbf{h}$ which would have several digits in any case.

3. The smoothing vector $\mathbf{h}$ lists for each of the n components the factors necessary to revise the estimated values of the coefficients $\mathbf{a}(T)$ in the model, according to the equation in the box on page 177. Note that this equation involves the transpose L': interchange the rows and columns of the matrix L given in the table.

4.–6. The last three parts of the tables, the variance of the coefficients, the variance of the forecast, and the standard deviation of the cumulative forecast error, will be discussed in Chapter 16.*

NOTE: Several of the entries in the table are very small decimal fractions. When there are three or more leading zeros after the decimal point and before the first significant digit, an exponential notation is used. Thus 0.0^4758 is $0.0000758 = 0.758 \times 10^{-4}$.

Three groups of models have been used frequently to describe processes for which forecasts are required. The first group (Fig. 12.1) includes simple polynomials of degree 0, 1, and 2, which were discussed in Chapters 7 and 9. The second group (Fig. 12.2) includes simple sinusoids re-

---

* Miss Joan Sullivan has written the general program by which such tables can be computed on the IBM 7090 for any model with up to ten degrees of freedom.

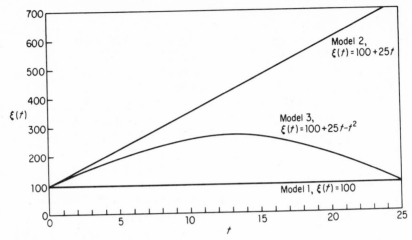

Fig. 12.1 Polynomial models.

quired to represent periodic processes with 12 observations per period. (Some businesses are beginning to use 13 accounting periods, of four weeks each, per year. Therefore, one example of a 13-point sinusoid is also included for seasonal sales forecasting in such a business.) The third group (Fig. 12.3) of models includes various combinations of linear and sinusoidal change in the process.

(1) *Constant process* (Table 12.1):

$$\xi(t) = a_1$$

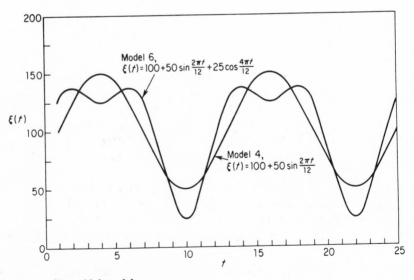

Fig. 12.2 Sinusoidal models.

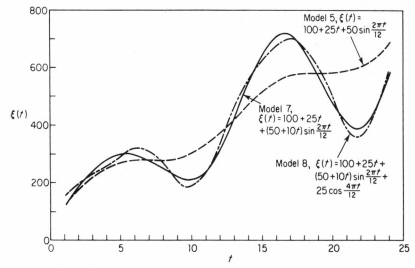

Fig. 12.3 Composite models.

This model corresponds to simple exponential smoothing and can be used whenever the process does not change in any deterministic way with time.

(2) *Linear process* (Table 12.2):

$$\xi(t) = a_1 + a_2 t$$

The computations for this case are the same as double exponential smoothing. The model is used whenever the process underlying the observations is growing (or falling) at a steady rate in time. The rate of growth can change by small random increments from time to time.

(3) *Quadratic process* (Table 12.3):

$$\xi(t) = a_1 + a_2 t + \tfrac{1}{2} a_3 t(t - 1)$$

This process is equivalent to that discussed under triple smoothing in Chapter 9, but note that the third fitting function is not simply t^2. The reason for using $\tfrac{1}{2} t(t - 1)$ stems from the canonical form of the transition matrix for polynomial fitting functions. Such a model might be used to forecast future positions of an automobile in which the acceleration is constant for substantial periods of time, but in the long run changes by small, random increments.

The equations for the components of **h** in the polynomial models were given in the summary at the end of Chapter 9.

(4) *Simple 12-point sine* (Table 12.4):

$$\xi(t) = a_1 + a_2 \sin \frac{2\pi t}{12} + a_3 \cos \frac{2\pi t}{12}$$

This model represents the first approximation to a periodic process, such as a seasonal sales pattern observed once a month, or the height of the tide, observed once an hour. Since there are three degrees of freedom (coefficients to be determined from the data), the effort required is the same as for triple smoothing—only the values of the constants are different. The model is equivalent to $\xi(t) = a_1 + A \sin \frac{2\pi}{12} (t - t_0)$.

(5) *Twelve-point sine with harmonic* (Table 12.5):

$$\xi(t) = a_1 + a_2 \sin \frac{2\pi t}{12} + a_3 \cos \frac{2\pi t}{12}$$

$$+ a_4 \sin \frac{4\pi t}{12} + a_5 \cos \frac{4\pi t}{12}$$

This process is equivalent to

$$a_1 + A_1 \sin \frac{2\pi}{12} (t - t_1) + A_2 \sin \frac{4\pi}{12} (t - t_2)$$

and includes one harmonic of the basic waveform, so that a somewhat more complex shape of pattern can be described.

(6) *Irregular 12-point periodic function* (Table 12.6):

$$\xi(t) = a_1 + \sum_{j=1}^{4} \left[a_j \sin \frac{2\pi j t}{12} + b_j \cos \frac{2\pi j t}{12} \right]$$

This model includes four harmonic frequencies and therefore can describe almost any periodic process with an irregular pattern that is observed 12 times during the period of the lowest frequency present. There are a total of 9 degrees of freedom. It would require 12 degrees of freedom to describe an arbitrary periodic factor exactly.

(7) *Irregular 13-point periodic function* (Table 12.7):

$$\xi(t) = a_0 + \sum_{j=1}^{4} \left[a_j \sin \frac{2\pi j t}{13} + b_j \cos \frac{2\pi j t}{13} \right]$$

This model differs from the previous one only in that there are 13 observations during the period of the lowest frequency present, applicable in sales forecasting in a company that observes its actual sales in four-week accounting periods instead of calendar months. There are a total of 9 degrees of freedom.

Dr. J. M. Dobbie has carried through the tedious algebra to obtain the components of **h** for the simple sinusoidal model

$$\xi(t) = a_0 + a_1 \sin \omega t + a_2 \cos \omega t$$

$$\mathbf{h}_1 = \frac{\alpha(1 + \beta^2 - 2\beta \cos \omega)}{2(1 - \cos \omega)}$$

$$h_2 = \frac{\alpha^2(1 + \beta)(1 + 2\cos\omega)}{2\sin\omega}$$

$$h_3 = \frac{\alpha[(1 + \beta)^2 - 2(1 + \beta^2)\cos\omega]}{2(1 - \cos\omega)}$$

The results have been generalized further to multiple frequencies, and exponentially-damped sinusoids. These results were obtained while this book was in proof, and will be published shortly.

(8) *Linear trend with simple sine wave* (Table 12.8):

$$\xi(t) = a_1 + a_2 t + a_3 \sin\frac{2\pi t}{12} + a_4 \cos\frac{2\pi t}{12}$$

This model would be used in place of (4), above, where the sinusoidal variation is superimposed on a steady growth (or decline).

(9) *Growing sine* (Table 12.9):

$$\xi(t) = (a_1 + a_2 t) + (a_3 + a_5 t)\sin\frac{2\pi t}{12} + (a_4 + a_6 t)\cos\frac{2\pi t}{12}$$

In this model, not only is the part of the process which an economist would call the *trend* growing, but so is the amplitude of the superimposed sinusoid. This model is suggested specifically to represent the monthly numbers of passengers in international air traffic.

(10) *Growing sine with harmonic* (Table 12.10):

$$\xi(t) = (a_1 + a_2 t) + (a_3 + a_5 t)\sin\frac{2\pi t}{12}$$

$$+ (a_4 + a_6 t)\cos\frac{2\pi t}{12} + a_7 \sin\frac{4\pi t}{12} + a_8 \cos\frac{4\pi t}{12}$$

This model is the same as the previous one (9) with the addition of a pair of terms to represent a significant six-month cycle in the air-passenger data. This model may not be encountered in many applications, but is included to illustrate the generality of the methods that have been developed.

INITIAL CONDITIONS FOR SINUSOIDAL MODELS. When the data can be represented by a simple sinusoid, the mean, amplitude, and phase angle can be determined by inspection, as in Fig. 4.5. When the data are more complicated, more formal methods may be warranted.

The models in Tables 12.4–12.7 include a constant, with coefficient a_1. The initial value of a_1 is the average, over any number of full cycles, of the data. The models also contain pairs of terms with fitting functions $\sin\omega t$ and $\cos\omega t$. The frequency ω can be written $\omega = 2\pi/p$ where p is the number of samples in one cycle. Let the coefficients of these terms be

Table 12.1   SMOOTHING COEFFICIENTS

Constant Model $\xi(T + t) = a_1$
Degrees of Freedom $n = 1$

Transition Matrix, L	Initial Values		
		f(0)	f(1)
1		$f_1 = 1$	1

Smoothing Vector, **h**				Variance of Coefficients			
$\beta =$	0.75	0.90	0.95	$\beta =$	0.75	0.90	0.95
$1 - \beta^n =$	0.25	0.10	0.05	$1 - \beta^n =$	0.25	0.10	0.05
$h_1 =$	0.25000	0.10000	0.05000	Var $a_1 =$	0.14286	0.05263	0.02564

Lead Time	Variance of the Forecast			Standard Deviation of Cumulative Forecast Error		
	$\beta = 0.7500$	0.9000	0.9500	0.7500	0.9000	0.9500
1	0.1429	0.0526	0.0256	1.0000	1.0000	1.0000
2	0.1429	0.0526	0.0256	1.6036	1.4868	1.4500
3	0.1429	0.0526	0.0256	2.0702	1.8638	1.7974
4	0.1429	0.0526	0.0256	2.5071	2.2005	2.1001
5	0.1429	0.0526	0.0256	2.9277	2.5131	2.3751
6	0.1429	0.0526	0.0256	3.3381	2.8098	2.6312
7	0.1429	0.0526	0.0256	3.7417	3.0950	2.8734
8	0.1429	0.0526	0.0256	4.1404	3.3717	3.1050
9	0.1429	0.0526	0.0256	4.5356	3.6419	3.3282
10	0.1429	0.0526	0.0256	4.9281	3.9068	3.5446
11	0.1429	0.0526	0.0256	5.3184	4.1676	3.7554
12	0.1429	0.0526	0.0256	5.7071	4.4248	3.9614

Table 12.2 SMOOTHING COEFFICIENTS

$$\text{Linear Model} \quad \xi(T + t) = a_1 + a_2 t$$
$$\text{Degrees of Freedom} \quad n = 2$$

Transition Matrix, L		Initial Values		
			f(0)	f(1)
1	0	f_1	1	1
1	1	f_2	0	1

Smoothing Vector, **h**				Variance of Coefficients		
$\beta =$	0.86603	0.94868	0.97468	$\beta =$	0.86603	0.94868	0.97468
$1 - \beta^n =$	0.25	0.10	0.05	$1 - \beta^n =$	0.25	0.10	0.05
h_1	0.25000	0.10000	0.05000	Var a_1	0.16937	0.06446	0.03173
h_2	0.01795	0.00263	0.0^3641	Var a_2	0.0^3740	0.0^4365	0.0^5422

Lead Time	Variance of the Forecast			Standard Deviation of Cumulative Forecast Error		
	$\beta = 0.86603$	0.94868	0.97468	0.86603	0.94868	0.97468
1	0.1900	0.0672	0.0324	1.0000	1.0000	1.0000
2	0.2121	0.0701	0.0331	1.5418	1.4609	1.4369
3	0.2357	0.0730	0.0337	2.0402	1.8457	1.7875
4	0.2607	0.0760	0.0344	2.5351	2.1970	2.0960
5	0.2873	0.0791	0.0351	3.0390	2.5305	2.3794
6	0.3153	0.0822	0.0358	3.5579	2.8540	2.6461
7	0.3448	0.0854	0.0365	4.0950	3.1720	2.9011
8	0.3758	0.0887	0.0372	4.6522	3.4872	3.1475
9	0.4082	0.0921	0.0380	5.2309	3.8016	3.3876
10	0.4422	0.0955	0.0387	5.8319	4.1166	3.6228
11	0.4776	0.0990	0.0394	6.4558	4.4331	3.8543
12	0.5145	0.1026	0.0402	7.1030	4.7519	4.0831

Table 12.3 SMOOTHING COEFFICIENTS

Quadratic Model $\xi(T + t) = a_1 + a_2 t + \frac{1}{2}a_3 t(t - 1)$
Degrees of Freedom $n = 3$

Transition Matrix, L				Initial Values	
				f(0)	f(1)
1	0	0	f_1	1	1
1	1	0	f_2	0	1
0	1	1	f_3	0	0

Smoothing Vector, **h**				Variance of Coefficients		
$\beta =$	0.90856	0.96549	0.98305	$\beta =$	0.90856	0.96549	0.98305
$1 - \beta^n =$	0.25	0.10	0.05	$1 - \beta^n =$	0.25	0.10	0.05
h_1	0.25000	0.10000	0.05000	Var a_1	0.18273	0.07038	0.03478
h_2	0.02394	0.00351	0.0^3855	Var a_2	0.00154	0.0^4758	0.0^5875
h_3	0.0^3765	0.0^4411	0.0^5487	Var a_3	0.0^5151	0.0^7100	0.0^9274

Lead Time	Variance of the Forecast			Standard Deviation of Cumulative Forecast Error		
	$\beta = 0.90856$	0.96549	0.98305	0.90856	0.96549	0.98305
1	0.2137	0.0745	0.0358	1.0000	1.0000	1.0000
2	0.2489	0.0789	0.0368	1.5622	1.4666	1.4394
3	0.2884	0.0835	0.0378	2.0921	1.8600	1.7937
4	0.3326	0.0882	0.0389	2.6322	2.2229	2.1071
5	0.3818	0.0932	0.0399	3.1963	2.5708	2.3964
6	0.4364	0.0984	0.0410	3.7912	2.9117	2.6700
7	0.4966	0.1039	0.0422	4.4215	3.2501	2.9328
8	0.5628	0.1095	0.0433	5.0901	3.5889	3.1881
9	0.6354	0.1154	0.0445	5.7995	3.9301	3.4380
10	0.7147	0.1215	0.0457	6.5516	4.2752	3.6841
11	0.8010	0.1279	0.0469	7.3483	4.6251	3.9275
12	0.8948	0.1345	0.0482	8.1909	4.9808	4.1692

Table 12.4 SMOOTHING COEFFICIENTS

Simple 12-point Sinusoidal Model

$$\xi(T + t) = a_1 + a_2 \sin \frac{2\pi t}{12} + a_3 \cos \frac{2\pi t}{12}$$

Degrees of Freedom $\qquad n = 3$

Transition Matrix L			Initial Values		
				$f(0)$	$f(1)$
1	0	0	f_1	1	1.00000
0	0.86603	0.50000	f_2	0	0.50000
0	−0.50000	0.86603	f_3	1	0.86603

Smoothing Vector $\mathbf{h}$				Variance of Coefficients			
$\beta =$	0.90856	0.96549	0.98305	$\beta =$	0.90856	0.96549	0.98305
$1 - \beta^n =$	0.25	0.10	0.05	$1 - \beta^n =$	0.25	0.10	0.05
h_1	0.08593	0.03347	0.01668	Var a_1	0.04512	0.01740	0.00853
h_2	0.04360	0.00640	0.00156	Var a_2	0.09012	0.03475	0.01706
h_3	0.16408	0.06654	0.03333	Var a_3	0.09456	0.03511	0.01711

	Variance of the Forecast			Standard Deviation of Cumulative Forecast Error		
Lead Time	$\beta = 0.90856$	0.96549	0.98305	0.90856	0.96549	0.98305
1	0.1505	0.0530	0.0257	1.0000	1.0000	1.0000
2	0.1471	0.0527	0.0257	1.5617	1.4696	1.4416
3	0.1395	0.0523	0.0256	1.9894	1.8316	1.7817
4	0.1330	0.0520	0.0256	2.3529	2.1407	2.0705
5	0.1309	0.0520	0.0256	2.6606	2.4101	2.3237
6	0.1322	0.0521	0.0256	2.9212	2.6473	2.5495
7	0.1333	0.0521	0.0256	3.1460	2.8591	2.7537
8	0.1322	0.0520	0.0256	3.3480	3.0522	2.9418
9	0.1309	0.0520	0.0256	3.5411	3.2339	3.1185
10	0.1331	0.0522	0.0256	3.7388	3.4111	3.2883
11	0.1396	0.0526	0.0257	3.9525	3.5894	3.4547
12	0.1472	0.0529	0.0257	4.1885	3.7719	3.6199

Table 12.5 SMOOTHING COEFFICIENTS

Twelve-point Sine Model with Harmonic

$$\xi(T + \tau) = a_1 + a_2 \sin \frac{2\pi t}{12} + a_3 \cos \frac{2\pi t}{12}$$

$$+ a_4 \sin \frac{4\pi t}{12} + a_5 \cos \frac{4\pi t}{12}$$

Degrees of Freedom $\quad n = 5$

Transition Matrix L					Initial Values		
						$\mathbf{f}(0)$	$\mathbf{f}(1)$
1	0	0	0	0	f_1	1	1.00000
0	0.86603	0.50000	0	0	f_2	0	0.50000
0	−0.50000	0.86603	0	0	f_3	1	0.86603
0	0	0	0.50000	0.86603	f_4	0	0.86603
0	0	0	−0.86603	0.50000	f_5	1	0.50000

Smoothing Vector $\mathbf{h}$				Variance of Coefficients			
$\beta =$	0.94409	0.97915	0.98979	$\beta =$	0.94409	0.97915	0.98979
$1 - \beta^n =$	0.25	0.10	0.05	$1 - \beta^n =$	0.25	0.10	0.05
h_1	0.05062	0.02003	0.01000	Var a_1	0.02791	0.01049	0.00513
h_2	0.00794	0.00115	0.0^{3}281	Var a_2	0.05552	0.02098	0.01026
h_3	0.10086	0.04006	0.02002	Var a_3	0.05631	0.02102	0.01027
h_4	0.02019	0.00297	0.0^{3}723	Var a_4	0.05645	0.02102	0.01026
h_5	0.09856	0.03994	0.02001	Var a_5	0.05663	0.02105	0.01027

Lead Time	Variance of the Forecast			Standard Deviation of Cumulative Forecast Error		
	$\beta = 0.94409$	0.97915	0.98979	0.94409	0.97915	0.98979
1	0.1463	0.0528	0.0257	1.0000	1.0000	1.0000
2	0.1414	0.0526	0.0257	1.5280	1.4589	1.4364
3	0.1389	0.0525	0.0256	1.9081	1.8029	1.7675
4	0.1395	0.0525	0.0257	2.2110	2.0861	2.0432
5	0.1389	0.0525	0.0256	2.4673	2.3309	2.2836
6	0.1389	0.0525	0.0256	2.7030	2.5535	2.5016
7	0.1391	0.0525	0.0256	2.9292	2.7618	2.7039
8	0.1387	0.0524	0.0256	3.1406	2.9564	2.8926
9	0.1393	0.0525	0.0257	3.3299	3.1357	3.0680
10	0.1390	0.0525	0.0256	3.5019	3.3021	3.2324
11	0.1398	0.0525	0.0257	3.6738	3.4636	3.3903
12	0.1448	0.0528	0.0257	3.8653	3.6285	3.5465

Table 12.6 SMOOTHING COEFFICIENTS

Irregular 12-Point Periodic Model

$$\xi(T + t) = a_1 + \sum_{j=1}^{4} \left(a_{2j} \sin \frac{2j\pi t}{12} + a_{2j+1} \cos \frac{2j\pi t}{12} \right)$$

Degrees of Freedom $\quad n = 9$

Transition Matrix, L									Initial Values	$f(0)$	$f(1)$
1	0	0	0	0	0 0	0	0	f_1	1	1.00000
0	0.86603	0.50000	0	0	0 0	0	0	f_2	0	0.50000
0	−0.50000	0.86603	0	0	0 0	0	0	f_3	0	0.86603
0	0	0	0.50000	0.86603	0 0	0	0	f_4	0	0.86603
0	0	0	−0.86603	0.50000	0 0	0	0	f_5	1	0.50000
0	0	0	0	0	0 1	0	0	f_6	0	1.00000
0	0	0	0	0	−1 0	0	0	f_7	1	0.00000
0	0	0	0	0	0 0	−0.50000	0.86603	f_8	0	0.86603
0	0	0	0	0	0 0	−0.86603	−0.50000	f_9	1	−0.50000

Smoothing Vector, **h**				Variance of Coefficients			
$\beta =$	0.96854	0.98836	0.99431	$\beta =$	0.96854	0.98836	0.99431
$1 - \beta^n =$	0.25	0.10	0.05	$1 - \beta^n =$	0.25	0.10	0.05
h_1	0.02784	0.01111	0.00556	Var a_1	0.01580	0.00585	0.00285
h_2	0.0^3752	0.0^3110	0.0^4267	Var a_2	0.03160	0.01170	0.00571
h_3	0.05569	0.02225	0.01113	Var a_3	0.03164	0.01170	0.00571
h_4	0.00164	0.0^3241	0.0^4587	Var a_4	0.03161	0.01170	0.00571
h_5	0.05566	0.02224	0.01113	Var a_5	0.03164	0.01170	0.00571
h_6	0.00294	0.0^3431	0.0^31049	Var a_6	0.03165	0.01169	0.00570
h_7	0.05558	0.02222	0.01111	Var a_7	0.03163	0.01169	0.00570
h_8	0.00573	0.0^3841	0.0^3205	Var a_8	0.03184	0.01171	0.00571
h_9	0.05527	0.02222	0.01113	Var a_9	0.03168	0.01171	0.00571

	Variance of the Forecast			Standard Deviation of Cumulative Forecast Error		
Lead Time	$\beta = 0.96854$	0.98836	0.99432	0.96854	0.98836	0.99432
1	0.1435	0.0527	0.0257	1.0000	1.0000	1.0000
2	0.1424	0.0527	0.0257	1.4947	1.4457	1.4299
3	0.1422	0.0526	0.0257	1.8254	1.7686	1.7502
4	0.1423	0.0526	0.0257	2.1119	2.0438	2.0218
5	0.1423	0.0526	0.0257	2.3638	2.2861	2.2609
6	0.1422	0.0526	0.0257	2.5872	2.5035	2.4763
7	0.1422	0.0526	0.0257	2.7981	2.7055	2.6754
8	0.1423	0.0526	0.0257	2.9904	2.8920	2.8600
9	0.1423	0.0526	0.0257	3.1712	3.0671	3.0333
10	0.1422	0.0526	0.0257	3.3467	3.2346	3.1982
11	0.1424	0.0527	0.0257	3.5048	3.3904	3.3532
12	0.1432	0.0527	0.0257	3.6675	3.5438	3.5036

Table 12.7 SMOOTHING COEFFICIENTS

Irregular 13-Point Periodic Function

$$\xi(T + t) = a_1 + \sum_{j=1}^{4}\left(a_{2j}\sin\frac{2j\pi t}{13} + a_{2j+1}\cos\frac{2j\pi t}{13}\right)$$

Degrees of Freedom $\quad n = 9$

Transition Matrix, L									Initial Values	$\mathbf{f(0)}$	$\mathbf{f(1)}$
1	0	0	0	0	0	0	0	0	f_1	1	1.000
0	0.885	0.465	0	0	0	0	0	0	f_2	0	0.465
0	−0.465	0.885	0	0	0	0	0	0	f_3	1	0.885
0	0	0	0.568	0.823	0	0	0	0	f_4	0	0.823
0	0	0	−0.823	0.568	0	0	0	0	f_5	1	0.568
0	0	0	0	0	0.120	0.993	0	0	f_6	0	0.993
0	0	0	0	0	−0.993	0.120	0	0	f_7	1	0.120
0	0	0	0	0	0	0	−0.354	0.935	f_8	0	0.935
0	0	0	0	0	0	0	−0.935	−0.354	f_9	1	−0.354

Smoothing Vector, $\mathbf{h}$				Variance of Coefficients			
$\beta =$	0.96854	0.98836	0.99431	$\beta =$	0.96854	0.98836	0.99431
$1 - \beta^n =$	0.25	0.10	0.05	$1 - \beta^n =$	0.25	0.10	0.05
h_1	0.02787	0.01112	0.00556	Var a_1	0.01577	0.00584	0.00285
h_2	0.0^{3}953	0.0^{3}139	0.0^{4}339	Var a_2	0.03151	0.01168	0.00569
h_3	0.05582	0.02234	0.01122	Var a_3	0.03158	0.01168	0.00569
h_4	0.00208	0.0^{3}308	0.0^{4}766	Var a_4	0.03154	0.01169	0.00570
h_5	0.05580	0.02236	0.01124	Var a_5	0.03159	0.01169	0.00570
h_6	0.00366	0.0^{3}540	0.0^{3}133	Var a_6	0.03158	0.01167	0.00568
h_7	0.05557	0.02222	0.01111	Var a_7	0.03157	0.01167	0.00568
h_8	0.00689	0.00101	0.0^{3}246	Var a_8	0.03179	0.01169	0.00569
h_9	0.05509	0.02214	0.01104	Var a_9	0.03163	0.01168	0.00569

Lead Time	Variance of the Forecast			Standard Deviation of Cumulative Forecast Error		
	$\beta = 0.96854$	0.98836	0.99432	0.96854	0.98836	0.99432
1	0.1437	0.0526	0.0256	1.0000	1.0000	1.0000
2	0.1420	0.0526	0.0256	1.5009	1.4482	1.4311
3	0.1420	0.0526	0.0256	1.8355	1.7728	1.7523
4	0.1420	0.0526	0.0256	2.1208	2.0475	2.0236
5	0.1418	0.0526	0.0256	2.3768	2.2915	2.2636
6	0.1419	0.0526	0.0256	2.6017	2.5095	2.4793
7	0.1419	0.0526	0.0256	2.8114	2.7110	2.6781
8	0.1418	0.0526	0.0256	3.0086	2.8994	2.8637
9	0.1419	0.0526	0.0256	3.1887	3.0744	3.0369
10	0.1420	0.0526	0.0256	3.3629	3.2413	3.2015
11	0.1419	0.0526	0.0256	3.5299	3.4007	3.3584
12	0.1420	0.0526	0.0256	3.6811	3.5497	3.5066

Table 12.8 SMOOTHING COEFFICIENTS

Linear Model with Superimposed Sinusoid

$$\xi(T + t) = a_1 + a_2 t + a_3 \sin \frac{2\pi t}{12} + a_4 \cos \frac{2\pi t}{12}$$

Degrees of Freedom $\quad n = 4$

Transition Matrix, L				Initial Values		
					f(0)	f(1)
1	0	0	0	f_1	1	1.00000
1	1	0	0	f_2	0	1.00000
0	0	0.86603	0.50000	f_3	0	0.50000
0	0	−0.50000	0.86603	f_4	1	0.86603

Smoothing Vector, $\mathbf{h}$				Variance of Coefficients			
$\beta =$	0.93061	0.97400	0.98726	$\beta =$	0.93061	0.97400	0.98726
$1 - \beta^n =$	0.25	0.10	0.05	$1 - \beta^n =$	0.25	0.10	0.05
h_1	0.12949	0.05024	0.02503	Var a_1	0.08510	0.03245	0.01593
h_2	0.00457	0.0^{3}660	0.0^{3}160	Var a_2	0.0^{4}866	0.0^{5}452	0.0^{6}526
h_3	0.04113	0.00605	0.00148	Var a_3	0.06879	0.02614	0.01281
h_4	0.12052	0.04977	0.02499	Var a_4	0.07074	0.02633	0.01283

Lead Time	Variance of the Forecast			Standard Deviation of Cumulative Forecast Error		
	$\beta = 0.93060$	0.97400	0.98726	0.93060	0.97400	0.98726
1	0.1720	0.0602	0.0291	1.0000	1.0000	1.0000
2	0.1798	0.0613	0.0293	1.5188	1.4545	1.4342
3	0.1825	0.0621	0.0296	1.9656	1.8224	1.7769
4	0.1824	0.0626	0.0297	2.3690	2.1440	2.0715
5	0.1822	0.0629	0.0298	2.7361	2.4325	2.3336
6	0.1827	0.0630	0.0298	3.0732	2.6951	2.5713
7	0.1836	0.0631	0.0298	3.3884	2.9379	2.7903
8	0.1853	0.0632	0.0298	3.6923	3.1666	2.9953
9	0.1898	0.0637	0.0299	3.9968	3.3872	3.1905
10	0.1997	0.0646	0.0301	4.3135	3.6054	3.3796
11	0.2152	0.0660	0.0304	4.6518	3.8255	3.5656
12	0.2332	0.0677	0.0308	5.0166	4.0504	3.7503

Table 12.9 SMOOTHING COEFFICIENTS

Growing Sinusoidal Model

$$\xi(T + t) = (a_1 + a_2 t) + (a_3 + a_5 t) \sin \frac{2\pi t}{12}$$

$$+ (a_4 + a_6 t) \cos \frac{2\pi t}{12}$$

Degrees of Freedom $\quad n = 6$

Transition Matrix, L						Initial Values		
							$\mathbf{f}(0)$	$\mathbf{f}(1)$
1	0	0	0	0	0	f_1	1	1.00000
1	1	0	0	0	0	f_2	0	1.00000
0	0	0.86603	0.50000	0	0	f_3	0	0.50000
0	0	-0.50000	0.86603	0	0	f_4	1	0.86603
0	0	0.86603	0.50000	0.86603	0.50000	f_5	0	0.50000
0	0	-0.50000	0.86603	-0.50000	0.86603	f_6	0	0.86603

Smoothing Vector, $\mathbf{h}$				Variance of Coefficients			
$\beta =$	0.95318	0.98259	0.99149	$\beta =$	0.95318	0.98259	0.99149
$1 - \beta^n =$	0.25	0.10	0.05	$1 - \beta^n =$	0.25	0.10	0.05
h_1	0.08595	0.03347	0.01668	Var a_1	0.05808	0.02176	0.01065
h_2	0.00203	0.0^3293	0.0^4713	Var a_2	0.0^4262	0.0^5134	0.0^6156
h_3	0.043751	0.00640	0.00156	Var a_3	0.11872	0.04384	0.02139
h_4	0.16408	0.06656	0.03335	Var a_4	0.11481	0.04331	0.02125
h_5	0.00104	0.0^4562	0.0^5667	Var a_5	0.0^4525	0.0^5269	0.0^6313
h_6	0.00389	0.0^3584	0.0^3143	Var a_6	0.0^4545	0.0^5271	0.0^6313

Lead Time	Variance of the Forecast			Standard Deviation of Cumulative Forecast Error		
	$\beta = 0.95318$	0.98259	0.99149	0.95318	0.98259	0.99149
1	0.1931	0.0674	0.0324	1.0000	1.0000	1.0000
2	0.2100	0.0697	0.0330	1.4909	1.4440	1.4290
3	0.2171	0.0708	0.0333	1.9353	1.8103	1.7708
4	0.2166	0.0710	0.0333	2.3254	2.1254	2.0619
5	0.2151	0.0710	0.0333	2.6598	2.3999	2.3169
6	0.2168	0.0712	0.0334	2.9402	2.6399	2.5434
7	0.2202	0.0715	0.0334	3.1753	2.8519	2.7474
8	0.2214	0.0717	0.0335	3.3793	3.0435	2.9344
9	0.2204	0.0717	0.0335	3.5701	3.2233	3.1101
10	0.2235	0.0721	0.0336	3.7670	3.4000	3.2796
11	0.2379	0.0735	0.0339	3.9889	3.5809	3.4471
12	0.2640	0.0762	0.0345	4.2497	3.7707	3.6154

Table 12.10 SMOOTHING COEFFICIENTS

Growing Sinusoidal Model with Harmonic

$$\xi(T + t) = (a_1 + a_2 t) + (a_3 + a_5 t) \sin \frac{2\pi t}{12} + (a_4 + a_6 t) \cos \frac{2\pi t}{12}$$

$$+ a_7 \sin \frac{4\pi t}{12} + a_8 \cos \frac{4\pi t}{12}$$

Degrees of Freedom $\quad n = 8$

Transition Matrix, L								Initial Values	$f(0)$	$f(1)$
1	0	0	0	0	0	0	0	f_1	1	1.00000
1	1	0	0	0	0	0	0	f_2	0	1.00000
0	0	0.86603	0.50000	0	0	0	0	f_3	0	0.50000
0	0	−0.50000	0.86603	0	0	0	0	f_4	1	0.86603
0	0	0.86603	0.50000	0.86603	0.50000	0	0	f_5	0	0.50000
0	0	−0.50000	0.86603	−0.50000	0.86603	0	0	f_6	0	0.86603
0	0	0	0	0	0	0.50000	0.86603	f_7	0	0.86603
0	0	0	0	0	0	−0.86603	0.50000	f_8	1	0.50000

Smoothing Vector, $\mathbf{h}$				Variance of Coefficients			
$\beta =$	0.96468	0.98692	0.99361	$\beta =$	0.96468	0.98692	0.99361
$1 - \beta^n =$	0.25	0.10	0.05	$1 - \beta^n =$	0.25	0.10	0.05
h_1	0.06367	0.02506	0.01251	Var a_1	0.04390	0.01636	0.00799
h_2	0.00113	0.0^3165	0.0^4401	Var a_2	0.0^4112	0.0^6569	0.0^7659
h_3	0.01858	0.00270	0.0^3658	Var a_3	0.08897	0.03290	0.01605
h_4	0.12547	0.05006	0.02504	Var a_4	0.08675	0.03258	0.01597
h_5	0.0^3332	0.0^4178	0.0^5211	Var a_5	0.0^4224	0.0^5114	0.0^6132
h_6	0.00224	0.0^3329	0.0^4804	Var a_6	0.0^4228	0.0^5114	0.0^6132
h_7	0.01507	0.00222	0.0^3542	Var a_7	0.03559	0.01316	0.00642
h_8	0.06090	0.02493	0.01251	Var a_8	0.03561	0.01317	0.00642

Lead Time	Variance of the Forecast			Standard Deviation of Cumulative Forecast Error		
	$\beta = 0.96468$	0.98692	0.99361	0.96468	0.98692	0.99361
1	0.1802	0.0637	0.0308	1.0000	1.0000	1.0000
2	0.1894	0.0651	0.0311	1.4936	1.4455	1.4298
3	0.1917	0.0656	0.0312	1.9056	1.7998	1.7656
4	0.1919	0.0656	0.0312	2.2504	2.0972	2.0481
5	0.1919	0.0656	0.0312	2.5439	2.3549	2.2947
6	0.1920	0.0656	0.0312	2.8014	2.5849	2.5161
7	0.1922	0.0657	0.0312	3.0324	2.7945	2.7190
8	0.1925	0.0657	0.0312	3.2406	2.9874	2.9067
9	0.1927	0.0657	0.0312	3.4304	3.1664	3.0819
10	0.1925	0.0657	0.0312	3.6133	3.3368	3.2483
11	0.1979	0.0663	0.0314	3.8082	3.5067	3.4103
12	0.2143	0.0681	0.0318	4.0344	3.6837	3.5722

a_2 and a_3. To estimate their initial values, proceed as follows: First construct the seasonal pattern. If there are several cycles of data, average corresponding samples across the cycles. If there is only one cycle, sketch a smooth curve through the data. If there are no data, estimate what the cyclic pattern should look like. In any event, the result will be a sequence of p numbers $\hat{x}_1, \hat{x}_2, \ldots, \hat{x}_p$.

Then form the sums

$$\hat{a}_2 = \frac{2}{p} \sum_{k=1}^{p} \hat{x}_k \sin \omega k$$

$$\hat{a}_3 = \frac{2}{p} \sum_{k=1}^{p} \hat{x}_k \cos \omega k$$

for each frequency ω that is to be included in the model.

The values of the coefficients for the model in Table 12.6 estimated from the data on Company B's imports (Table C.9) are:

$$\hat{a}_1 = 2484.5,$$

$$\omega_1 = \frac{2\pi}{12}, \quad \hat{a}_2 = 341.0, \quad \hat{a}_3 = -85.9, \quad A_1 = 351.7$$

$$\omega_2 = \frac{4\pi}{12}, \quad \hat{a}_4 = -65.8, \quad \hat{a}_5 = -142.2, \quad A_2 = 156.7$$

$$\omega_3 = \frac{6\pi}{12}, \quad \hat{a}_6 = -33.8, \quad \hat{a}_7 = -30.7, \quad A_3 = 45.7$$

$$\omega_4 = \frac{8\pi}{12}, \quad \hat{a}_8 = -341.1, \quad \hat{a}_9 = -42.4, \quad A_4 = 366.5$$

The amplitude $\sqrt{a_{2j}^2 + a_{2j+1}^2} = A_j$ is also shown.

A NOTE ABOUT EXPONENTIAL MODELS. The derivation of Chapter 11 includes fitting functions that are exponential functions of time, such as $e^{\lambda t}$ and $te^{\lambda t}$. It is necessary to know the value of λ to write down the transition matrix, and hence the computations would be special to each application. The most frequent cases where the exponential functions are encountered involve returns on financial investments, or population growth, where one can replace $e^{\lambda t}$ by $(1 + r)^t$, where r is some fraction (percentage) considerably less than unity. From the binomial theorem we can write

$$(1 + r)^t = 1 + rt + \tfrac{1}{2}(t - 1)r^2 + \ldots + \binom{t}{k} r^k$$

The exact expression includes all terms up to $k = t$. But when r is reasonably small, a simple polynomial in t is sufficient, since the higher powers of r will be indistinguishable from zero. Hence when the process is exponential, but the rate of growth is not known (but certain to be a few percent), use a polynomial in time. That is, instead of the exponential model of the process, we use a Taylor series expansion of that model, in which only a few items are significant.

For example, suppose that some process were growing at the rate of 2 percent in each sampling interval and that a forecast was wanted for up to 12 sampling intervals in the future. A growth of 2 percent per month actually compounds to 26.82 percent in a year. The quadratic approximation to this exponential would yield 26.64 percent in a year, a difference of less than one-tenth of 1 percent. The cubic term gives the correct result to four figures. This example is extreme, with a high rate of growth and a long lead time. The forecasts are revised frequently, so that in most exponential processes the polynomial model should be eminently satisfactory.

Work Sheet

To illustrate the use of these methods, let us turn to another work sheet. Recall from Chapter 4 that the Warmdot Filter sales data (Fig. 12.4

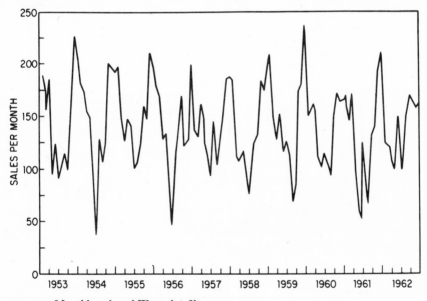

Fig. 12.4 Monthly sales of Warmdot filters.

plotted from Table C.13) could be described rather well by a simple sinusoidal model

$$\xi(t) = C + A \cos \frac{2\pi}{12} (t - t_0)$$

$$= a_1 + a_2 \sin \frac{2\pi t}{12} + a_3 \cos \frac{2\pi t}{12}$$

In Fig. 4.5, we estimated the initial values of these coefficients (as of December, 1952) as

$$\hat{a}_1(0) = 150$$

$$\hat{a}_2(0) = 0$$

$$\hat{a}_3(0) = 50$$

Table 12.4 gives the program constants needed to revise these estimated coefficients each month in the light of new observations. We can use the middle value of the discount factor $\beta = 0.96549$ ($\beta^3 = 0.9$). The three equa-

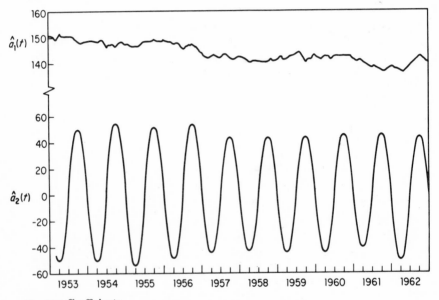

Fig. 12.5 Coefficients.

tions for revising the coefficients are shown in the heading of Work Sheet No. 8. The numerical constants in the first terms on the right side of the equation are the three rows (zeros omitted) of the transpose L'; the last term is the corresponding component of the smoothing vector $\mathbf{h}$.

The forecast for the next month is $\hat{\mathbf{a}}(T)\mathbf{f}(1)$, where $\mathbf{f}(1)$ is given in Table 12.4. Forecasts for the second and third month would use

$$f(2) = \begin{bmatrix} 1 \\ 0.866 \\ 0.500 \end{bmatrix} \quad f(3) = \begin{bmatrix} 1 \\ 1.000 \\ 0 \end{bmatrix}$$

The forecast error is the difference between a forecast for one month and the actual observation.

Exercise. Complete the computations of Work Sheet No. 8.

Work Sheet No. 8 GENERAL EXPONENTIAL SMOOTHING

DATA: Warmdot Filter sales (Table C.14)
MODEL: Simple 12-point sine (Table 12.4)

$$\xi(T + t) = a_1 + a_2 \sin \frac{2\pi t}{12} + a_3 \cos \frac{2\pi t}{12}$$

SMOOTHING: $\beta = 0.96549$ equivalent to $\alpha = 0.10$
$\hat{a}_1(T) = \hat{a}_1(T - 1) + 0.03347e_1(T)$
$\hat{a}_2(T) = 0.86603\hat{a}_2(T - 1) - 0.50\hat{a}_3(T - 1) + 0.00640e_1(T)$
$\hat{a}_3(T) = 0.50\hat{a}_2(T - 1) + 0.86603\hat{a}_3(T - 1) + 0.06654e_1(T)$
FORECASTS: $\hat{x}_1(T) = \hat{a}_1(T) + 0.5000\hat{a}_2(T) + 0.86603\hat{a}_3(T)$

$$\hat{x}_\tau(T) = \hat{a}_1(T) + \hat{a}_2(T) \sin \frac{2\pi \tau}{12} + \hat{a}_3(T) \cos \frac{2\pi \tau}{12}$$

ERROR: $e_1(T) = x(T) - \hat{x}_1(T - 1)$

Date	Data	Coefficients			Forecasts			Error
t	$x(t)$	$a_1(t)$	$a_2(t)$	$a_3(t)$	$\hat{x}_1(t-1)$	$\hat{x}_2(t-2)$	$\hat{x}_3(t-3)$	$e_1(t)$
Initial		150	0.0	50.0	...	...	...	..
1	191	150	−25.0	43.1	193	...	...	−2
2	158	149	−43.3	23.7	175	175	...	−17
3	184	151	−49.2	1.3	148	150	150	+36
4	97	150	−43.4	−25.5	127	124	125	−30
5	124	150	−24.7	−42.6	106	109	106	+18
6	92	150	−0.2	−49.8	101	99	101	−9
.					107	107	106	
.						125	125	
.							150	
.								

Figure 12.5 shows how the coefficients vary. The constant term $\hat{a}_1(t)$ drifts slowly downward, but at each month represents the current estimate

of the average month's sales. (Contrast these values with a 12-month moving average of the same data.)

The sinusoidal coefficient $\hat{a}_2(t)$ follows a sine wave, reflecting the changes in the origin of time with each observation. The values vary somewhat

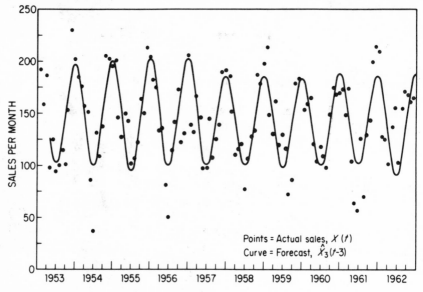

Fig. 12.6 Forecasts of Warmdot's filter sales.

from a pure sine wave, to reflect the change in estimates of the amplitude and phase angle. (The other coefficient $\hat{a}_3(t)$ could vary in a similar way, about 90° out of phase.)

Figure 12.6 compares the actual observations $x(t)$ with the forecast $\hat{x}_3(t - 3)$ made from data three months prior.

13 Probability Models

The probability model is conceptually quite different from the time-series model. In the time-series model, the significant abstraction from the observations is the process that changes with time, and one thinks of the observations as being that process, with some superimposed noise. In some problems, it is much more relevant to pay attention to the shape of the distribution from which the noise samples are drawn. The process in these cases is usually constant and may even be nearly zero.

The time-series model is some function of time, with coefficients whose values are to be estimated from the observations to date. In the probability model, we shall estimate *probabilities* rather than coefficients. We shall define n mutually exclusive and collectively exhaustive *events*. For example, if the observations are the number of units of a product ordered by successive customers, we could define the three events:

(1) The quantity is less than 5 pieces.

(2) The quantity is at least 5 pieces, and less than 20.

(3) The quantity is at least 20 pieces.

No matter what quantity is ordered, we can associate it with one and only one of these events.

In the example discussed in Chapter 5, the observations were the times you arrive home in the evening. The events were (1) arrive home before 5:19:59; (2) arrive home between 5:20:00 and 5:29:59, . . . and so on, up to (8) arrive home after 6:20:00.

In each case, the observations (units of time) can be measured on a single scale. The n *events* are defined in terms of $n + 1$ *class limits*, which we can call

$$X_0 < X_1 < X_2 < \ldots X_n$$

The event associated with the observation $x(t)$ corresponds to the number of the interval in which the observation falls. Any possible observation must either be equal to one (and only one) of the class limits or must fall between some pair. That is, there is only one k such that

$$X_{k-1} < x(t) \leqslant X_k$$

and therefore we associate the kth event with the observation $x(t)$. Note especially that this means that the first class limit X_0 must be less than any observation that can occur, and the last limit X_n must be larger than any observation that can occur. Since no one can be absolutely and mathematically certain that the observations will be bounded, there are two alternatives available in designing the system. The obvious one is perhaps to set $X_0 = -\infty$ and $X_n = +\infty$. As we shall see, this may lead to some difficulties. Another way is to set X_0 as large as can be reasonably expected to be less than any observation, and X_n as small as can be *reasonably* expected to be greater than any observation. Then when an observation occurs—and it will—outside these reasonable bounds, provide for the system to cry "TILT"; you'll want to look at the unusual occurrences before processing them routinely.

In this chapter, we shall discuss a very simple method for estimating the probabilities $\hat{p}_k(t)$ associated with the various events $X_{k-1} < x(t) \leqslant X_k$. Since there is a total of n possible events, there are $n - 1$ degrees of freedom, since the sum of the probabilities must be equal to one. That is, not all n of the values p_k are independent.

Start with some initial prediction (what the Bayesian statisticians would call the *prior estimate*) of the various probabilities $\hat{p}_k(0)$, $k = 1, 2, \ldots, n$. Some analysis of past data, or judgment about the future, made it possible to set the class limits at various points along the scale on which the observations are measured (Chapter 5). The same study should provide at least a rough estimate of the probabilities associated with the various events.

Now suppose that the observation $x(t)$ is associated with the kth event $X_{k-1} < x(t) \leqslant X_k$. We shall construct a unit vector $\mathbf{u}_k$ which has zeros for $n - 1$ components, and a one in the kth component. It is the kth column from a unit matrix of rank n. For example, suppose there were five class intervals, and the observation fell in the second. Then the corresponding unit vector would be $\mathbf{u}_2' = (0\ 1\ 0\ 0\ 0)$.

We can consider the previous values of the n probabilities as an n-component column vector $\mathbf{p}(t)$. The process of revising these estimates in the light of current information is *vector smoothing*, according to the rule

$$\hat{\mathbf{p}}(t) = \alpha\mathbf{u}_k + (1 - \alpha)\hat{\mathbf{p}}(t - 1)$$

Each component of the vector is modified by simple exponential smoothing of either a zero or a one. For example, if there are five class intervals, and the observation falls in the second one,

$$\hat{p}_1(t) = (1 - \alpha)\hat{p}_1(t - 1)$$

$$\hat{p}_2(t) = (1 - \alpha)\hat{p}_2(t - 1) + \alpha$$

$$\hat{p}_3(t) = (1 - \alpha)\hat{p}_3(t - 1)$$

$$\hat{p}_4(t) = (1 - \alpha)\hat{p}_4(t - 1)$$

$$\hat{p}_5(t) = (1 - \alpha)\hat{p}_5(t - 1)$$

If the vector $\hat{\mathbf{p}}(t - 1)$ is a probability vector, all of its components must be non-negative, and their sum must be exactly one. The process of vector smoothing described above cannot make any component negative, and the sum of the resulting components is the same as the sum of their previous values. Hence if $\hat{\mathbf{p}}(t - 1)$ is a probability vector, so is $\hat{\mathbf{p}}(t)$.

Consider one class interval, say the kth one. The value of the estimate $\hat{p}_k(t)$ is the result of exponential smoothing of a string of ones and zeros. If the probability distribution governing the observations $x(t)$ doesn't change, then the probability that we use a one as the "data" in smoothing is just the true probability of the kth event $\bar{p}_k$, and the probability that we use a zero is $\bar{q}_k = 1 - \bar{p}_k$. The expected value of the "data" is exactly $\bar{p}_k$, and the expected value of the estimate $\mathcal{E}[\hat{p}_k(t)] = \bar{p}_k$, the correct probability.

Furthermore, if the process continues long enough, the initial estimates will be completely discounted. Therefore vector smoothing will, on the average, yield the probabilities of the n mutually exclusive and collectively exhaustive events described by the class limits.

Successive values of any particular component of the unit vector $\mathbf{u}(t)$ used in revising the probability vector represent samples from a binomial distribution. Hence the variance of the kth component is $\bar{p}_k(1 - \bar{p}_k)$. In Chapter 8, we discussed the variance of the result of exponential smoothing in terms of the variance of the input. The variance of the estimates of the kth probability is

$$\sigma_k^2 = \frac{\alpha}{2 - \alpha}\ \bar{p}_k(1 - \bar{p}_k)$$

where α is the smoothing constant used in revising the estimates of the probability vector. Now there are two kinds of choices available to the systems designer. The class limits can be set so that p_k is either very large (nearly one) or very small (nearly zero). Then the variance of the components of the probability vector will be small. If the shape of the distribution is changing with time, a larger smoothing constant can be used to discount old information rapidly.

Alternatively, if the probability distribution is constant in time, there is no need to discount old data, and a smaller smoothing constant can be used to decrease the variance of the estimates. Then it is possible to use fewer class intervals, with probabilities that are not small.

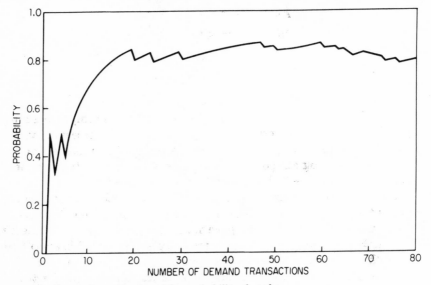

Fig. 13.1 Successive estimates of the probability that the interval will be less than fifteen days.

In many practical applications, one might select class limits so that near one tail there were five intervals, each with an associated probability on the order of 0.02, for ease in interpolation. Then the rest of the distribution could be considered one event, with probability 0.9.

Exercise. Compute the variance of the estimates of the probabilities for each of the two types of events, $\tilde{p}_1 = 0.02$ and $\tilde{p}_2 = 0.9$. Plot the results as a function of α.

As an example, we might apply vector smoothing to the data in Table C.15, to estimate the distribution of the numbers of days between demand for HF 2815-343-2678, a bearing shell half, stocked by the Navy. The average interval between transactions is a little over six days. One might expect that interarrival times follow an exponential distribution. Therefore the following class limits were selected, so that there would be ten events, each with probability initially estimated as $\hat{p}_k(0) = 0.1$:

$X_0 = 0$		X_6	$= 6$
$X_1 = 1$		X_7	$= 8$
$X_2 = 2$		X_8	$= 10$
$X_3 = 3$		X_9	$= 15$
$X_4 = 4$		X_{10}	$= \infty$
$X_5 = 5$			

One way of estimating the probability that the next transaction will occur within fifteen days is dividing the number of occasions when the next

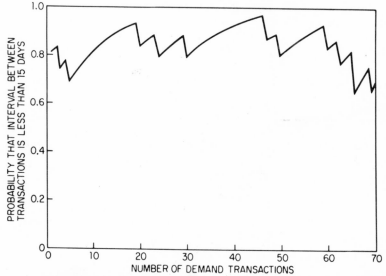

Fig. 13.2 Cumulative probabilities that the interval will not exceed fifteen days.

transaction has been within fifteen days by the total number of occasions reported. This fraction is a good estimate of the required probability. Figure 13.1 is a plot of what these estimates would have been, if made with each successive transaction. Note that initially the estimates swing wildly, but then become more stable as the fractions are based on larger and larger numbers. After 60 transactions, even a significant change in the distribution of interarrival times could hardly affect this estimate.

By contrast, Fig. 13.2 shows how the successive estimates would have varied, if they had been computed by vector smoothing, with a smoothing constant $\alpha = 0.1$. The zigzag pattern is more marked throughout the sequence. The fluctuations are smaller initially. There seems to be an increase in the chance that more than fifteen days will elapse between transactions, after the sixtieth observation. This change is tracked quite well.

Exercise. Use the data from Table C.2. Use the first year (1956) to estimate the initial probabilities, that the demand will be less than 150, 151–200, 201–25, 226–50, or 251 and over. Set up a work sheet like Work Sheet Number 9, and carry out vector smoothing.

Work Sheet No. 9 VECTOR SMOOTHING

DATA: Demand Transactions, Table A.1
CLASS LIMITS: 0, 150, 200, 225, 250
SMOOTHING CONSTANT: $\alpha = 0.1$

Date	Demand	0–150	151–200	Interval 201–25	226–50	251 and Over
t	$x(t)$	$k = 1$	$k = 2$	$k = 3$	$k = 4$	$k = 5$
Initial		0.9091	0.0114	0.0000	0.0568	0.0227
Jan. 3, 1951	2	0.9182	0.0102	0.0000	0.0511	0.0205
5	40					
8	60					
11	75					
12	12					
.	40					
.						
.						

A handy, but apparently little-known device for tallying information has been used* for at least half a century by the Quebec woodsmen in counting the number of logs in a pile. The tallies go by tens, with dots and lines around a square, thus

$$1 = \cdot \qquad 2 = \cdot\cdot \qquad 3 = \vcenter{\hbox{$\cdot\;\cdot$}} \qquad 4 = \vcenter{\hbox{$\cdot\;\cdot$}} \qquad 5 = \underline{\cdot\;\cdot}$$
$$6 = \lfloor\cdot \qquad 7 = \lceil \qquad 8 = \square \qquad 9 = \boxslash \qquad 10 = \boxtimes$$

I have found that, once I got used to it, this scheme is fast and accurate. When we count the data from Table C.2 for 1956, the results look like this:

* H. S. Graves, "Woodsman's Handbook," U.S. Department of Agriculture, *Bulletin* 36 (1903), p. 122.

Interval	Tally	Total	Fraction
0–150	⊠ ⊠ ⊠ ⊠ ⊠ ⊠ ⊠ ⊠	80	0.9091
151–200	.	1	0.0114
201–25		0	0.0000
226–50	:	5	0.0568
251 and over	..	2	0.0227
		88	1.0000

A NOTE ON PROCESSING SPORADIC DATA. One of the frequent difficulties encountered in trying to design an automatic forecast system, especially in industrial inventory control, is sporadic data. In an inventory control system, one wants to forecast demand during the lead time that it takes to replenish stock, as a basis for setting reorder levels. The data-processing system may be set up to summarize the demand once a month and to revise all of the forecasts at that time.

A significant fraction of items in some inventories will have no activity at all during a particular month. There are likely to be several months in a row with no demand. That does not mean, of course, that the item should not be in the inventory. It may be a vital spare part for some machinery and be needed promptly when it is needed at all, so that there must always be some in stock.

If the item is important, like an expensive spare part, then it may be worth the effort to deal with demand-during-a-lead-time (see Chapter 18), or to forecast the distribution of times between successive demands.

For a large number of items, however, the individual part isn't worth that much special treatment. It is not worthwhile to design a special forecasting routine for such items. The cost of keeping track of which system applies to which items would be uneconomical. One obvious solution, of course, is to use a probability model, as discussed above. Then the probability that there is no demand in a month would be estimated as one of the events.

Exercise. How would you handle customer returns for credit? What is the probability distribution for demand during a lead time if it takes three months to replenish the supply?

Another simplification might be considered. If, in any period, there is no activity, skip the forecast computations. That is, the estimate of the coefficients (or other parameters) in the forecast model would not change if the observation were zero; therefore, the forecast would be exactly the same as the one computed previously.

Obviously, the results of this scheme cannot be interpreted as the average rate of demand (as would be required in computing an order quantity, for example) since a large number of periods with no demand would be ignored. Rather, one treats the result as "the average rate of demand-when-there-is-any." When there is no demand, the inventory status doesn't change. One of the principal purposes of a forecast is furnishing the basis for deciding when to order more material. If the inventory status doesn't change, obviously one doesn't want to order more material.

Forecasting

"One forms provisional theories and waits for time or
fuller knowledge to explode them."

Sussex Vampire

The correct solution to a problem should be patently correct. That is, the proof should be so clear to someone who knows the material that he can explain to anyone else why the right answer is right. The obvious answer to a problem, on the other hand, is not always the right one.

By now, I think we can safely assume that the data being analyzed are current and clean; that the model chosen to represent the process has all the terms necessary to explain the systematic variation in the observations, but no unnecessary terms that merely amplify the random noise; and that the coefficients or other parameters in the model can be accurately estimated by some simple and robust smoothing technique. What could be more obvious as a forecast than the evaluation of that model at the relevant future time?

This section intends to discuss some other ways to use the available information to obtain a more useful forecast. If you can think of two or three "obviously right" answers, you must dig a little deeper and understand why one of them is better than the alternatives. That understanding should lead to a far better result. My aim is not to confuse, but to stimulate thought.

There is such a wide variety of forecasting problems that it would not be possible to solve them all in the compass of one book. The list of alternatives for forecasting presented here is not complete. But the list is longer than just the obvious evaluation of the model with the current estimates of the coefficients; perhaps the discussion will suggest further alternatives that are worth consideration in your particular problem.

When you watch a duck flying, you want to use the recent information to decide where the duck will be when your shot gets to the same point in space. Usually, one would assume that his observations of past positions had been exact. But radar observations of the progress of an airplane are not exact: there are various sources of noise that mean that the observations are merely estimates of past positions. Still, an air traffic controller wants to know where the airplane will be in two minutes, or when the airplane will be over a certain marker. The observation at the future time will also contain noise; the forecast is an estimate of what the observation would be if there were no noise.

The aircraft (or the duck) might start to turn, or climb. Then the problem is deciding where the target could be in the future. Now there is a new element that results in a difference between the future observation and that estimated from the current model: an intentional or systematic change in the values of one or more of the coefficients in the model.

You may estimate that the gasoline consumption in your car is about 20 miles per gallon. If you now have 1 gallon in the tank, would you pass a service station, knowing that the next station is 20 miles away? Probably not. There are times when you don't get 20 miles per gallon, because of road and traffic conditions; the gauge that shows 1 gallon may not be entirely accurate; the next station may be a little more than 20 miles away. Here, the forecast problem is estimating a worst possible consumption, not the average, and a longest possible distance to the next replenishment opportunity. If you are certain that your present supply will last at least until the next station, then you can pass this one.

Forecasting demand for an inventory control system presents somewhat the same problem. There may be an underlying pattern of growth and seasonal variation. But the demand at any time is the true demand that must be satisfied. The noise—the difference between the actual observation and the model—cannot simply be averaged out as in the case of tracking an airplane on radar.

Decisions based on the forecast therefore must recognize that future observations will be samples from some probability distribution. The time-series model can be used to estimate the mean of that distribution, if there is no significant change, such as intentional evasion. Section V will deal with estimates of the other parameters of that distribution.

Action taken now—including the deliberate decision not to take any positive action—generally has an effect some time in the future. You shoot at a duck now, but the duck isn't hit for some seconds. You tell the pilot of an airplane to turn, because he will be at a specific point in space in a few minutes. You pass a gas station now, because you'll have some gas left when you get to the next one. You order more stock now, which will be delivered in six months. Chapter 14 is a short discussion of these lead times:

the time by which your decision must lead the effect, and therefore the time over which the forecast is required.

In Chapter 15, we shall consider some of the alternatives for using a time-series model to forecast what the price of a stock will be in two weeks, or what the total demand will be during the next two months. If the original observations were transformed in some way (recall Chapter 3), then the inverse transformation must be applied to the forecasts.

We shall also discuss the use of a routine objective forecast computation to help competent management make more useful predictions. The objective forecast can be one of the pieces of information considered in producing the final subjective prediction.

Although the values of the coefficients have been carefully estimated to give an accurate model of past observations, it may be a good idea not to use all of them in the forecast; or any of the values may be deliberately changed to take account of deliberate evasion. Chapter 16 discusses the variance of these estimates caused by the noise in the observations as a basis for deciding whether a coefficient is significant.

Chapter 17 discusses the use of a probability model in forecasting, covering both the problem of interpolation between the class limits used to define the events, and the problem of convolution to obtain estimates for lead times that are longer than the intervals used in sampling the process.

Three special techniques for getting the sort of forecasts required in an inventory control system do not fit into the pattern of using a model to represent the data, and an explicit smoothing technique. These are reported in Chapter 18 to suggest alternative ways of tackling the problem.

Lead Times

The forecasts are only a part of some larger control system. If the forecast were generated as an end in itself, then it wouldn't matter how the forecast was obtained. Somehow the forecast is going to be used, as the basis for deciding whether to take some specific action. You may want to shoot at an enemy target or direct a friendly one to a specific place. You may want to budget production, decide whether to hire more people or lay some off, or arrange for operating capital. You may want to decide whether, and how much, to buy to replenish stocks or to hedge against price changes.

In order to make good decisions about action, you want a good forecast of what the process $\xi(t)$ will be at some time in the future. How far in advance do you need the forecast? For some capital budgeting decisions, an estimate of the total market over the next ten years may be required. Annual budgets look a year ahead, but perhaps should consider the second year as well. Production and transportation of material takes time, so that there may be a natural lead time for an inventory system. The distance by which you should lead a moving target is implicitly defined in terms of the relative velocities of the target and the missile.

There may even be two kinds of lead time. A short lead time is dictated by the shortest practical time that may elapse between making a final commitment and the time that the effect of that commitment is felt. This would be the time of flight of a ballistic shot, or the normal production cycle time in a factory. It may be wise to have a forecast over a longer period of time, too. Suppose you were to order enough of a seasonal product to last one lead time. At the end of that time, you may find that there isn't enough manufacturing capacity to satisfy the peak need. Hence, one may look farther ahead to decide whether it will be possible again to make a routine commitment. The longer projection need not be as accurate, since there will be an opportunity later—when there is better information—to modify a plan. The longer-range preliminary forecast helps one plan for major peaks and valleys.

When there is noise in the observed data, that noise gets amplified by the forecast. In general, the longer the lead time, the greater the amplification. In Section VII, we shall discuss the use of all the available information in making preliminary plans and final commitments in a variety of situations. In each case, the action recommended will be a compromise between conflicting objectives—the sort of rubber stamp problem illustrated by Fig. 3.1. At best there is some risk of loss. That risk depends on the variance of the forecast errors. Hence, the greater the amplification of noise, the greater the minimum risk that must be incurred.

The lead time necessary in making the final commitment should be as short as possible. Part of the problem in the design of an over-all control system, therefore, is taking any possible steps to shorten the lead time. Another part of the design of the control system is providing for advance planning over longer lead times, so that the peaks and valleys can be smoothed out. The final commitments should be minor modifications of the longer-range plan.

One way of solving the forecast problem is getting data about the process that contain no noise: then an accurate forecast is simple to produce. Another way is shortening the lead time. If you don't have to plan in advance, it doesn't matter how you forecast. But there is almost always some irreducible minimum of noise and some minimum lead time.

Let's look at a few specific examples: Handicaps for sports car rallies are based on a simple forecast of the contestant's performance. The lead time is trivial. It is necessary only to forecast what the expected performance is at the next rally. The lead time is simply one more observation.

Next let's take a very simple problem of aiming at a moving target. Figure 14.1 shows the target now at point T, the observer at point O and the estimated impact point I. We shall suppose that the range is short enough that we can expect the shot to travel at a constant speed V_m during the time the target continues at constant velocity V_t. The aiming angle θ is given simply by the law of sines

$$\sin \theta = \frac{V_t}{V_m} \sin \psi$$

where ψ is the target angle, between the target's path and the line of sight from the observer. Again, it is a simple matter of trigonometry to find the target angle, since

$$\cos \psi = \frac{1}{V_t} \frac{dR}{dt}$$

It can be determined from the target's velocity, and the rate at which the range is decreasing.

The target will not always continue to move at constant velocity, of course. If the range is great, the shot may not travel at constant velocity

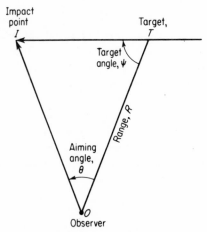

Fig. 14.1 Aiming at a moving target.

either. Then the problem becomes more complicated and is one reason for developing guided missiles. The general plan is made when the missile is launched in a given direction. The plan is continually modified, however, by changing the course of the missile in flight. The effect of the errors in forecasting target motion over very long times is minimized.

Now let's consider the problems of corporate planning for a manufacturing enterprise. The amount of work to be done depends on incoming orders, whereas the income depends on shipments of finished products. If the demand is seasonal, the forecasts should always extend at least one full cycle into the future. It may be necessary to build up some inventory in the slack season to compensate for lack of capacity to manufacture to demand during the peak season. The number of production workers can be changed by hiring or laying off, but such changes cost money and take time. A long-range plan will build up about the right amount of inventory, with about the right size of the labor force.

The actual production rates should be reviewed periodically, once a month, or even once a week. The most recent revision of a short-range forecast can be used to decide whether to modify the long-range plan. It may be possible to use a short work week, or overtime, to compensate for the local variations in demand. If the basic plan is sound, the variation should be small and within the compass of such changes. But if the long-range plan is lacking, it may be impossible to respond to fluctuations in demand or to the seasonal rise and fall.

In the same way, the treasurer can make a long-range basic plan for financing, in the light of an annual forecast of income and expense. The actual borrowings and repayments would be based on much shorter-range forecasts, that are presumably more accurate representations of the current conditions.

Finally, let me give a short sermon on the manufacturing lead times that need to be considered in an inventory control system. The basic plan for controlling the stock of any item in inventory should be based on a forecast that extends through the next seasonal peak, if any, or over a long enough period of time to recognize growth in demand. (See Chapter 18 for a discussion of the expected remaining life of an item.)

The final commitment as to whether to order more stock now depends on the manufacturing lead time. The risk is measured by the amount of safety stock required to assure some level of routine service, as an alternative to substitution, expediting, or other premium-cost methods of satisfying the customer. If the lead time is long, the safety stock will be high.

The lead time here starts when an order to replenish stock is released and ends with the first receipt of material against that order. Let's look at some of the events that occur and contribute to the total elapsed lead time. We'll start when the final posting to the inventory record is made. Later transactions cannot affect the procurement decision made now: they will affect the next procurement decision. It takes some time for the information to flow to the point where the forecasts are computed. The summary of demand is to be the data from which the forecast will be revised. Then there is a time to accumulate enough work to make it worthwhile to process the files and to revise the forecasts. Then there is a lapse of time while the orders are reviewed and finally released.

In some companies, all this takes only a few hours; in others, it takes literally months. Perhaps there is a significant opportunity for improvement in the elimination of unnecessary waiting time, or even unnecessary steps in the process.

Then there are the external factors that influence the length of the lead time. Some managers have been startled to find what a small fraction of the total elapsed time is consumed by something actually happening to the order. If you have not done so, you may find it instructive to carry out the following experiment:

Count the time that it takes an order to get from your stock control section to the mail room—the time when the order is actually moving through space, not the time that it is sitting waiting for someone to pick it up. Then count the time in the mail, from the postmark to the receiving stamp in the vendor's office. Next, how long does it take for the piece of paper to get from the mail room to the shop—again excluding the time waiting for some action.

In the shop, add the set-up hours allowed on each operation, and the number of process hours for the quantity ordered. Count the time when material is actually moving from one point to another. Continue this process through packing and shipping, and the transit time in a moving truck from the plant to your warehouse.

At the end of such an accounting you may have accumulated a total *active* time of four days, five hours, and twenty-seven minutes, or call it one work week. Why does it take eight months for material to arrive, counting total elapsed calendar time from the date the order was released? Of course, some slack time must be allowed in the system, for the various queues in which the order waits. If you find that the total elapsed time is more than five times the active time, however, there are probably opportunities for improvement in tightening up the scheduling procedures, that will far outweigh any improvements you can make in forecasting over an absurdly long lead time.

Techniques for achieving shorter lead times are outside the scope of this book. The systems designer may feel that they are outside the scope of his assignment, if he has been asked to develop better forecasts.

I suggest that the organization that uses a system with clean data, simple techniques, and short lead times will be a good deal happier than it would have been had all the design effort been concentrated on finding the optimum value of the smoothing constant in a model with nine degrees of freedom, with bad data, and a tremendous lead time.

The lead time that is relevant in forecasting may be sharply defined by external factors, such as manufacturing processes, or cyclic peaks, or it may be a nominal time, such as a year ahead. In some cases, physical factors determine the lead time that elapses between the decision and its effect, but the length of the lead time varies from time to time. Sometimes it may be necessary to forecast the length of the lead time itself by inference from past data. If the lead times do vary substantially, then it is usually worth some appreciable effort to try to find the cause of the variation and eliminate it. If the lead times become less variable, they will also, on the average, become shorter.

Finally, note that the same basic smoothed coefficients can be used to generate forecasts over several different lead times, required for different kinds of plans.

15 Forecasting with Time-Series Models

The systems designer must make two classes of decision in developing the procedures for getting a forecast with a time-series model of the process. The first depends on the nature of the process being observed: whether one wants a forecast of the observation at a specific time in the future, or whether one wants a forecast of the total of all observations through a specific future time, starting with the next observation.

The second class of decision offers a much wider scope for choice. You have very carefully set up the procedures for getting successive observations $x(t)$. You have selected some set of functions of time $\{f_i(t)\}$ so that the process underlying the observations can be satisfactorily represented by some linear combination of these functions

$$\xi(T + \tau) = a_1 f_1(\tau) + a_2 f_2(\tau) + \ldots + a_{nn}(f\tau)$$

The smoothing techniques give a best estimate of the current values of the coefficients that describe recent data $\hat{a}_i(T)$. What description should you use to describe data in the near future? An obvious answer is to plug the current best estimates of the coefficients into the model. Later on in this chapter, we shall consider when it might be appropriate to replace the estimated values by some other value for one or more of the coefficients before evaluating the model as a forecast.

Discrete versus Cumulative Forecasts

First let us be quite clear about the distinction between a forecast evaluated *at* a given point in time and a forecast evaluated *through* a given point in time. Think first of an essentially continuous process, like the position of an aircraft or the price of soy beans. To come within the scope of this book, the continuous process would be observed at discrete intervals, by a scanning radar, or in weekly market reports. There is a position, or a price, at any instant in time, whether one observes it or not. It is usual, for such a process, to want a forecast *at* a particular future time. What will the aircraft position be two minutes from now, if it continues at its present course and speed? What will the price of soy beans be next March?

When the basic process is continuous, the forecast is obtained as the evaluation of a model at a specific point in time. There is, of course, nothing to prevent the evaluation of the model for each of the next several observations, to provide a sequence of forecasts for different lead times.

Now consider the demand for an item kept in inventory. The actual demand occurs in discrete pulses. The data observed as a basis for the forecasting are the cumulative sum of these pulses over some interval of time, like a week, or a month. As soon as the sum is observed, it is set back to zero, to start accumulating the pulses in the next interval of time. Thus the data are not really demand at all, but the average rate of demand per unit time.

In some applications, it is of interest to forecast the demand in a particular future period: a best estimate of what the observed demand will be when we get there. More generally, for production planning and for inventory control systems, one wants a forecast of the total demand during the next lead time: what the cumulative sum would be if it started now and kept on adding demand until the end of the lead time.

The difference between a spot forecast and an accumulative forecast should not be hard to see, and in most cases, it is obvious from the application which is the correct one to use. The accumulative forecast can always be generated as the running sum of spot forecasts for each of the successive future observations.

The two types of problem can be viewed in common. The continuous process, such as target position or commodity price, is the sum of the *changes* during the lead time. That is, one can think of the target's velocity or of the price change as the basic process. Then the future position is the present position plus the sum of the moves in successive sampling intervals, or the future price is the present price times the percentage changes in each sampling interval. (We are consistently dealing only with additive models; if a percentage change in price is relevant to the process, one can use an exponential model. See, however, the comment on polynomial approximations to exponential processes in Chapter 12.)

Polynomials are frequently used to describe the average rate of demand per unit time. Table 15.1 gives the sums of powers of the integers, together with sums of trigonometric functions required for periodic phenomena.

Table 15.1   SUMS OF SINUSOIDS AND OF POWERS OF THE INTEGERS

$$\sum_{k=1}^{N} k = N$$

$$\sum_{k=1}^{N} k = \frac{N(N+1)}{2}$$

$$\sum_{k=1}^{N} k^2 = \frac{N(N+1)(2N+1)}{6}$$

$$\sum_{k=1}^{N} k^3 = (\Sigma k)^2 = \frac{N^2(N+1)^2}{4}$$

$$\sum_{k=1}^{N} k^4 = \frac{N}{30}(6N^4 + 15N^3 + 10N^2 - 1)$$

$$\sum_{k=1}^{N} \sin k\omega = \frac{\sin (N\omega/2) \sin [(N+1)/2]\omega}{\sin \omega/2}$$

$$\sum_{k=1}^{N} \cos k\omega = \frac{\cos (N\omega/2) \sin [(N+1)/2]\omega}{\sin \omega/2} - 1$$

$$\sum_{k=1}^{N} k \sin k\omega = \frac{\sin (N+1)\omega}{4 \sin^2 \omega/2} - \frac{(N+1) \cos [(2N+1)/2]\omega}{2 \sin \omega/2}$$

$$\sum_{k=1}^{N} k \cos k\omega = \frac{(N+1) \sin [(2N+1)/2]\omega}{2 \sin \omega/2} - \frac{1 - \cos (N+1)\omega}{4 \sin^2 \omega/2}$$

Exercise. If the model of the observations is $x_t = a_0 + a_1 t + a_2 t^2 + a_3 t^3$ what combination of the a_i would you use to forecast the accumulative total for the next four observations?

Coefficients in the Forecast Equation

Now let us turn to the intriguing problem of what values to use for the coefficients $\hat{a}_i(T)$ when making either a spot forecast or an accumulative forecast. There are a number of possibilities. If the value of a coefficient $\hat{a}_i(T)$ estimated by the smoothing process at time T will continue to be the value appropriate for future observations, then, of course, that value should be used. If the estimated value is too large, a smaller value should be used;

conversely, if the estimate is too small, a larger value should be used. Perhaps the value is correct now, but it should change with time into the future.

The model that was chosen—that is, the family of functions, such as terms of a polynomial, or the transcendental functions, or empirical functions of time—is supposed to represent local segments of the time series adequately. The accuracy of the fit is usually discounted for observations obtained either very far in the past, or very far in the future.

The whole point of making a forecast, of course, is that one doesn't know what the future observations will be. The estimated values of the coefficients are based on past data alone. They are the best possible values to use, if one were to forecast backward in time. Let us look more closely at some of the reasons why they may not be the best values to use in the future.

Consider a physical process, like tracking the position of an aircraft. There is a maximum acceleration that any given aircraft can attain. Generally, there is very little change in speed at a given altitude. There is a strictly limited rate of climb and a limited (although larger) rate of descent. There is a minimum radius for the tightest turn that an aircraft can make. These physical restrictions are known to the people that are tracking the aircraft, as soon as the type has been identified.

If the aircraft has been maneuvering during the most recent few observations, the apparent (linear and radial) accelerations will be simple functions of the coefficients in the model used to describe the position as a function of time. Because of the noise in the observations, the coefficients will not be an exact representation of the actual path of the aircraft. Therefore it is possible to compute an absurd acceleration for the aircraft, which would lead to an absurd forecast of future positions.

Exercise. Discuss the relative merits of tracking systems that (1) use the computed values of the coefficients in forecasting; (2) compare the apparent accelerations with the maximum possible for the type of aircraft, and limits the accelerations used in the forecast to the maximum; (3) compare the apparent with maximum acceleration and warn the operator when the apparent is above maximum.

DISCOUNTING FORWARD IN TIME. The goodness of fit of the model to past data has been discounted in time in order to allow for a slow drift in the values of the coefficients that best describe the current series of observations. An analogous idea is the discounting of coefficient values in future time. Consider a Taylor series polynomial, where the coefficients represent derivatives of successively higher orders.

$$x_t = a_0 + a_1 t + \frac{a_2 t^2}{2} + \ldots + \frac{a_n t^n}{n!}$$

The higher-order derivatives should generally be zero, or close to it. If the value computed from recent data is not zero, one could reason that the value will soon return to zero. One way of representing this belief is by the use of another discount factor $\gamma < 1$. The forecast equation, derived from the polynomial model, would be

$$\hat{x}(t + \tau) = a_0 \gamma^{o\tau} + a_1 \gamma^\tau \tau + \frac{a_2 \gamma^{2\tau} \tau^2}{2} + \ldots + \frac{a_n \gamma^{n\tau} \tau^n}{n!}$$

The higher-order derivatives are then discounted as exponential functions of the lead time τ. Look back at Fig. 9.1. What time constant seems to be appropriate in describing the exponential decay of the linear and quadratic coefficients in the model that describes the movement of IBM common stock prices?

FORECASTS AS A BASIS FOR MANAGEMENT PREDICTIONS. There is another possibility to consider. Although the aircraft may have been maneuvering in the past, the acceleration must change at some time in the future. Therefore, although the tracking system is a perfectly adequate representation of the past path, the pilot may deliberately change his maneuver. It may be worth considering three forecasts: (1) future position if the present path is continued; (2) future position if the acceleration(s) increase to the maximum possible value; (3) future position if the acceleration(s) decrease to the minimum possible value.

Even in a non-physical situation, such as the demand for a manufactured product, it may be possible to predict the maximum possible change in pattern. Such a prediction could be used either to check the reasonableness of the computations on past data or to investigate the future course of demand under alternative assumptions.

Prediction is definitely an art, based on the skillful subjective weighing of a great many factors. Some of these factors, such as past trends or seasonal patterns in the data, can be measured explicitly and objectively by the methods discussed in this book. Other factors, such as the impact on the market of a new product, price changes, or a new promotional campaign, may be measured quantitatively, in that a numerical value is assigned to the estimate, but true skill and judgment will have a great effect on getting the correct numerical value. In still other cases there will be only a qualitative feeling for the direction that changes in the national economy may take.

In our discussions of the iterative techniques for computing estimates of coefficients in the various models from current data, we have required some estimate of the initial values of these coefficients. For some applications, it will be worthwhile to design a "one-shot" program that will analyze past data to get these starting conditions. For many cases, however, there will be no past data. When a new product is launched, that product has no history. It may be similar to some other products, and that similarity may be helpful in estimating the proper initial coefficient values. But the problem of getting started is basically one of exploiting the best judgment available.

Planning the financial budgets for a company rightly deserves the careful attention of the best managers. They may predict prices, incoming order rates, labor and production costs, raw material availability, and so on. To the extent that changes that will change the historical pattern are anticipated, these predictions must be based on managerial judgment. To the extent that a manager looks at past trends and extrapolates them into the future, however, routine computations can help him do the job more quickly and accurately, by taking more significant factors into account, or detect the subtle beginnings of a change in the historical patterns.

In many companies, it is now the practice to summarize a routine forecast computation for the management, as one of the factors they must consider. There may, for example, be a routine system of forecasting the demand of each of the products manufactured for stock, as part of the inventory control system. The sum of these forecasts is one possible measure of the forecast of total business for those products. Management can look at the total and decide whether there are any extra factors not present in the recent pattern of demand that are likely to change the future pattern.

If there appear to be no significant changes, then the forecasts are adequate for all planning operations. If there is some significant change, management can add the modification to the summary forecast.

It is not uncommon to find that management accepts the forecasts prepared in this way 95 percent of the time. Only very rarely will there be a major new customer account, or an impending strike, or the introduction of a new product line that should affect the demand forecast from the historical data. The fact that management does predict such a departure is a clear signal that the forecasts for some of the individual items should be changed before making final commitments on stock levels, production, and procurement.

A military commander has the same problem, as he watches the track of a target forecast by the fire-control apparatus. Most of the time he will be justified in planning his actions on the assumption that the target will continue as it has up to the present. Occasionally, however, he may predict a change: some maneuver that he anticipates.

In either case, the prediction amounts to a restatement of the best values of the coefficients to describe future action. There are many ways to proceed with this information:

(1) One could use the predicted coefficients in the forecast equation, but continue to compute smoothed estimates from the data as that comes in. The smoothing constant might be increased in order to discount old information more rapidly, so that the system will respond to the change when it actually becomes apparent. In this way, management need not predict what the change will be; it need predict only that there will be a change.

(2) A second course of action, especially when there is much confidence in the prediction, is replacing the stored values of the coefficients so that the estimated coefficients modify the predictions in the light of continuing data.

(3) A third course, all too often found in industrial practice, is ignoring the management prediction, usually because the word doesn't get down to the people who must use the forecasts in making day-to-day decisions.

The use of an objective forecast as one of the factors considered by management has a number of advantages:

Most of the time, no further computation is required, and operational plans can proceed on the basis of the forecast.

It is clear what factors have been taken into account in computing the forecast, so that novel factors can be identified.

The forecast provides a standard of measurement against which to judge the improvement that the subjective prediction affords. To the extent that a manager improves the quality of the estimate, he should be encouraged to make further modifications.

It should require less effort to estimate the change from the normal level caused by some known new factor in the market than to estimate the total level, including the effect of that factor.

Experience has shown that well-designed statistical techniques can, in fact, usually detect the beginning of a change more quickly than management judgment can (see Chapter 18).

Forecasts Derived from Transformed Data

The data which are smoothed to estimate coefficients in a model may not always be the original observations of the process. In Chapter 3, we discussed a number of transformations. One was the installation rate: the fraction of refrigerators that have the optional left-hand doors. Another was the bias in the predictions furnished by major customer accounts. Still another was the standardization of rally scores. Missile tracking data must be transferred to earth-centered coordinates. (Copernicus's contribution to modern astronomy was the transformation of data about the planets to heliocentric coordinates.) In other applications, still other transformations may be useful.

These transformations try to get a sequence of derived data that can be represented by a much simpler model than is required for the original sequence. The fewer the degrees of freedom in the model, the less work there is in smoothing, and the less the amplification of the noise in the observations. Of course, the process of transformation itself introduces extra work and noise amplification. The transformation is justified only when the over-all work, or the over-all amplification, or both are decreased.

The rally scores are something of a special case. The objective of the transformation from points earned to a standard score is making the results on one rally comparable with those on another. The transformation of the obvious data is merely a scale factor to reduce the scores to a common basis. Once the scores have been measured in standard units, a constant model is adequate, and the forecast is merely the currently estimated value of the average. The forecast lead time is one observation: the next rally that the contestant enters.

The optional installation rates, or prediction bias, however, was intended to reduce the problem to one where the sequence of derived observations could be represented by a model with fewer degrees of freedom. Therefore, the inverse transformation must be applied after the smoothing and extrapolation steps in order to obtain a forecast of the real process of interest.

Exercise. Set up a copy of Work Sheet No. 10. Use the data from Table C.3 on the installation rates of refrigerator doors. The installation rates can be represented by a constant model; therefore use single exponential smoothing, with a smoothing constant $\alpha = 0.1$. The initial conditions are the average installation rate for the last seven months of 1957.

The forecasts for each of the next three months are the current smoothed rate multiplied by the production schedule. For inventory planning, it is also necessary to have the current projection of the total requirements in the next three months. These forecasts should be recorded on the line for the month to which they refer rather than the line on which they were computed.

Repeat this exercise. The second time, use a linear model to allow for possible trends in the installation rate. Are the forecasts better or worse? Is the computed value of the linear coefficient (trend) significantly different from zero?

(Work Sheet No. 10 is on page 226.)

Work Sheet No. 10 INSTALLATION RATES

DATA: Refrigerator production and left-hand door option, Table C.3
TRANSFORMATION: Installation rate: Doors per refrigerator
MODEL: Constant
SMOOTHING: Exponential smoothing, $\alpha = 0.1$
FORECAST: Current smoothed rate × future production
INITIAL CONDITIONS: Average last seven months 1957

$$= \frac{2839}{7400} = 0.384$$

Date	Production	Doors	Rate	Smoothed Rate	Forecasts			Three Months Total
t	$R(t)$	$D(t)$	$x(t)=\dfrac{D(t)}{R(t)}$	$S_t(x)$	$\hat{x}_1(t-1)$	$\hat{x}_2(t-2)$	$\hat{x}_3(t-3)$	
	Initial Conditions			0.384				
Jan., 58	1,200	458	0.382	0.384	461	·	·	·
Feb.	1,500	414	0.276	0.384	576	576	·	·
Mar.	1,500	489	0.326	0.373	560	576	576	1,613
April	1,500	306	0.204	0.368	552	560	576	1,728
May	1,500	654	0.436	0.360	528	552	560	1,680
June	1,500	458	0.305	0.355	540	528	552	1,656
July	1,500	507	0.338	0.353	533	540	528	1,584
Aug.	1,000	362	0.362	0.354	353	355	360	1,440
Sept.	1,000	·	·	·	354	353	355	1,243
Oct.	1,000	·	·	·	·	354	353	1,059
Nov.	750	·	·	·	·	·	266	974
						·	·	·

16 Variances of Coefficients and Forecasts

Throughout the discussion, we have been considering a process $\xi(t) = \tilde{\mathbf{a}}'\mathbf{f}(t)$. For the purposes of this chapter, we assume that we know what the fitting functions $\mathbf{f}(t)$ are; furthermore, we shall not take explicit account of any changes in the true coefficients $\tilde{\mathbf{a}}$. The process is observed at discrete sampling intervals, and the observations $x(t) = \xi(t) + \epsilon(t)$ include noise $\epsilon(t)$. We shall take the mean of the noise to be zero, the variance to be σ_ϵ^2, and stipulate that there is no serial correlation among the noise samples.

The smoothing process estimates values of the coefficients $\hat{\mathbf{a}}(T)$ from the observations $x(0), x(1), \ldots, x(T)$. If there were no noise, and if we use the correct model of the process, for any of the smoothing techniques discussed we shall get the correct estimates of the coefficients. Initial conditions are significant in exponential smoothing and its generalizations, but after a sufficiently long period, the computed values of the coefficients would equal the true values.

When there is noise in the observations, the best we can hope for is that the expected value of each coefficient is equal to the true value $\mathcal{E}(\hat{a}_i) = \tilde{a}_i$. The collection of estimates over time will have a variance caused by the noise. This chapter seeks to investigate that variance and its consequences.

One consequence to be discussed in detail is the effect on the forecast equation

$$\hat{x}(T + \tau) = \tilde{\mathbf{a}}'(T)\mathbf{f}(\tau)$$

If there were no noise and the model were correct, then the forecast would be equal to the process $\hat{x}(T + \tau) = \xi(T + \tau)$. The noise in the observations causes the distribution of estimates of the coefficients which in turn causes a distribution of the forecasts. It has been shown elsewhere that the mean of that distribution (under these assumptions) is the process itself. We propose to investigate the variance of the distribution. In the next section, we shall combine the variance of the forecasts with the noise in the future observations in order to get the distribution of forecast errors.

Distribution of Coefficients

Throughout this book we have encountered several techniques for computing the variance of some element in the system. It is sometimes convenient to deal with the average lagged product, which is equal to the autocovariance if the mean of the input is zero. Then the autocovariance for a zero lag is the variance sought.

Another technique, useful for the output of a linear system, is the sum of the squares of the impulse responses (if the inputs are not correlated).

The most powerful attack (which can handle correlated inputs if necessary) is to develop the variance-covariance matrix (Appendix A).

In Appendix A, we consider the general problem of weighted regression. The observations x_t are to be represented by a model $\hat{x}_t = \hat{\mathbf{a}}'\mathbf{f}(t)$. The values of the coefficients $\hat{\mathbf{a}}$ are to be chosen in such a way as to minimize the sum of weighted square residuals

$$S_a = \sum_{t=1}^{T} w^2(x_t - \hat{x}_t)^2$$

It is proved that the expected values of the coefficients are equal to the true values.

In the exponential smoothing processes, the weights assigned have the particularly simple form $w_{T-j}^2 = \beta^j$ where β is the discount factor, slightly less than unity. We have already encountered the F-matrix

$$F = \sum_{j=0}^{\infty} \beta^j \mathbf{f}(-j)\mathbf{f}'(-j)$$

The discussion of the variance of the coefficients requires another similar matrix, with the square of the weights

$$K = \sum_{j=0}^{\infty} \beta^{2j}\mathbf{f}(-j)\mathbf{f}'(-j)$$

The variance-covariance matrix for the coefficients is

$$V\sigma^2 = F^{-1}KF^{-1}\sigma^2$$

The (i, j) element V_{ij} is the covariance between a_i and a_j.

$$\text{cov } \{a_i, a_j\} = V_{ij}\sigma_\epsilon^2$$

where σ_ϵ^2 is the variance of the (uncorrelated) noise in the observations.

For some of the simpler cases, the results can be carried through analytically. It may be instructive to go through the case of a first-order (linear) polynomial model

$$\xi(t) = a_1 + a_2 t$$

for which the fitting functions are

$$\mathbf{f}(t) = \begin{bmatrix} 1 \\ t \end{bmatrix}$$

The F-matrix is

$$F = \sum_{j=0}^{\infty} \beta^j \begin{bmatrix} 1 & -j \\ -j & j^2 \end{bmatrix} = \begin{bmatrix} \dfrac{1}{1-\beta} & \dfrac{-\beta}{(1-\beta)^2} \\ \dfrac{-\beta}{(1-\beta)^2} & \dfrac{\beta(1+\beta)}{(1-\beta)^3} \end{bmatrix}$$

The inverse is

$$F^{-1} = \begin{bmatrix} 1 - \beta^2 & (1-\beta)^2 \\ (1-\beta)^2 & \dfrac{(1-\beta)^3}{\beta} \end{bmatrix}$$

The matrix with squared weights is

$$K = \sum_{j=0}^{\infty} \beta^{2j} \begin{bmatrix} 1 & -j \\ -j & j^2 \end{bmatrix} = \begin{bmatrix} \dfrac{1}{1-\beta^2} & \dfrac{-\beta^2}{(1-\beta^2)^2} \\ \dfrac{-\beta^2}{(1-\beta^2)^2} & \dfrac{\beta^2(1+\beta^2)}{(1-\beta^2)^3} \end{bmatrix}$$

Let us introduce the smoothing constant $\alpha = 1 - \beta$ wherever it is convenient. Then the variance-covariance matrix is

$$V = F^{-1}KF^{-1} = \frac{\alpha}{(1+\beta)^3} \begin{bmatrix} 1 + 4\beta + 5\beta^2 & \alpha(1 + 3\beta) \\ \alpha(1 + 3\beta) & 2\alpha^2 \end{bmatrix}$$

The variances of the coefficients are given by the diagonal terms.

$$\text{var } \{\hat{a}_1\} = \frac{\alpha(1 + 4\beta + 5\beta^2)}{(1+\beta)^3} \sigma_\epsilon^2$$

$$\text{var } \{\hat{a}_2\} = \frac{2\alpha^3}{(1+\beta)^3} \sigma_\epsilon^2$$

These are the same results obtained by another method in Chapter 10.

In addition, we have the fact that

$$\mathrm{cov}\,\{a_1,\,a_2\} = \frac{\alpha^2(1+3\beta)}{(1+\beta)^3}\,\sigma_\epsilon^2$$

The variance-covariance matrix is always symmetrical $V' = V$.

For more elaborate models, the algebra of computing the inverse F^{-1} gets too tedious to be borne. In the process of computing the numerical

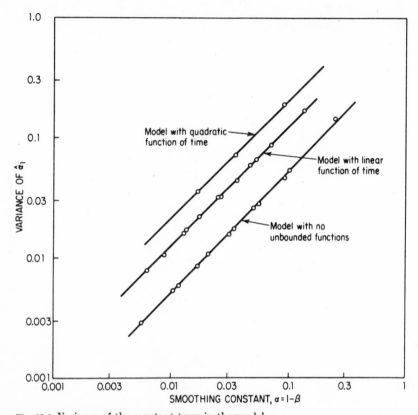

Fig. 16.1 Variance of the constant term in the model.

values on a large electronic computer, however, it is simple to compute the matrix V. Tables 12.1–12.10 list the diagonal elements V_{ii} in part 4 of each table. These are the variances of the coefficients, expressed as a multiple of the variance of the noise σ_ϵ^2.

Although it is not practical to derive the formal expressions for these variances in all models, it is still possible to discover some orderly relationships. Each of the ten models includes a constant term (fitting function $f_1(t) = 1$). Figure 16.1 is a plot of the variance of the coefficient $\hat{a}_1$, for the

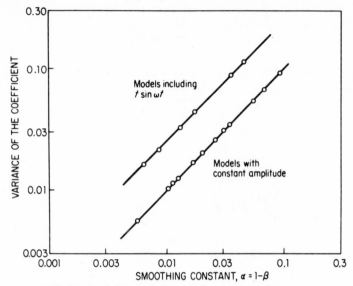

Fig. 16.2 Variance of the coefficient of the sine term in the model.

three values of β tabulated in Chapter 12. It is most revealing to plot the variance factor V_{11} against the complement $\alpha = 1 - \beta$, on log-log scales. It is immediately apparent that the variance in every case is very nearly

proportional to $1 - \beta$ and that there are three classes of models. When the model also includes a quadratic function $f_3(t) = t^2$, the variance of the constant term is approximately 2.1α. When the model includes terms, such

Table 16.1 APPROXIMATE RELATIONSHIPS FOR THE VARIANCE
OF THE COEFFICIENTS ($\alpha = 1 - \beta$ IS SMALL)

Fitting Function $f_i(t)$	Character of Complete Model	Variance Ratio var $\{a_i\}/\sigma_\epsilon^2$
1	(a) No unbounded functions	0.5α
	(b) Linear polynomials	1.25α
	(c) Quadratic polynomials	2.1α
$\sin \omega t$ or $\cos \omega t$	(a) Constant amplitude	α
	(b) Terms in $t \sin \omega t$	2.5α
t	(a) No higher-order polynomials	$0.25\alpha^3$
	(b) Quadratic polynomials	$1.75\alpha^3$
$t \sin \omega t$	All frequencies	$0.5\alpha^3$
t^2	No higher-order polynomials	$0.175\alpha^5$

as $f_2(t) = t$, or $f_5(t) = t \sin \omega t$, then the variance of the term is approximately 1.25α. In Chapter 8, we showed that, for single exponential smoothing, the variance of the coefficient is $\alpha/(2 - \alpha)\sigma_\epsilon^2$, but when α is small, the factor is very nearly 0.5α.

Figure 16.2 shows a similar proportionality for the coefficients of $f_3(t) = \sin \omega t$ (for all frequencies ω) and $f_5(t) = t \sin \omega t$.

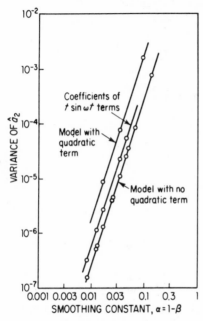

Fig. 16.3 Variance of the coefficient of t in the model.

In Fig. 16.3, the variance of the coefficient of $f_2(t) = t$ is seen to behave like α^3. There are only three points available for the quadratic coefficient $f_3(t) = t^2$, but they are consistent with α^5.

Table 16.1 summarizes the relationships that can be used for small values of α (less than 0.2).

As a check on the theoretical development, we have run two simulations. The input data were the 1000 random numbers in Table D.8. These numbers have a uniform distribution with mean 4.78679×10^4 and variance 8.4787×10^8. Two models were used to represent the data

(1) Quadratic model (Table 12.3) $\beta = 0.96549$

$$\xi(T + \tau) = a_1 + a_2\tau + \tfrac{1}{2}a_3\tau(\tau - 1)$$

(2) Growing sine with harmonic (Table 12.10) $\beta = 0.99361$

$$\xi(T + \tau) = (a_1 + a_2\tau) + (a_3 + a_5\tau) \sin \frac{2\pi\tau}{12} + (a_4 + a_6\tau) \cos \frac{2\pi\tau}{12}$$

$$+ a_7 \sin \frac{4\pi\tau}{12} + a_8 \cos \frac{4\pi\tau}{12}$$

In each case, the initial value of $a_1 = 5.0 \times 10^4$, and all other $a_i = 0$.

The simulation revised all the coefficients in each model according to each of the 1000 random numbers in turn. At the end of the run, the variance of each sequence of coefficient values was computed. Table 16.2 summarizes the computed variances and the values that would have been expected from the factors in part 4 of the corresponding tables in Chapter 12.

For example, in Table 12.3, for a discount factor $\beta = 0.96549$, the variance of a_2 is 0.0^4758 times the variance of the noise in the input. In this simulation, the input is pure noise with variance $\sigma_\epsilon^2 = 8.4787 \times 10^8$. Hence, we should estimate the variance of the coefficient a_2 to be

$$\sigma_{a_2}^2 = 0.758 \times 10^{-4} \times 8.4787 \times 10^8 = 6.427 \times 10^4$$

The actual results of the simulation check reasonably well at 5.577×10^4: about 13 percent less than the factor would predict. The other cases in Table 16.2 show reasonably good agreement.

Table 16.2   A SIMULATION TO VERIFY FACTORS FOR ESTIMATING
THE VARIANCE OF THE COEFFICIENTS

Model	Table	Coefficient	Variances	
			From Simulation	From Factor
Quadratic	12.3	a_1	5.121×10^7	5.967×10^7
		a_2	5.577×10^4	6.427×10^4
		a_3	7.02×10^0	8.479×10^0
Growing sine	12.10	a_1	5.799×10^6	6.774×10^6
		a_2	5.214×10^1	5.587×10^1
		a_3	1.867×10^7	1.361×10^7
		a_4	1.826×10^7	1.354×10^7
		a_5	1.441×10^2	1.119×10^2
		a_6	1.409×10^2	1.119×10^2
		a_7	4.220×10^6	5.443×10^6
		a_8	4.240×10^6	5.443×10^6

Application to Forecasting

As we have seen, the smoothing computations will compute a numerical value for each coefficient in the model chosen to represent the data. If the fitting functions are those that actually describe the underlying process, the expected values of the estimates will be the correct values of the coefficients. If the model includes a term that is not necessary to describe the process, the expected value of the coefficient will be zero. But at any one time, the computed value may not be zero.

There are many processes—especially economic series—where one does not know what terms are required for an adequate model. A Taylor series expansion as a polynomial may be a very adequate representation. The derivatives above the second (involving t^2) can usually be neglected. The other derivatives may change at random by small amounts.

Thus a quadratic polynomial may be a reasonably elaborate model of local segments of the time series. In some intervals, however, the "true" value of the second derivative, or even the first, may be zero. If it is zero, a simpler model will suffice and will not amplify the noise as greatly.

A possible strategy is the following: Fit a quadratic model (Table 12.3) to the data. After each sampling interval compare the values of a_2 and a_3 with their standard derivations caused by the noise. In the case of the simulation summarized in Table 16.2,

$$\sigma_{a_2} = 250$$

$$\sigma_{a_3} = 2.8$$

If the observed values $\hat{a}_2(T) > 250k_2$, and $\hat{a}_3(T) > 2.8 \cdot k_3$, then forecast according to the model

$$\hat{x}(T + \tau) = \hat{a}_1(T) + \hat{a}_2(T)\tau + \tfrac{1}{2}\hat{a}_3(T)\tau(\tau - 1)$$

But if either of the coefficients is less than the threshold, set the coefficient $a_i = 0$ before computing the forecast.

Such a test makes routine the management prediction of coefficients discussed in the previous chapter.

Another application has been used on prices in the stock market. The procedure can be oversimplified as follows: In certain periods of time, the basic forces acting on the price of a stock force an upward trend. The growth cannot continue indefinitely. At some point, the forces will have a net downward resultant on the price. Soon after a high point in the price movement, the first and second derivations a_2 and a_3 should be significantly negative. Soon after a low point, both should be significantly positive. Routine tests of significance can be used to select from all stocks being traded those that are most attractive for consideration today.

In both these applications there is obviously a problem for the rubber stamp of operations research. The variable to be fixed is the safety factor k in the test of a_i versus $k_i\sigma_i^2$. If the factor is large, then many significant effects will be unnoticed. If the factor is small, many trivial effects will be brought to one's attention. The selection of the safety factors is discussed in Section VII.

NOTE: strictly speaking, if one rejects the coefficient for a higher-order term in a polynomial model, one should re-estimate each of the other coefficients, since the fitting functions are not orthogonal. As a practical matter the change made by doing so is insignificant.

Variance of the Forecasts

Once we know the variance-covariance matrix V for the coefficients $\hat{\mathbf{a}}$ in the forecast equation,

$$\hat{x}(T + \tau) = \hat{\mathbf{a}}(T)\mathbf{f}(\tau)$$

$$= \sum_{i=1}^{n} \hat{a}_i(T)f_i(\tau)$$

we can also compute the variance of the forecasts, var $\{\hat{x}\}$. It is shown in Appendix A that

$$\text{var } \{\hat{x}_\tau\} = \sum_{j=1}^{n} \sum_{k=1}^{n} f_j(\tau) \text{ cov } \{a_j, a_k\} f_k(\tau)$$

$$= \mathbf{f}'(\tau) V \mathbf{f}(\tau) \sigma_\epsilon^2$$

In the earlier example of a first-order polynomial model

$$\mathbf{f}(t) = \begin{bmatrix} 1 \\ t \end{bmatrix}$$

we found the variance-covariance matrix

$$V = \frac{\alpha}{(1 + \beta)^3} \begin{bmatrix} 1 + 4\beta + 5\beta^2 & \alpha(1 + 3\beta) \\ \alpha(1 + 3\beta) & 2\alpha^2 \end{bmatrix}$$

When we carry through the multiplication $\mathbf{f}'(\tau) V \mathbf{f}(\tau) \sigma_\epsilon^2$, we get

$$\text{var } \{\hat{x}_\tau\} = \frac{\alpha}{(1 + \beta)^3} [1 + 4\beta + 5\beta^2 + 2\alpha(1 + 3\beta)\tau + 2\alpha^2\tau^2]\sigma_\epsilon^2$$

For the usual range of the smoothing constant, this expression could be approximated by

$$\text{var } \{\hat{x}_\tau\} = \alpha[1.25 + \alpha\tau]\sigma_\epsilon^2$$

Part 5 of the tables of Chapter 12 lists these variance estimates for lead times $\tau = 1, 2, \ldots, 12$. For example, Table 12.2 refers to this same linear model. With a discount factor $\beta = 0.86603$ and a lead time $\tau = 6$, the table says that var $\{\hat{x}_6\} = 0.3153\sigma_\epsilon^2$, which is exactly the value given by the preceding formula.

The five models in Chapter 12 that do not contain any unbounded polynomial fitting functions have very nearly the same variance of the forecasts for all lead times. Note that it is the equivalent discount factor β^n that is relevant for estimating the variance of the forecasts in these cases.

Equivalent Smoothing Constant $\alpha = 1 - \beta^n$	Approximate Variance Ratio for the Forecasts $\text{var}\,\{\hat{x}_\tau\}/\sigma_\epsilon^2$
0.25	0.145
0.10	0.053
0.05	0.026

As a rule of thumb, one could use $\text{var}\,\{\hat{x}_\tau\} = [(1 - \beta^n)/2]\sigma_\epsilon^2$ for any of these models.

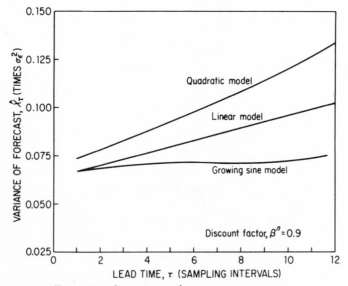

Fig. 16.4 Forecast variance versus time.

When there is a polynomial fitting function, the variance of the forecasts does depend on the lead time. For reasonably small values of the equivalent smoothing constant $\alpha = 1 - \beta^n$, the variance of the forecast with a linear model is linear with the lead time, and with a quadratic model it is quadratic (Fig. 16.4).

We developed the approximate rule

$$\text{var } \{\hat{x}_\tau\} \doteq (1.25\alpha + \alpha^2\tau)\sigma_\epsilon^2$$

for the linear model from the exact form. By inspection of the results in Table 12.3 we can infer a similar approximate model for the variance of forecast with the quadratic model

$$\text{var } \{x_\tau\} \simeq (2\alpha + 3\alpha^2 + 3\alpha^3\tau^2)\sigma_\epsilon^2$$

The simulations run to check the variance of the coefficients give a verification of these factors for the variance of the forecasts made for lead times of $\tau = 1$, 6, and 12 sampling intervals.

There is reasonably good agreement of the trial with the estimates based on the factors from Tables 12.3 and 12.10, which were computed numerically, rather than derived analytically. For example, the model from Table 12.10 was tested using $\beta = 0.99361$. The variance of the forecast for the sixth observation ahead would be estimated as

$$\text{var } \{\hat{x}_6\} = (0.0312) \times 8.4787 \times 10^8 = 2.645 \times 10^7$$

whereas in the actual trial the result was 2.937×10^7. Table 16.3 compares the other results.

Table 16.3   A SIMULATION TO VERIFY FACTORS FOR ESTIMATING
THE VARIANCE OF THE FORECAST

Model	Table	Forecast	Variances From Simulation	From Factor
Quadratic	12.3	$\hat{x}_1$	5.429×10^7	6.317×10^7
		$\hat{x}_6$	7.192×10^7	8.343×10^7
		$\hat{x}_{12}$	9.854×10^7	11.404×10^7
Growing sine	12.10	$\hat{x}_1$	2.833×10^7	2.611×10^7
		$\hat{x}_6$	2.937×10^7	2.645×10^7
		$\hat{x}_{12}$	2.947×10^7	2.696×10^7

Forecast Errors

Although the variance of the forecasts may be of some interest in itself, the principal motivation for the foregoing discussion is the analysis of the forecast errors

$$e_\tau(t) = x(t) - \hat{x}_\tau(t - \tau)$$

There are two sources of variation: the noise added to the true process

$\epsilon(t) = x(t) - \xi(t)$, and the variation in the forecast $\hat{x}_\tau$ resulting from noise samples in the observations before time $T = t - \tau$.

We consider here only the case where all noise samples are serially independent. That is the variance is $\sigma_\epsilon^2 = R_{\epsilon\epsilon}(0)$, and all other autocorrelations are $R_{\epsilon\epsilon}(k) = 0$. (If there is non-zero correlation among noise samples, then the methods discussed in Chapter 21 are more appropriate.)

The variance of the sum of independent random samples is the sum of the variances. Hence, the variance of the forecast error is simply

$$\text{var } \{e_\tau\} = [1 + \mathbf{f}'(\tau) V \mathbf{f}(\tau)]\sigma_\epsilon^2$$

The tables in Chapter 12 give values for the factor $\mathbf{f}'(\tau) V \mathbf{f}(\tau)$ in part 5 of the table. The variance of the forecast error is 1.0 plus that factor, multiplied by the variance of the noise.

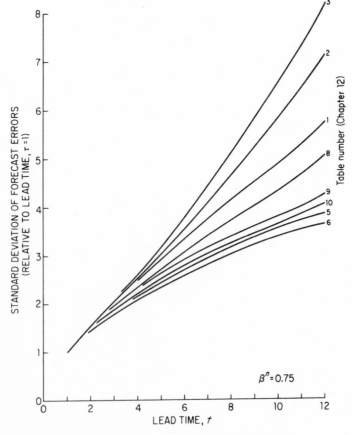

Fig. 16.5a Standard deviation of the forecast error versus lead time.

Let us turn our attention now to the accumulative forecasts

$$\hat{X}_\tau(T) = \sum_{i=1}^{\tau} \hat{x}_i(T)$$

$$= \sum_{i=1}^{\tau} \hat{a}(T)f(i)$$

$$= \hat{a}(T) \sum_{i=1}^{\tau} f(i)$$

Such forecasts are required in many inventory control and production-planning systems. The forecast error that must be considered is the difference between the total forecast and the total of the observations in the next τ sampling intervals.

$$E_\tau(t) = \hat{X}_\tau(t - \tau) - \sum_{i=0}^{\tau-1} x(t - i)$$

$$= \sum_{i=1}^{\tau} [\hat{x}_i(t - \tau) - x(t - \tau + i)]$$

$$E_\tau(t) = \sum_{i=1}^{\tau} e_i(t - \tau + i)$$

The variance of the error in the total forecast accumulated over a lead time of τ sampling intervals is the sum of the variances of the forecast errors for each of the τ discrete forecasts.

The system control decisions, discussed in Section VII, are usually

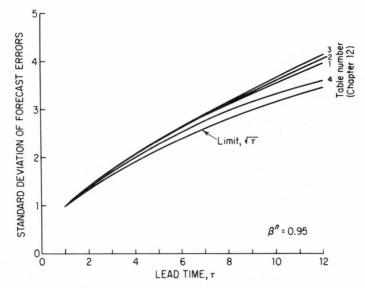

Fig. 16.5b Standard deviation of the forecast error versus lead time.

based on the standard deviation of the forecast error, rather than the variance.

$$\sigma_{E_\tau} = \sqrt{\left(\tau + \left[\sum_{i=1}^{\tau} \mathbf{f}(i)\right]' V \left[\sum_{i=1}^{\tau} \mathbf{f}(i)\right]\right)} \, \sigma_\epsilon$$

Part 6 of the tables in Chapter 12 lists, for lead times $\tau = 1, 2, \ldots, 12$, the ratio $\sigma_{E_\tau}/\sigma_{E_1}$, which is independent of the variance of the noise.

Section V will discuss the estimates of the standard deviation of the forecast error for a lead time of one sampling interval. The factors in part 6 of the tables of Chapter 12 therefore make it possible to estimate the standard deviation of the error in an accumulative forecast that covers any longer lead time.

The factors are plotted against lead time in Fig. 16.5. Figure 16.5(a) is for the case of the lowest equivalent discount factor $\beta^n = 0.75$. In the case of the first-order (linear) polynomial model, the factors could for convenience be taken to be proportional to the lead time

$$\sigma_{E_\tau} \simeq (0.50 + 0.54\tau)\sigma_{E_1}$$

The quadratic model factors grow more rapidly, and those for the other models, with bonded fitting functions, behave more like the square root of the lead time.

Figure 16.5(b) shows that when the discount factor grows, so that the equivalent smoothing constant $\alpha = 1 - \beta^n$ becomes very small, the effect of the variance of the forecasts is minimized, and the accumulation of the noise samples dominates the result. A dashed line shows the limiting case where the factor is equal to $\sqrt{\tau}$.

The simulation with pure random input gives the data to verify some of the factors in part 6 of the tables of Chapter 12. The program also computed the errors in forecasting 1, a total of 4, and a total of 12 sampling intervals into the future. At the end of the run, the variances of these errors were computed.

Since the variance of the noise was 8.479×10^8, we should expect the variance of the forecast errors for one sampling interval to be

$$1.0745 \times 8.479 \times 10^8 = 9.111 \times 10^8 \quad \text{for Table 12.3,} \quad \beta = 0.96549$$

$$1.0308 \times 8.479 \times 10^8 = 8.740 \times 10^8 \quad \text{for Table 12.10,} \, \beta = 0.99361$$

The actual results were 9.166×10^8 and 8.694×10^8, respectively.

The variance of the error in forecasting a total of four sampling intervals, with the quadratic model (Table 12.3) should be

$$(2.2229)^2 \times 9.166 \times 10^8 = 4.529 \times 10^9$$

in comparison with the observed result 4.689×10^9.

The other results are summarized in Table 16.4:

Table 16.4   A SIMULATION TO VERIFY FACTORS FOR ESTIMATING
THE VARIANCE OF FORECAST ERRORS

Model	Table	Discount Factor β	Error	Variances From Simulation	From Factor
Quadratic	12.3	0.96549	E_4	4.689×10^9	4.529×10^9
			E_{12}	2.054×10^{10}	2.274×10^{10}
Growing sine	12.10	0.99361	E_4	3.703×10^9	3.647×10^9
			E_{12}	9.744×10^9	11.094×10^9

Forecasting with Probability Models

A probability model abstracts from a sequence of observations information about the shape of the distribution and suppresses information about the sequential pattern in time. Therefore, the vector of probabilities $\mathbf{p}(t)$ which is the current estimate of the probabilities of the n distinct events is also the estimate of these probabilities for any time in the future. The process is believed to change very slowly, if at all.

Two points should be discussed. One is the problem of interpolation. Given the vector of probabilities that the observation will fall in each of n distinct class intervals on some scale, how does one find the number that should be exceeded P percent of the time, where P has a predetermined value? The other question has to do with the lead time. An accumulative function, such as the demand on an inventory, may be sampled regularly, say, once a quarter. The lead time is some multiple of the sampling interval, such as a year. How can one estimate the Pth percentile in the distribution of the total demand during the lead time?

Interpolation

Let's take up the interpolation question first. The sequence of observations can be represented by $x(t)$ where x is measured on some numerical scale, $X_0 \leqslant x \leqslant X_n$ where X_0 and X_n are the minimum and maximum possible values that the observation can reasonably take. (There will obviously be occasional exceptions. When an observation does not fall in the range estimated in advance to be reasonable someone should be roused to investigate the reasons thoroughly before going on with the routine computations.)

The Pth *percentile* is a number x_P such that P percent of the time $X_0 \leqslant x(t) \leqslant x_P$, and for $100 - P$ percent of the time $x_P < x(t) \leqslant X_n$. There is no reason to suppose that for a given value of P x_P coincides with any one of the class limits X_k. We have a current estimate of the probabilities that the observation will fall in any one of the n distinct classes, $\hat{p}_k(t)$, $k = 1, 2, \ldots, n$. Therefore, we also know the cumulative probability that the observation will fall to the left of any of the class limits

$$Pr\{x \leqslant X_k\} = P_k = \sum_{i=1}^{k} p_i$$

Obviously $P_0 = 0$ and $P_n = 1.0$.

It is fair to assume that when you set up the process of estimating the probabilities in a probability model, you have some estimate of where the Pth percentile point will fall, for any value or values of P in which you will be interested. There will be a number of class limits above and below this estimated point. (If you knew in advance exactly where the point was going to fall, you wouldn't need a forecast.) It is important that the Pth percentile point does not fall in the top class interval. If P is very large, so that you are interested in the largest possible observation, or the next to the largest, then it is better to use the concept of ranked samples, discussed in the next chapter.

The collection of mutually exclusive and collectively exhaustive events that is the probability model should be so arranged that there are many events near the estimated point of interest. One event can easily be used to account for the 75 percent to 90 percent of the observations among which there is no interest in distinguishing.

We're given a value P of the percentile of interest. For consistency with the probabilities, let's assume that it's expressed as a fraction, rather than as a percentage. Then we can leave out the bothersome factor of 100. If $P = P_k$ for some class limit k, then there is no problem. Let us therefore take the case where

$$\sum_{i=1}^{k-1} p_i(t) = \hat{P}_{k-1}(t) < P < \hat{P}_k(t) = \sum_{i=1}^{k} p_i(t)$$

The cumulative probability $\hat{P}_{k-1}(t)$ at one class limit X_{k-1} is less than the desired probability, which in turn is less than the cumulative probability $\hat{P}_k(t)$ and the next class limit X_k. We include the hat to denote estimate of the value, and the time index (t) to show that we are dealing with the current estimate.

The simplest estimate of the desired percentile point is obtained by linear interpolation:

$$\hat{x}_p(t) = \frac{(\hat{P}_k(t) - P)X_{k-1} + (P - \hat{P}_{k-1}(t))X_k}{\hat{P}_k(t) - \hat{P}_{k-1}(t)}$$

For example, the initial conditions of Work Sheet No. 9, with the individual demand transaction data from Table C.2 could be summarized in a table like the following:

k	Class Limit X_k	Probability $\hat{p}_k(0)$	Cumulative Probability $\hat{P}_k(0)$
0	0		0.0000
		0.9091	
1	150		0.9091
		0.0114	
2	200		0.9205
		0.0000	
3	225		0.9205
		0.0568	
4	250		0.9773
		0.0227	
5	infinity (400)		1.0000

If one wanted to estimate the ninety-fourth-percentile point $(P = 0.94)$, the calculation for linear interpolation would be

$$x_{0.94} = \frac{(0.9773 - 0.94)(225) + (0.94 - 0.9205)(250)}{(0.9773 - 0.9205)} = \frac{13.2675}{0.0568} = 233.6$$

If the class limits are rather closely spaced in the region of interest (so that P_k is not very different from P_{k-1}), then linear interpolation should be sufficient. It is possible to "fit" higher-order polynomials to a larger number of points surrounding the point of interest.*

Exercise. Extend the example in Work Sheet No. 9 to estimate the ninety-fourth-percentile point after every tenth transaction.

Near the tail of a distribution, one might expect that, even for empirical distribution functions, the cumulative probability behaves like

---

* See, for example, W. E. Milne, *Numerical Calculus* (Princeton, N.J.: Princeton University Press, 1949).

$$P(x) = 1 - \gamma^x \quad \text{or} \quad P(x) = 1 - \delta^{x^2}$$

where γ or δ is a number less than one. Such a function can be fitted to the current estimates of the cumulative probabilities at each of the class limits. The process can be illustrated by the previous example.

k	Class Limit x_k	Cumulative Probability $P_k(0)$	$\log(1 - P)$	$\dfrac{\log(1 - P)}{x}$
0	0	0.0000	0	
1	150	0.9091	−1.0414	−0.00694
2	200	0.9205	−1.0996	−0.00550
3	225	0.9205	−1.0996	−0.00489
4	250	0.9773	−1.6440	−0.00658
5	400	1.0000	−∞	

If $P(x) = 1 - \gamma^x$, then $\log \gamma = [\log(1 - P)/x]$. The average value of this ratio, for the three upper class limits, is $\log \gamma = -0.00598$. Hence the ninety-fourth-percentile point would be estimated as

$$x_{0.94} = \frac{\log(1 - 0.94)}{-0.00598} = \frac{-1.22185}{-0.00598} = 204.3$$

Accumulating over a Lead Time

Finally, let us turn to the problem of forecasting the total value of the observations over a lead time that is longer than the sampling intervals at which the data are observed. This might occur in an inventory control application, where the observed data are the weekly total quantities demanded from the inventory, and the replenishment lead time is five weeks.

The mean demand in a period of five weeks will be five times the mean demand in one week. If the demand shows no serial correlation from week to week, then the variance of the demand in a period of five weeks will be five times the variance of the demand in one week. Finally, the shape of the distribution for the total in five weeks will be very nearly described by a normal distribution, regardless of the shape of the distribution for the demand in one week.

Since the only information required is the mean and variance of demand—not the shape of the distribution for a week—one is thrown back on the time-series models. The mean demand can be estimated by a moving average or by single exponential smoothing. One way of defining the variance is the mean square minus the square of the mean.

$$\sigma_x^2 = \overline{x^2} - \overline{x}^2$$

The mean square $\overline{x^2}$ can be estimated by a moving average or single exponential smoothing of the square of the observations.

If there is a valid reason for suspecting that the shape of the distribution of demand during the lead time is significantly different from normal, then the observations should be taken once per lead time, rather than once a week. (See Chapter 18.) Then a probability model can be set up directly for these data.

The following exercise may serve to illustrate just how fast the central limit theorem acts. If x is a random sample from any distribution that has a mean m and a finite variance σ^2, then the sums of n such random samples are (in the limit for large n) normally distributed with mean nm and variance $n\sigma^2$. That is, for large enough values of n, the probability that a sum will lie between any two values can be calculated accurately by the normal distribution. Let us show by example that *large enough* can mean $n = 5$.

Consider a random variable x that is uniformly distributed between zero and one. The frequency function is

$$f(x) = 1 \quad 0 \leqslant x \leqslant 1$$
$$0 \quad \text{elsewhere}$$

Now let y_N be the sum of N such random samples. The frequency function that describes the distribution of these sums is

$$f_N(y) = \frac{1}{(N-1)!}\left[y^{N-1} - \binom{N}{1}(y-1)^{N-1} + \binom{N}{2}(y-2)^{N-1} - \ldots \right]$$

where $0 < y < N$, and the summation is continued as long as the argument $(y - k)$ is positive. The mean of this distribution is

$$\bar{y} = \frac{N}{2}$$

and the variance is

$$\sigma_y^2 = \frac{N}{12}$$

Now consider the Pth percentile points in this distribution. We can express the point y_p in terms of the mean and standard deviation as

$$y_p = \bar{y} + k_p\sigma_y$$
$$= \frac{N}{2} + k_p\sqrt{\frac{N}{12}}$$

Table 17.1 gives the values of $k_p(n)$ for $P = 0.99, 0.95, 0.90,$ and $0.80,$

and for $N = 1, 2, 3, 4, 5$, and infinity. The case of $N = \infty$ is exactly the normal distribution.

The rapidity of convergence to the normal distribution is illustrated

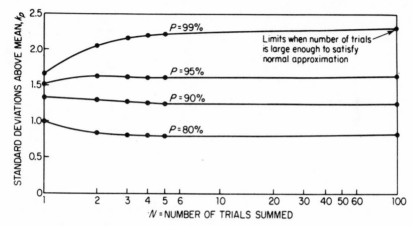

Fig. 17.1 Locus of the pth percentile points.

dramatically by Fig. 17.1, which plots the locus of the Pth percentiles as a function of the number of independent uniform samples summed.

Table 17.1 APPROXIMATIONS TO THE NORMAL DISTRIBUTION*

	1	2	3	4	5	Normal Curve
N = number of trials summed	1	2	3	4	5	
σ_y = standard deviation	0.2887	0.4082	0.5000	0.5774	0.6445	

Upper tail probability $(1 - P)$	k_p standard deviations above mean					
1%	1.70	2.10	2.22	2.25	2.27	2.33
5	1.56	1.67	1.66	1.65	1.65	1.645
10	1.38	1.35	1.31	1.30	1.29	1.28
20	1.04	0.90	0.86	0.85	0.84	0.84

* These calculations were carried out by Mr. Gordon Crook.

Special Direct Forecasts

This book is organized into a chain of steps that is intended to help the systems designer to think carefully through each step in the design of a forecast system, which is to be embedded in some sort of control system. From time to time, however, he may encounter special situations which do not fit the general mold. By this point, I hope the reader has firmly in mind, almost to the point of a conditioned reflex, the sequence: data, model, smoothing, forecast. The sequence should organize and stimulate creative systems design effort.

The sequence of steps is not an ironclad rule, however. This chapter is intended to break the flow and show that there are other approaches to special problems. We shall consider three topics that have been developed for inventory control or production-planning applications. Some readers, who have analogous problems, may find the suggestions of direct benefit. I hope that the suggestions will encourage other readers to think for themselves. If you're having trouble in solving a given problem by conventional methods, perhaps it is worthwhile to restate the problem. Some restatement may have a simple and obvious solution.

These three topics are restatements of the forecasting problem. First we shall look at the problem of estimating the maximum demand-during-a-lead-time, as a basis for setting the reorder levels in an inventory control system. The second topic deals with a way of periodically revising the reorder levels, without requiring any posting of the demand information. Finally, we shall deal with the problem of the final buy, or an all-time supply: how much material will last from now on?

Maximum Demand-during-a-Lead-Time

One reason for forecasting demand in an inventory control system is furnishing the basis for deciding whether it is now time to order more material to replenish the stock of some item. The problem may arise in a retail store or a warehouse, which will order the replenishment from a factory. It may arise in the factory, in deciding whether to make more of a stock part. The purchasing department faces the problem of ordering more raw materials from another source.

There are many ways of setting up a routine control system that will flag any item when it is time to order replenishment of the stock.* A formalization of the "two-bin" system is one rule that is frequently used and will serve our purpose here. We shall call the stock on hand, plus any stock already ordered but not yet received, the *available stock*. At each transaction, the stock on hand is adjusted from the previous balance by adding any receipts and subtracting any disbursements. The available stock figure is similarly revised by adding the quantities ordered for replenishment and subtracting the disbursements from the previous balance.

The *reorder level* is a number posted in the unit stock record. After each posting that affects the available stock, the new balance is compared with the reorder level. If the available stock is greater than the reorder level, no action is required. If the available stock has dropped to a point equal to, or less than, the reorder level, more stock is ordered. The quantity is added to the available stock balance so that it is now larger than the reorder level.

The system works fine, so long as the numerical value of the reorder level is correct. If the reorder level is high, then replenishments will be ordered earlier than necessary, with the result that there consistently is some stock on hand when the new lot arrives. The level could be reduced, with an attendant reduction in inventory investment and no other ill effects.

If the reorder level is too low, the stock will not be ordered soon enough. The stock now on hand will be exhausted before the new lot arrives. The excess demand may be backordered, or the customer may go else-

* J. F. Magee, *Production Planning and Inventory Control* (New York: McGraw-Hill, 1958).

where with his business. It may be possible to expedite delivery of some stock already on order to provide a substitute. In any case, some effort, expense, or lost profit accrues to the organization. If the reorder level were raised, there would be a larger average investment in the inventory, but a decrease in the costs (in a general sense) of not having enough material in stock. (Chapter 25 deals in detail with the problems of finding the best compromise.)

"Too high" a reorder level corresponds to available stock that is greater than the demand during the lead time required to replenish the stock. "Too low" a reorder level corresponds to available stock that is less than the demand during the lead time. Hence, we are led inexorably to the conclusion that the right reorder level is the maximum reasonable demand during a lead time. The word *reasonable* is inserted, since it may be good strategy to run short by a little bit now and again: the cost of being short occasionally is less than the cost of supporting the inventory that would prevent the shortage.

Thus, the reorder level depends on a forecast of what the future demand will be. The lead time covered by the forecast is the time required from the release of an order to the receipt of the material. If the lead time is known, then the general methods that are the major theme of this book can be used to advantage in forecasting the total demand through that period of time.

There are many instances, however, where the lead time itself is a stochastic variable. Think, for example, of a factory that manufactures a variety of products. When the demand rate is high, generally, there are many items to be made, so there is a lot of work in the shop. The queues in front of the work stations get longer, and the legitimate manufacturing cycle is longer. Hence, high demand tends to generate longer lead times.

A converse example is that of a warehouse that stocks many products made by the same factory. If the demand is high, the warehouse will order more items, and it will take less time to accumulate a truckload that can economically be shipped back to the warehouse. When the demand is low, reorders fall off, and it takes more time for the truckload to accumulate. Here, high demand tends to generate shorter lead times.

When you order material from independent vendors, particularly those that have few formal controls in their own production planning, the lead times can vary widely from order to order.

Nevertheless, in any of these situations, the correct reorder level is still the maximum reasonable demand during a lead time. One could forecast the distribution of lead times, using the same methods that are appropriate for forecasting the distribution of demand per unit time. The order point, conceptually, could be determined from the joint probability distribution of lead times and demand. But joint probability distributions are much harder to handle than distributions that involve only one variable. It is not always possible to deal with the distributions as if they were independent (see Chapter 25).

The problem can be restated: the reorder level should be the maximum reasonable demand-during-a-lead-time, where the phrase "demand-during-a-lead-time" is a single variable. If the data in a forecast system are measured in units of demand-during-a-lead-time, and if the model is in the same terms (whether time series or probability model), then the forecasts that result will be estimates of the demand-during-a-lead-time, and we can pick the level that is the maximum reasonable level to use as a reorder level.

It is possible to measure the demand-during-a-lead-time directly, by a simple bookkeeping device. Somewhere in the unit stock record, keep a running total of the demand since the beginning of the year. Many organizations already accumulate sales year-to-date, for sales analysis. At the end of the year, the total figure is automatically the annual sales volume, which is used for several planning functions.

NOTE: Total annual sales is, in effect, a moving average of one observation, where the sum is sampled once a year.

The unit record also contains a space to record information whenever a replenishment order is released: the quantity ordered, date due, price, vendor, and so on. Add one more piece of information to that already recorded for each order when it is released: the total sales year-to-date for the item.

Later on, when material is received, the record is posted to show that the material was actually received, what the quantity was, and so on. At that time, again post the current sales year-to-date. Suppose, for example, that a replenishment order was released on June 12, for 250 pieces. At that time, the sales year-to-date were 688 pieces. Then material is received against that order on August 3, when the sales year-to-date are 875 pieces. During the lead time that it actually took for that order, the actual demand was $875 - 688 = 187$ pieces. The difference between the two cumulative sales figures is automatically the demand-during-a-lead-time, since it is a sum that started when the lead time is defined as starting and ended when the lead time is defined as ending.

If material is delivered in several partial installments, count the end of the lead time when the first shipment is received. Unless there is something radically out of control in the system, the remainder of the material must be received at an average rate that is higher than the rate material is being withdrawn from stock. Therefore, the stock level must be at its lowest point just before the first delivery.

The demand-during-a-lead-time is another transformation of the original data in order to make the information more closely represent the process of real interest. The sampling intervals are irregular: once per receipt of material, rather than once a week, or once a month. The data can be represented with either a time-series model, or by a probability model, as is appropriate. The forecast lead time is one observation—how much will the demand be in the next lead time?

Exercise. Set up a copy of Work Sheet No. 11. Use the transaction data from Table C.2. From the tables of random numbers in Appendix D, construct a sequence of numbers that represent lead times between fifteen and twenty-five days. (Treat the number in the table as a decimal fraction between 0 and 1; multiply each successive number by 10, and add the result to 15. Round off the result to whole days.)

Calculate the demand-during-a-lead-time, starting with each date in turn. NOTE: The months in Table C.2 have exactly twenty (working) days each.

The dates are converted, for convenience, to a cumulative shop date. The cumulative demand year to date on each line is subtracted from the cumulative demand as of the shop date that is equal to the current shop date, plus the lead time. For example, the shop date at the beginning is $t = 1$, and the lead time is 21. Thus, material ordered now would be delivered at $t = 22$. At that time the cumulative demand is 312. The demand-during-a-lead-time is $312 - 88 = 224$.

The transformed data could be represented by a time-series model. (What one would you use?) It could be set up as a probability model. Where would you put the class limits to estimate the level that would be exceeded 7 percent of the time?

Work Sheet No. 11 DEMAND-DURING-A-LEAD-TIME

Calendar Date	Shop Date	Demand Trans- action	Cumu- lative Demand	10 Times Random Number	Lead Time	Demand- during-a- Lead-Time
	t		Year to Date			
Jan. 1, 1956	1	83	88	6	21	224
7	7	25	113	7	22	321
11	11	45	158	7	22	276
14	14	30	180	7	22	296
17	17	75	263	2	17	221
18	18	12	275			
19	19	12	287			
20	20	25	312			
Feb. 3	23	42	354			
6	26	50	404			
9	29	30	434			
14	34	50	484			

If the item is not very expensive, it may be good strategy not to run out at all—the extra inventory required is cheap compared with the penalty of being caught short. Then the reorder level is the maximum demand-during-a-lead-time. The result could be forecast from the average demand-during-a-lead-time and the distribution around that average. Or, one could sample the numbers generated in Work Sheet No. 11, to pick the largest value in each month: January $x(t) = 459$, February, $x(t) = 520$, and so on. If these observations were smoothed by single exponential smoothing, the result would be the average of the maximum demand-during-a-lead-time.

There is an even simpler way that is most appropriate for hand-posted records rather than mechanical stock control systems. The demand-during-a-lead-time is visible, as in Work Sheet No. 11, at any time. Whenever the reorder level should be revised, look at all the values of demand-during-a-lead-time for about the last 10 entries. Pick the largest one. That was the maximum demand-during-a-lead-time. In any situation in which a constant model is warranted, it can be a good estimate of the future maximum demand-during-a-lead-time.

Exercise. Extend Work Sheet No. 11 by one more column. On each line post the largest demand-during-a-lead-time from the most recent 10 lines.

RANKED SAMPLES. The number of past entries that is scanned to pick the largest will determine the probability that the chosen number will be exceeded by the next observation. The most recent N observations $x_1, x_2, \ldots, x_N$ represent a set of N samples from some distribution, which has a distribution function $\theta(x)$. We can relabel the observations so that the subscript refers to size, rather than to the sequence in which they were drawn. Under the new scheme of indices,

$$x_1 > x_2 > \ldots > x_N$$

Therefore, x_k is the kth largest number in the set of N observations. The chance that another observation will exceed x_k is

$$y_k = \int_{x_k}^{\infty} \theta(t) \, dt$$

We shall show that
$$y_k = \frac{k_k}{N + 1}$$

For example, there is one chance in ten that the largest of nine samples will be exceeded on the next draw by a sample from the same distribution.

It may be useful to know something about the distribution of the statistic y, so that we can pick the sample that corresponds to a definite probability or percentile point.

For any distribution function, the probability that a value of y falls in the interval from y to $y + dy$ is exactly dy. The chance that there are $k - 1$ values that are smaller is y^{k-1}, and the chance that the other $N - k$ values are larger is $(1 - y)^{N-k}$. There are $N!/[(k - 1)!(N - k)!]$ different ways of arranging these observations. Hence, the distribution of y is

$$p(y) \, dy = \frac{N!}{(k - 1)!(N - k)!} y^{k-1}(1 - y)^{N-k} \, dy$$

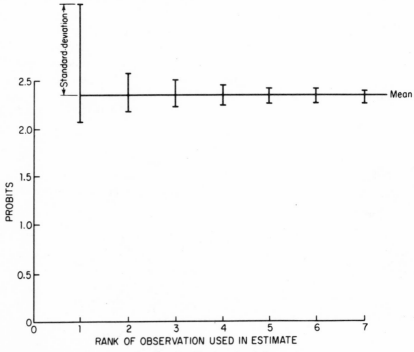

Fig. 18.1 Values of x_k for estimating the 99 percent point.

The expected value of any moment of the distribution is of the form

$$E(y^m) = \int_0^1 y^m p(y) \, dy$$

The integrals can be evaluated quite easily in terms of the beta function, since

$$B(r, q) = \int_0^1 x^{r-1}(1 - x)^{q-1} \, dx = \frac{\Gamma(r)\Gamma(q)}{\Gamma(r + q)} = \frac{(r - 1)!(q - 1)!}{(r + q - 1)!}$$

Therefore, $\quad \mathcal{E}(y^m) = \dfrac{(m + k - 1)(m + k - 2) \ldots (k)}{(m + N)(m + N - 1) \ldots (N + 1)}$

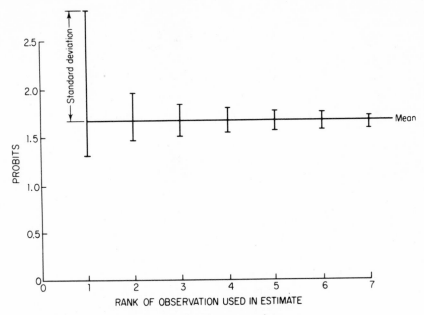

Fig. 18.2 Values of x_k for estimating the 95 percent point.

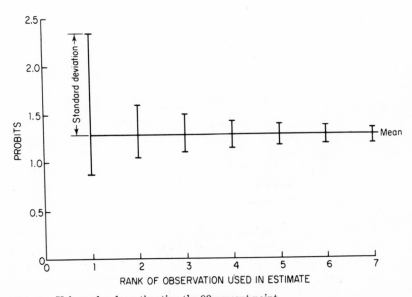

Fig. 18.3 Values of x_k for estimating the 90 percent point.

The mean is

$$\mathcal{E}(y) = \frac{k}{N + 1}$$

and the variance is

$$\sigma_y^2 = \mathcal{E}(y^2) - \mathcal{E}^2(y) = \frac{k(N + 1 - k)}{(N + 1)^2(N + 2)}$$

Note that these results do not make any assumption about the form of the distribution $\theta(x)$. Figures 18.1–18.3 show how the accuracy of estimating the Pth percentage point increased with the number of observations. For example, the 95 percent point in the distribution can be estimated by the largest in a sample of 19, the next-to-largest in a sample of 39, or the seventh largest in a sample of 139. The horizontal line in each figure represents the expected value of the Pth percentile point, in a normal distribution with zero mean and unit variance. The vertical lines represent one standard deviation for the distribution of the estimates, for samples of size $N = 1, 2, \ldots, 7$. Note that there is a large reduction in uncertainty if the estimate is based on the next-to-largest figure in a larger sample, compared with the largest in a smaller sample. In a manually posted record there may not be much extra cost in using a longer historical record.

Exercise. From the first 21 samples in Work Sheet No. 11, what is the chance that demand-during-a-lead-time in the future will exceed 490?

Setting Order Points without Posting Demand

In many inventories, as many as half the total number of items stocked collectively represent less than 5 percent of the total value. Since there is no real money tied up in these items, it isn't worthwhile to have a very sophisticated stock control system for them. A simple reorder level system, with pretabulated standard order quantities, is all that can be justified. If possible, records should be eliminated—the stock that can be lost wouldn't pay for the clerical or mechanical data-processing effort necessary to keep records. It is necessary, of course, to have some way to set the reorder level at approximately the right number. If the stock of one of these insignificant items is exhausted, it represents just as much of a problem as a larger item, and those costs should also be avoided.

There are various modifications, but the following will illustrate how a simple control system can be quite effective. Suppose that we are dealing with miscellaneous minor parts that are used in assembling a number of different products. Whenever anyone on the assembly floor wants more, he draws a reasonable quantity from the stock room. (A stock chaser may actually go and get the parts.) No requisition. No counting. Just take what you want from the stock room.

The stock room clerk has a list of all the items in the stock room, in sequence by storage location. The list gives the present reorder level. Every day, he spends a few minutes touring some section of the stock room. He looks at each bin and estimates whether the number in the bin is definitely larger than the reorder level on the list, or about equal to it. If he thinks that the stock on hand has reached the reorder level, he notes that item on the list and goes to the next location. Many companies do not even require the clerk to count stock at this stage. The comparison is made by an estimate.

The list is returned to the stock control center. There is a deck of punched cards, with one for each item on the list. Someone pulls the card corresponding to each item that was noted as having reached the reorder level. That card becomes the requisition for more stock, since it has pre-punched all the information about source, price, and quantity needed to order, if the item is required. When the cards have been pulled, the re-mainder of the deck is thrown away since none of the rest is to be ordered.

The vendor may even be willing to use that card as his order. In some vertically integrated organizations, the same card can be a picking ticket, shipping ticket, and invoice detail card. Material is now received into stock in response to the order. The only essential piece of paper in the process enters now, the receiving slip—which could still be the same original punched card!

The stock room clerk takes the material to its proper location, counts the stock now in the bin, counts the new stock, and notes both counts on the receiving report. The count of material in the bin is made when the clerk had to be in that location anyhow, to put stock away. It is made when the number of pieces to be counted is at the absolute minimum. It is possible to use the order quantity, the invoice quantity, or the vendor's estimate, if you like, for the quantity received. It is necessary to know that material was received and approximately how much. The receiving slip, with these counts, is returned to the stock control center.

So much for the overt operational details of the procedures. There is lots of slack and room for error. But for these items, the errors will gen-erally cost a great deal less than the measures taken to prevent them.

Now let's look at the internal logic that makes it possible to set a reorder level to print on that list the stock clerk takes with him in his tour. Note that nowhere is any record kept of what people take from the stock room.

The technique is making a guess at a reorder level. Not a forecast, nor a prediction, nor an average. Just a guess. A very high guess, to start with. If the demand for the item were high, a high order point would be justified.

Therefore, the stock would be down to that order point when the list was first taken around the stock room. Therefore, that high order point was correct. If the order point wasn't correct, the stock would not have dropped to the reorder level, since the demand wasn't as high as was assumed in setting the high order point. So we guess again, a little lower this time. This process of repeatedly guessing lower and lower order points will ultimately converge: the stock will drop to the current guess of the reorder level. Therefore, that must have been the right reorder point.

The procedure can be explained this way. Suppose that it is decided to maintain an average safety stock P pieces, which will be enough to protect service against any kind of fluctuation in the rate of demand, or the length of the replenishment lead time. If the current rate of demand were D and the lead time were L units of time, then the reorder level R should satisfy

$$R = DL + P$$

Now call the stock on hand, at the time of the last receipt, I (what was received, plus what was already in the bin), and call the time of that receipt t_1. When the stock reaches the reorder level, at time t_2, we can estimate the demand rate D by

$$D = \frac{I - R}{t_2 - t_1}$$

Substitute this expression for the demand rate in the equation defining the reorder level,

$$R = L\frac{I - R}{t_2 - t_1} + P$$

or

$$R = R(t_2) = \frac{LI + (t_2 - t_1)P}{t_2 - t_1 + L}$$

The reorder level can be viewed as a function of the lead time L, the safety stock P (both of which are known reasonably well), and the time since the last receipt $t_2 - t_1$. Now think of t_2 as "today," and you can calculate the reorder point that is appropriate to today, at any time, with no record of what the demand has been.

As an example, suppose the lead time is $L = 4$ months, and that the protective stock is $P = 7$ pieces. At time $t_1 = 0$, the actual inventory was $I = 45$ pieces. When we substitute these numbers into the equation for the reorder level, we get

$$R(t_2) = \frac{4 \times 45 + 7t_2}{4 + t_2}$$

Furthermore, if the stock has dropped to the reorder level at time t_2, the average rate of demand is

$$D(t_2) = \frac{45 - R}{t_2} = \frac{38}{4 + t_2}$$

For example, at the end of three months since the last receipt, the reorder level would be $R = 29$ pieces, and the apparent demand, if the stock reaches that level, would be $D = 5.3$ pieces per month.

Exercise. Compute the reorder levels that would be published in successive months, and the apparent rate of demand. Plot these results as a function of the time that has elapsed since the last receipt. What happens to the estimates if the item is reordered when the actual stock is 50 percent above the reorder level?

All-Time Supplies

There is a typical pattern to the life cycle of demand for a spare part, used to repair some piece of equipment such as an automobile, an appliance, or a construction machine. When the new model of the equipment is first built, there is a gradual rise in demand for parts. Some of the rise is caused by the larger population of equipment needing the part; some by the increasing probability that the part will have to be replaced. The renewal equation* can be used to estimate the distribution of the quantities required in this phase of the life cycle. Ultimately, the average rate of usage per unit of equipment in the population will reach a steady state, when the effects of the different ages of the population disappear.

EXPONENTIAL DECAY. In the terminal phase, it is characteristic that the population of that particular model declines at an exponential rate. Since we know that the rate of usage per unit of population is constant, we should expect the demand for the parts to decline at a similar exponential rate. Figure 18.4 is taken from *Automobile Facts and Figures*, Automobile Manufacturers Association, 1957. It shows the percentage of automobiles produced from 1927 that survive to an age of up to fourteen years. After age ten years, the population of automobiles decreases by roughly 35 percent a year. Only 65 percent of the cars registered in one year are registered in the following year. The 65 percent rate appears to be constant from age ten on. Similar data have been noted for other repairable equipment. A small sample of ship's repair parts used by the Navy shows a steady decline of 30 percent in annual usage in each succeeding year.

If the demand in one year $x(t)$ can be expressed as a fraction $\lambda x(t - 1)$ of the demand in the previous year, where λ does not depend on time, then the demand in any future year can be expressed by the model

$$\hat{x}(t) = x(0)\lambda^t$$

* William Feller, *An Introduction to Probability Theory and Its Applications* (New York: Wiley, 1950).

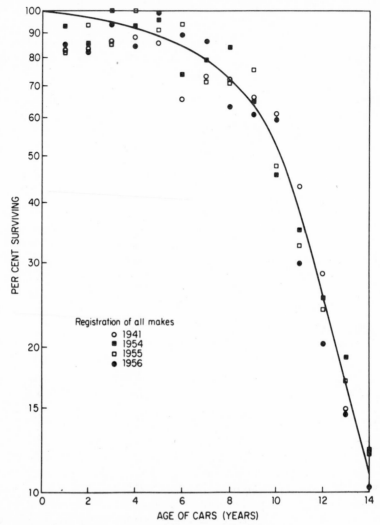

Fig. 18.4 Percentage of total passenger car production surviving.

Therefore, the sum of the demand for the next t years is

$$\hat{X} = \sum_{j=1}^{t} \lambda^t x(0)$$

As the future time becomes very large, the estimate of total remaining demand is

$$\hat{X} = x(0) \frac{\lambda}{1 - \lambda}$$

In the case of spare parts for automobiles, for example, after age ten years

$$\hat{X} = x(0)\,\frac{0.65}{0.35} = 1.86x(0)$$

Therefore, if 250 pieces were sold last year, of a part used on a model that is at least ten years old, 465 pieces should satisfy all demand from now on. If production tools are to be scrapped, the stock could be brought up to a total available quantity of 465 pieces. If there is a large stock, all but 465 pieces could be scrapped.

LINEAR DECLINE. One way of looking at the total remaining requirements is based on an exponential decay in the population as the model. In some applications, it may be appropriate to use a linear model of demand. The demand in any time period can be described by a process

$$\xi_t = a_0 + a_1 t$$

The values of the coefficients can be estimated by any of the smoothing techniques just discussed. If the estimate $\hat{a}_1(t)$ is negative, that is a sure sign that the demand is declining, at least at the moment. The apparent time required for the rate of demand to become zero is

$$\hat{t} = -\frac{\hat{a}_0}{\hat{a}_1}$$

and the total demand in that length of time is

$$X = \hat{t}\hat{a}_0 + \frac{\hat{t}(\hat{t}+1)}{2}\,\hat{a}_1 = -\frac{\hat{a}_0}{2\hat{a}_1}\,(\hat{a}_0 + \hat{a}_1)$$

Suppose, for example, that at some point in time $\hat{a}_0 = 15$, and $\hat{a}_1 = -3.5$. By this formula, the total demand that will occur before the demand rate drops to zero is

$$X = \frac{15}{2 \times 7}\,(15 - 3.5) = 12.3 \text{ pieces}$$

Therefore, no matter what the economical order quantity computation (or the purchasing department) says, it would not seem reasonable to order more than the difference between the current available stock and 13 pieces. (We assume that if the demand picks up again later, more can be ordered at not much extra cost.)

Error Measurement and Analysis

"If it should ever strike you that I am getting a little over-confident in my powers, or giving less pains to a case than it deserves, kindly whisper 'Norbury' in my ear, and I shall be infinitely obliged to you."

The Yellow Face

On the hillside behind the tiny village of Cromdale, in Morayshire, there is a thriving business that has no forecasting problems, even though the production lead time is ten years. They make only one product, straight malt Scotch whiskey, and sell to only one customer, a large blending combine in London. The total sales are exactly equal to the total production, which is exactly equal to the plant capacity, which hasn't changed significantly since 1795.

Even when there are more products and more customers, it is sometimes still possible to make very accurate forecasts. At one time, a company had such a large share of the market for a canned food product that it could always manage by the end of any year to sell precisely what it had forecast at the beginning of that year. If at any time it found that sales were running ahead of forecast, it could ration shipments to grocers. If sales were behind forecast, it could offer a variety of incentives to get grocers to order more.

In both these cases, the total system of planning and selling could adjust the observed sales to the forecast. Some economists feel that the same feedback control operates to create a depression when the government forecasts one. It is beyond the scope of this book to discuss the complete loop from periodic observations of sales, through forecasts, the planning system, production, and marketing, and finally to the ultimate effect on future observations of sales. Just bear in mind that it is sometimes possible that the forecast will be used in a way that makes future events conform to the forecast.

A guided missile may be launched along a course that is based on a forecast of the target's future path. In some cases, it is conceivable that the target may try to alter its path because a missile has been launched against it. The guidance system modifies the path of the missile in response to such intentional evasion or to correct for the errors caused by the noise in the observed data. Such guidance correction is analogous to expediting production in order to fill customer demand when it turns out to be different from the initial plan.

There are many situations, of course, where the future course of the observed process is not causally affected by the forecast, which is based only on past observations. The future observations may be strongly related to past observations, but they won't be affected by the forecast itself. For example, on January 25, 1962, the United States launched a rocket that was supposed to land cameras on the moon. The path was very carefully calculated (forecast), taking into account all the known factors. Although astronomical orbits can be calculated with astonishing accuracy, the rocket missed the moon by some 20,000 miles—about 10 percent of the distance of the moon from the earth. Very small variations in the controllable factors governing the initial path were amplified to produce a substantial miss.

The scientists and engineers had done all they could to make the rocket go where they wanted it. There was no error in forecasting the moon's future position, just instability in the control system. Businessmen want, just as desperately, sales to match forecast. In the business system there is generally accurate control over production and distribution; the uncertain element is the customers' demand pattern.

In either case there is a difference between initial intent and final accomplishment. The difference is the net result of the interaction among a very large number of small causes. Some of the more significant causes can be studied and, when they are understood, eliminated or at least taken into account in forecasting future events. There will always remain some variation that cannot be accounted for exactly. The situation may be made clearer if you think of flipping a coin. It is theoretically impossible to know enough about all the forces that act on the coin during its flight from thumb to table to be able to forecast whether this particular toss will land on edge, fall with heads up, or fall with tails up. Even after the coin has made initial contact with the table surface, one can only state the relative chances for any of the final states of rest.

Thus, you can't expect to forecast future observations of a real system exactly. It is frustrating to try to forecast specific events, since it can't be done. It is possible, however, to forecast the *probability distribution* that describes the relative chances that any one of several possible events will be observed in the future. This section is concerned with estimates of these distributions. There are three types of statement that must be made regarding these distributions. The first statement is the form of the distribution: normal, poisson, lognormal, exponential, gamma, negative binomial, rectangular, and so on and on and on. Chapter 19 discusses the evidence in favor of the normal distribution as a representation of forecast errors.

The second statement is the current estimate of the values of enough parameters to specify the distribution. The poisson and exponential distributions are completely described by the value of one parameter, usually the mean. Values must be given for two parameters to specify most other common distributions. There are distributions that require three or four parameters. When there are two parameters, one is usually the mean and the other the standard deviation, but other related parameters are sometimes used. In Chapter 20, we shall consider that the value of the mean has been estimated by the forecasts discussed in the preceding sections on time-series models and forecasts. We shall discuss the mean absolute deviation as a measure of variation in the two-parameter distributions. It is simpler to compute than the standard deviation.

The third statement that must be made is the serial correlation between successive samples from the distribution. Random samples have no serial correlation. If one observation is known to be above the mean of the distribution, that knowledge conveys no information about whether the next observation will be above the mean, or below it. When there is positive serial correlation, then knowledge that a particular observation was above the mean increases the likelihood that the next observation will also be above the mean. If the serial correlation were negative, successive observations are likely to be on opposite sides of the mean. Techniques for measuring the serial correlation are discussed in Appendix A; the use of serial correlation in forecasting is discussed in Chapter 21.

Three quite different stochastic elements are encountered in problems of forecasting. Any one of them can be described by a particular probability distribution and the correlation between successive samples. The basic element is the *noise* $\epsilon(t)$ which obscures the true process underlying the sequence of observations $x(t) = \xi(t) + \epsilon(t)$. The noise may have any distribution; it will have zero mean, and it is common to analyze problems in which there is no serial correlation. Of course, the problems encountered in real life may not conform to the simplicity of analysis.

The second stochastic element is the *residual*, the difference between a model and the actual observation. The noise in a set of observations $x(0), \ldots, x(T)$ will prevent one from getting the exact values of the true coefficients $\mathbf{a}(T)$; the model fitted to the observations may not be an accurate representation of the true process; and finally the true coefficients in the true process may be changing slowly with time, so that the current process is not the same as the process generating earlier observations. These factors combine to create the residual $x(T - j) - \hat{\mathbf{a}}'(T)\mathbf{f}(-j)$. The mean of the distribution of these residuals will be zero, and the form of the distribution will be similar to the distribution of the noise—unless there is a substantial difference between the true process (which is never known) and the model fitted to the observations. For fixed T, the correlation between successive residuals will be the same as the correlation between successive noise samples. The residuals at a fixed time $t = T - j$ for successive estimates of the coefficients in the model, at time T, $T + 1$, and so on, will have a very definite autocorrelation induced by the particular method of computing the coefficients.

Finally there is the third stochastic element which we shall call *forecast error*, or simply *error*. The error is like a residual in that it is the difference $e(T + t) = x(T + t) - \mathbf{\hat{a}}'(T)\mathbf{f}(t)$ between the actual observation and the model fitted. The distinction is that the forecast is forward in time, so that the observation $x(T + t)$ was not one of the observations used in estimating the coefficients $\mathbf{\hat{a}}(T)$.

The mean of the distribution of forecast errors will be zero only if the model of the underlying process that was correct until now continues to be a correct description throughout the forecast lead time. When the process is a physical one, like the path of a ballistic missile, then the same model is relevant both to past and future observations, and the correct model can be selected according to the physics of the process. There is no corresponding physical understanding for economic series, such as demand on an inventory or the price of a corporate share. The models used in forecasting such series are descriptive rather than structural. Therefore, the appropriate model can change from time to time. If it does change, the average forecast error will not be zero. The fact that the average error is not zero can be used to detect such a change.

The distribution of *forecast errors* will not be the same as the distribution of the *residuals:* the differences between the model and the past observations. We have seen repeatedly that the forecasting process amplifies the noise. That is, there is a distribution of the forecast itself, caused by past noise. Since the forecast is a linear combination of past observations, the distribution of forecasts will tend to be normal. The distribution of forecast errors is the convolution of the noise distribution and the forecast distribution. The noise samples may be random or correlated; the forecasts are definitely correlated.

Note that we compare the distribution of forecast errors with the distribution of noise in the past observations—not the distribution of the observations themselves. The distribution of observations is equal to the distribution of noise only when the model is a constant. If you use any polynomial or trigonometric model, then the noise will be vastly different from the observations. For example, suppose that the observations actually come from an exact sine wave, at regular intervals. That is, $x(t) = A + B \sin \omega(t + t_0)$. If the model used is

$$\xi(t) = a_1 + a_2 \sin \omega t + a_3 \cos \omega t$$

then, after three observations, the model will represent the observations exactly, if the coefficients are estimated as in Chapter 12. There will be no forecast error, because there was no noise. Still, the observations can be described as correlated samples from a particular distribution.

Exercise. What is the form of the distribution of equally spaced observations of a sine wave?

Chapter 20 covers some novel methods that have been used very satisfactorily in forecasting the margin for error required in economic forecasts used in sales and financial budgeting, inventory control and production planning, and raw material purchasing. Chapter 21 summarizes the more rigorous theory of forecasting in stationary time series, when the mean and autocovariance function (or power spectrum) are known.

19 The Normality of Forecast Errors

In this chapter, we deal with forecast errors. The word *error* is used in its mathematical, rather than its moral sense. The forecast error is merely the difference between the forecast and the (later) actual observation. To quote Webster's *New Collegiate Dictionary*, "error . . . suggests inaccuracy where accuracy is impossible."

One can't hope to forecast a specific future observation exactly. It is possible, however, to be quite accurate in estimating the characteristics of the distribution that describes the long-run probability of forecasting within a given range of error. In a way, we want to forecast the forecast errors. To develop this forecast system, in this chapter we shall consider the *data* to be used and the *model* that describes those data. Then in Chapter 20, we shall develop *smoothing techniques* to estimate values of the parameters in the model and finally the *forecast* of the future errors.

Data

First, let's think through alternative methods of observing the forecast error. The data from which one might hope to forecast future forecast errors are quite obviously past observations of forecast errors. The current forecast error can be observed by comparing the current observation of the actual process with any of the forecasts prepared earlier. The problem of deciding which data to use therefore resolves into two components: one, which of the previous forecasts to use; the other, how to make the comparison. Neither of these questions is very esoteric, once it is stated carefully. Nevertheless, it is apparently worthwhile to spend a little effort to plonk through a statement of the alternatives that make the selection obvious: no other author has published any analysis of forecasting the necessary allowance for error.

Continuing with our previous notation, we shall call the current instant of time T, and the current observation of the process $x(T)$. In the past, we may have made several forecasts of what the observation would be at time T. Since the emphasis of the discussions is now changed to analysis of prior forecasts, from the problem of making the forecast, we shall change notation again. The symbol $\hat{x}_\tau(T)$ means a forecast (the hat over the x), made at time T, for a lead time of τ periods. Previously, we used $\hat{x}(T + \tau)$ to mean the same thing.

$$\hat{x}_\tau(T) = \hat{x}(T + \tau) = \mathbf{a}'(T)\mathbf{f}(\tau)$$

A number of forecasts could be compared with the observation $x(t)$: They include $\hat{x}_1(t - 1)$, $\hat{x}_2(t - 2)$, and so on, up to $\hat{x}_\tau(t - \tau)$ for some maximum forecast horizon τ. Note that, in the previous notation, these would all reduce to something of the form $\hat{x}(t - j + j) = \hat{x}(t)$. The subscript is used in this chapter to emphasize how long ago the forecast was made.

If the lead time, from final commitment to the result of the action, is τ periods, then it might seem logical to compare the current observation $x(t)$ with the forecast $\hat{x}_\tau(t - \tau)$. (If the observations are discrete samples of a continuous process, then the current observation would be compared with the forecast at the tth observation—see Chapter 15. If the observations are totals of production or demand during the period between observations, then the actual total production or demand during the lead time τ should be compared with the sum of the forecasts covering the same period.)

This particular comparison has two disadvantages: One, the past τ forecasts must be recorded, which can be something of a problem for each of several thousand items in an inventory, but is quite reasonable for total departmental sales. Second, some characteristic of the forecast error may be changing, and one must then wait a lead time τ to discover the change.

Therefore, one may consider an alternative, the comparison between $x(t)$ and $\hat{x}_1(t - 1)$. Only one forecast need be recorded, and the error is measured in one period, instead of τ. We don't know what the distribution of the noise was, in the past observations. If we did, however, we could use the amplification factors tabulated in Chapter 12 and discussed in Chapter

16 to estimate the distribution of forecast errors for any lead time. The measurement of error for a lead time of one observation is a calibration of the curves (Fig. 16.5), in effect, an estimate of the noise in past observations. Therefore, when we know the noise amplification curves for one lead time, we can use them to estimate the errors for another.

In the case of many thousands of items in an inventory, the formal analytical results are quite satisfactory. For total departmental sales or the orbit of a single satellite, it is worth the extra effort to keep the extra records necessary to measure the error at the end of the lead time directly. A slanted chart is a useful device for recording forecasts and forecast errors for several different lead times. The last three columns of Work Sheet No. 8 are such a slanted chart with forecasts for one, two, and three months in the future.

Exercise. Retrieve each of the forecast Work Sheets from earlier chapters. Record the forecasts that would be made for lead times of one, two, three, . . . , up to six observations in the future in a slanted chart.

It is particularly important to note that the same analysis can be applied to subjective predictions as well as to objective forecasts. If the estimate of future sales is predicted by management, record the predictions in a similar slanted chart, so that they can later be compared with actual sales.

So much for the alternatives of which forecast to compare with the current observation. Now let us consider some of the alternatives for making the comparison. Possibly the simplest comparison is the difference

$$e(t) = x(t) - \hat{x}_1(t - 1)$$

When it becomes desirable to distinguish among several estimates of forecast error, based on different forecasts, we shall include a subscript indicating the lead time:

$$e_j(t) = x(t) - \hat{x}_j(t - j)$$

When the subscript is omitted, the error will be measured from the forecast made as of the previous observation $e(t) = e_1(t)$. In either case, the forecast $\hat{x}$ can be replaced with a subjective prediction. That is, the estimate can be merely someone's opinion, or guesstimate, of what the next observation will be; it is not necessarily restricted to the formal forecasts generated from a model fitted to observed data.

In some cases, the error can be normalized to obtain a relative error

$$y(t) = \frac{x(t) - \hat{x}_1(t - 1)}{\hat{x}_1(t - 1)}$$

The relative error may be particularly useful when the process is growing exponentially. A forecast of the bias in customers' predictions may be expressed as a relative error. Note that special provisions must be taken to guard against the instability caused by minor variations in the forecast $\hat{x}_1(t-1)$ if the average value of the forecast is close to zero. Except for this problem, a relative error may prove to be appropriate in some highly seasonal patterns.

If the original observations were transformed in some way to get a simpler pattern, then it may be appropriate to compare the current observation directly with the forecast that has been transformed back into the original units. Rally scores would be measured in standard (transformed) scores, rather than raw scores, since the degree of difficulty changes so radically from rally to rally. In planning the production of refrigerators, the error in forecasting will dictate the number of doors to be held in safety stock. Comparison of the actual number of doors used with the number forecast allows not only for noise in the measured installation rate, but also for any noise caused by unexpected changes in the production schedule.

Exercise. Retrieve Work Sheet No. 5, on which you estimated the values of the coefficients in a linear model, by exponential smoothing, for the Warmdot Thermostat data in Table C.12. Add two more columns in which to record the forecast one week ahead and the error (see Work Sheet 5a). How would you describe the sequence of errors?

Model

The forecast (or the prediction) for any process is a single number, an estimate of what the future observation of the same process will be: actual gasoline consumption is 19.8 miles per gallon; the target will travel 1462 feet during the time of flight for a rocket; total division sales will be $26.5 million next quarter; Ted Patton will achieve a standard score of -2.1 on the next rally; and so on.

In each case, these estimates are based on either a formal, objective analysis of past data, or an informal, subjective estimate of a number of quantitative and qualitative factors. Since there was noise in the past information there will be errors in the forecasts. Gasoline consumption may be somewhere between 18.5 mph and 21.2 mph, depending on driving conditions, and so on. The target may move 1430 feet or 1520 feet, depending on wind gusts, evasion, inaccurate estimates of present position, and so on. The total division sales may be anything from $23 million to $28 million, depending on competition, promotional success, the economic climate, and so on. Ted Patton may get a standard score of -4.0 or $+0.5$, depending on whether his navigator happens to notice the distinction between "an intersection" and "a crossroads" in the route clues for the next rally, and so on.

Usually then, we want one or two other numbers in addition to the forecast. In Section VII, we shall go into the "rubber stamp" problem of deciding what probability P is appropriate to use in a given application. Then the number that is relevant for taking action is the answer to a question like one of the following: What is the lowest reasonable gasoline mileage, such that there's only one chance in a hundred that I'll run out if I act on the assumption that mileage will be better than that number? What is the reasonable volume of space in which the target will lie, such that there is a 75 percent chance that I'll hit the target if the proximity fuse is set accordingly? What are the reasonable limits on sales, such that there's an 80 percent chance of having enough cash to operate if sales are above the lower limit, and a 93 percent chance of having enough stock and production capacity if the sales are below the upper limit? What is the best reasonable score that Ted Patton could achieve that would give him 5 chances in 55 entries of winning a trophy?

To answer these questions, we want to represent the data on forecast errors by a probability distribution. Three types of information must be supplied about the distribution. First, what is the form of the distribution? We shall show by analysis and simulation that in a very great number of cases, the distribution is approximately normal. Even if the distribution isn't exactly normal, you'll take the correct action if you assume that the distribution is normal.

Second, what are the values of the mean and variance of this distribution? We shall show that if the noise in past data has zero mean and variance σ_ϵ^2 then the mean forecast error will also be zero (so long as the process doesn't change), and the variance can be estimated from the response characteristics of the forecast system. Of course, if the mean noise isn't zero, the mean forecast error won't be zero; the *tracking signal* is developed to detect whether the model does represent the observations. The *mean absolute deviation* is proportional to the standard deviation of any distribution, but is much simpler to compute.

Third, what is the serial correlation among successive samples from the distribution? Discussion of the effects and use of autocorrelation is deferred to Chapter 21.

Hence, the model to which we shall give most attention as a description of forecast errors is a normal distribution with mean zero, and variance proportional to the square of the mean absolute deviation.

THE NORMALITY OF FORECAST ERRORS. In what follows, we shall develop the characteristic function (moment-generating function) for a linear, discrete, time-invariant system. If the input sequence x_t has mean $\bar{x}$ and variance σ_x^2, and there is no serial correlation between successive observations, then the characteristic function can be used to compute the mean and variance of the output sequence y_t. Finally, if the input sequence x_t comes from a normal distribution, the output sequence will also be normally distributed. The following proof is due to Ronald Howard.

Consider any linear, discrete, time-invariant system, such as the various forecasting systems that have been described in this book. Let the impulse response (see Appendix B) of the system be $h(n)$. The input to such a system is x_t, which takes on values only at integral values of time t, but the values of the observations x may take on real value. The output will also have values y_t only at integral values of t. The output is represented by the convolution of the impulse response with the input signal

$$y_t = \sum_{k=0}^{\infty} h(k)x_{t-k}$$

The statistics of the output function y_t are related to the statistics of the input function x_t. In general, an infinite set of joint probability density functions is required to describe the statistics of the input, and hence, of the output. Even if the successive values of the input function were statistically independent, the output function could exhibit high-order correlations. In the present discussion, we shall restrict ourselves to the case of independent input values and consider only the first-order statistics of the output. The correlations will be considered in the next chapter.

Let $P_1(x)$ be the density function of the input amplitude x_t and $P_2(y)$ be the first-order density function of the output y_t. The *characteristic function* of the input amplitude, $F_x(j\omega)$, is the Fourier transform of the density function.

$$F_x(j\omega) = \mathcal{E}(e^{-j\omega x}) = \int_{-\infty}^{\infty} e^{-j\omega x} P_1(x) \, dx$$

The first-order characteristic function of the output is similarly given by

$$F_y(j\omega) = \mathcal{E}(e^{-j\omega y})$$

The output characteristic function can be written as

$$F_y(j\omega) = \mathcal{E}\left\{ \prod_{k=0}^{\infty} \exp - \left[j\omega h(k)x_{t-k} \right] \right\}$$

Since the successive values of x_t are independent, the expected value of the product may be written as the product of the expected values. Therefore

$$F_y(j\omega) = \prod_{k=0}^{\infty} F_x(j\omega h(k))$$

The first-order characteristic function of the output can be obtained by multiplying together the characteristic function of the input with ω replaced by ω times successive values of the impulse response.

The kth moment of y, $\overline{y^k}$ can be expressed in terms of the derivatives of the characteristic function of y at the origin by

$$\overline{y^k} = j^k \left.\frac{\partial^k F_y(j\omega)}{\partial \omega^k}\right|_{\omega=0}$$

The mean of the output function is

$$\bar{y} = \bar{x} \sum_{k=0}^{\infty} h(k)$$

When input values are independent, the average value of the output is the average value of the input multiplied by the sum of the values of the impulse response. The variance is

$$\sigma_y{}^2 = \sigma_x{}^2 \sum_{l=0}^{\infty} h^2(l)$$

Thus, under the same conditions of independent input values, the variance of the output is the variance of the input times the sum of the squares of the values in the impulse response.

Now, let us suppose that x_t is normally distributed with mean m and standard deviation σ. Then

$$F_x(j\omega) = \exp - \left\{ \frac{\omega^2 \sigma^2}{2} + j\omega m \right\}$$

and

$$F_y(j\omega) = \exp - \left\{ \frac{\sigma^2 \omega^2}{2} \sum_{k=0}^{\omega} h^2(k) + j\omega m \sum_{k=0}^{\infty} h(k) \right\}$$

Therefore, by comparison of the characteristic functions we have proved that the output y is normally distributed with mean

$$\bar{y} = m \sum_{k=0}^{\infty} h(k)$$

and variance

$$\sigma_y^2 = \sigma^2 \sum_{k=0}^{\infty} h^2(k)$$

Since the output amplitude y has been shown to be the sum of independent samples from $P_1(x)$ weighted by the values of the impulse response, we should expect from the central limit theorem that, for a very large class of input amplitude distributions $P_1(x)$, the output amplitude y would be approximately normally distributed.

We have represented the input data as the sum of a "true" process and the noise

$$x(t) = \xi(t) + \epsilon(t)$$

(In physical systems, the true value may be supported by some physical reasoning. In economic systems, the true value is merely the value of the descriptive model of the observations.)

The mean of the noise is zero and the forecasting processes are linear, so that the superposition theorem holds. Therefore, the mean of the forecast will be the expected value of the "true" process. For simplicity, therefore, we shall consider the case $\xi(t) \equiv 0$, so that the input signal is the noise $x(t) = \epsilon(t)$. The mean is $\mathcal{E}(x) = 0$, the variance σ^2, and there is no serial correlation. The variance of the *forecasts* will be equal to the variance of the noise multiplied by the sum of the squares of the impulse responses. The variance of the *forecast errors* will be the sum of the variance of the noise and the variance of the forecast, since, for the moment, we stipulate that the successive noise samples have no serial correlation.

SIMULATION. In order to investigate the effect of distributions of data other than normal on the distribution of forecast errors, we set up a simulation. There were three runs. In each run, the data consisted of 100 random samples from one of the following distributions:

(1) Normal, mean 99.19, standard deviation 24.75
(2) Uniform between 56.7 and 143.3; mean 99.12, standard deviation 25.1
(3) Triangular distribution between 64.6 and 170.7, with the mode at 64.6; mean 99.34, standard deviation 25.5

(The data were generated* to have a mean of 100 and standard deviation 25; the values just cited refer to the actual samples picked.) The data were described by a constant model, and the value of the constant was estimated by single exponential smoothing, $\alpha = 0.1$. With more elaborate models, effectively smoothing more past data, the central limit theorem will have even greater validity.

The observation $x(t)$ at each time period was compared with the forecast $\hat{x}_1(t - 1) = S_{t-1}(x)$. The error in the forecast is $e(t) = x(t) - \hat{x}_1(t - 1)$.

We should expect the mean of the forecast to be the mean of the input data and the mean forecast error to be zero. The standard deviation of the forecasts should be

$$\sigma_{\hat{x}} = \sigma_x \sqrt{\alpha/(2 - \alpha)}$$

The standard deviation of the forecast errors should be

$$\sigma_y = \sigma_x \sqrt{2/(2 - \alpha)}$$

The actual results are compared with these theoretical estimates in Tables 19.1 and 19.2. The expected results were borne out by the simulation.

* See Chap. 24.

Table 19.1 MEAN AND STANDARD DEVIATION
OF SIMULATED FORECASTS

Input Distribution	Simulation Forecast		Theoretical Forecast	
	Mean	Standard Deviation	Mean	Standard Deviation
Normal	99.32	6.06	99.19	5.68
Uniform	99.43	5.37	99.12	5.76
Triangular	99.67	5.84	99.34	5.85

Table 19.2 MEAN AND STANDARD DEVIATION
OF SIMULATED FORECAST ERRORS

Input Distribution	Errors in Simulation		Theoretical Errors	
	Mean	Standard Deviation	Mean	Standard Deviation
Normal	+0.06	25.06	0.00	25.39
Uniform	−0.36	25.85	0.00	25.75
Triangular	−0.37	26.28	0.00	26.17

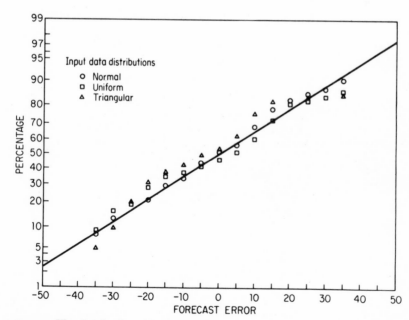

Fig. 19.1 The distribution of forecast errors.

The real objective of the simulation, however, was finding out what sort of distribution function would describe the distribution of forecast errors. When the input data are normally distributed around a constant mean, then the errors will also be normally distributed. But the triangular distribution is not normal. It is highly skewed. Neither is the uniform distribution normal; the fourth moment is too large. Figure 19.1 is a plot, on normal probability scale, of the distributions of forecast errors in the three simulations. It is apparent that one would set the same confidence levels, for a given probability of including the error, for all three input distributions,

The simulation with 1000 random numbers for Table D.8 gives additional information on the distribution of the forecast error, analyzed for the case of forecasting with the quadratic model (Table 12.3), discount factor $\beta = 0.96549$ ($\beta^n = 0.9$).

The cumulative distribution of the errors for one sampling interval are more nearly uniform than normal (Table 19.3), since the noise is uniform even though the forecasts are normal. The contribution to the variance of the forecasts is only 0.0745 times the variance of the noise.

When the errors in forecasting the total of only four samples are examined, however, the distribution (Table 19.4) is extremely close to the normal.

Table 19.3 DISTRIBUTION OF ERRORS IN FORECASTING ONE SAMPLING INTERVAL

[A simulation with 1000 random numbers with a uniform distribution, quadratic model (Table 12.3) $\beta = 0.96549$.]

Error Less Than ($\times 10^4$)	Actual Number of Occurrences	Theoretical Number of Occurrences Normal Distribution	Uniform Distribution
−6	3	23.8	0
−5	36	49.5	23.3
−4	128	93.4	118.7
−3	200	161.1	214.0
−2	300	254.6	309.4
−1	394	370.7	404.7
0	496	500.0	500.0
1	594	629.3	595.3
2	684	745.4	690.7
3	792	839.9	786.0
4	901	906.6	881.3
5	973	950.5	976.7
6	998	976.2	1000.0
7	1000	989.6	1000.0

Table 19.4   DISTRIBUTION OF ERRORS IN FORECASTING TOTAL
OVER FOUR SAMPLING INTERVALS

Error Less Than ($\times 10^4$)	Actual Number of Occurrences	Theoretical Number of Occurrences Normal Distribution	Uniform Distribution
−18	4	4.3	0
−16	10	9.6	0
−14	35	20.6	0
−12	46	39.9	0
−10	76	71.8	78.6
−8	124	120.5	162.5
−6	198	188.6	246.4
−4	266	279.9	330.3
−2	368	384.4	414.1
0	486	498.0	498.0
2	612	611.6	581.9
4	714	716.1	665.7
6	807	807.4	749.6
8	876	875.5	833.5
10	926	924.2	917.4
12	963	956.1	996
14	978	975.4	996
16	990	986.4	996
18	994	991.7	996
20	995	994.3	996

Exercise. Set up a Work Sheet to carry out single exponential smoothing on the transaction data in Table C.2. Compute the forecast errors as the difference between the current transaction and the previous estimate of the average quantity. Are these forecast errors normally distributed? Was the original data normally distributed?

I have adduced some persuasive evidence that the forecast errors will be normally distributed. Before you rely heavily on that model, however, be sure that the facts in your own particular application warrant the use of a normal distribution.

PARAMETERS IN THE MODEL. If the distribution is normal, it is necessary only to specify the values of two parameters, the mean and the variance, and then the probability of any particular event can be obtained from tables (see Table D.6). The values of the mean and the variance can be estimated from the error data in the conventional way. In what follows, we shall discuss two related parameters: the *mean absolute deviation*, and the *tracking signal*. These estimates can be used where data-processing simplicity is of paramount importance.

THE MEAN ABSOLUTE DEVIATION. In analytical problems of deriving the formal expression for some result in a stochastic process, it is most convenient to deal with the variance σ^2 as a measure of the scatter of the data around the mean. Many of the mathematical manipulations are simplest in terms of the variance. For one thing, the variance of the sum of independent events is just the sum of their individual variances. Therefore in decision problems, it is common to deal with the standard deviation (the square root of the variance), which is measured in the same units as the data.

The computation of the standard deviation from actual data is something of an involved process, involving sums of squares and square roots. Even with moderate-sized computers, it is usually well to avoid the requirement for square roots, especially when a large number of them must be obtained. Therefore, the mean absolute deviation is a more meaningful statistic to consider in systems where there are a large number of forecasts to be produced. The mean absolute deviation is proportional to the standard deviation. We shall show that, for four specific distributions, the constant of proportionality is approximately 0.8.

In a general stochastic process y, the data can be described by a probability distribution $p(y)$. If there are only a countable number of values y_i, then the probabilities of each value can be represented by p_i, $i = 1, 2, \ldots$. If the form of the function $p(y)$, or the values p_i, are given, then we require estimates for two parameters, frequently the mean

$$\mu = \int_{-\infty}^{\infty} yp(y) \, dy = \sum_{i=0}^{\infty} y_i p_i$$

and the variance

$$\sigma^2 = \int_{-\infty}^{\infty} (y - \mu)^2 p(y) \, dy = \sum_{i=0}^{\infty} (y_i - \mu)^2 p_i$$

In what follows, we shall be concerned with the mean absolute deviation

$$\Delta = \int_{-\infty}^{\infty} |y - \mu| p(y) \, dy = \sum_{i=0}^{\infty} |y_i - \mu| p_i$$

Let us define a normalized variable by

$$t = \frac{y - \mu}{\sigma}$$

Then the mean absolute deviation is

$$\Delta = \int_{-\infty}^{\infty} |t\sigma| p(t) \, dt$$
$$= \sigma \int_{-\infty}^{\infty} |t| p(t) \, dt$$

Hence, the mean absolute deviation is proportional to the standard deviation, and the ratio may depend on the form of the distribution $p(t)$, but the dependence is slight. The ratios in Table 19.5 are derived for four distributions.

The average squared residual is a minimum when measured from the mean μ, and hence one uses the variance σ^2 to measure dispersion. The average absolute value of the residuals, on the other hand, is a minimum when measured from the median m, and one could use the mean absolute deviation Δ_m as an alternative measure of dispersion. In a symmetrical distribution $\mu = m$, so $\Delta_\mu = \Delta_m$; but in a skewed distribution $\Delta_\mu > \Delta_m$. For example, in the exponential distribution $\Delta_m = 0.693 \lambda$, whereas $\Delta_\mu = 0.736 \lambda$. Since the forecasts estimate the mean rather than the median, Table 19.5 gives Δ_μ rather than Δ_m.

Table 19.5 RATIO OF MEAN ABSOLUTE DEVIATION TO
THE STANDARD DEVIATION

Distribution	Ratio Δ/σ
Normal	$\sqrt{2/\pi} = 0.79788$
Exponential	$2/e = 0.73576$
Uniform	$\sqrt{3}/2 = 0.86603$
Triangular	$16/27\sqrt{2} = 0.83805$

Normal distribution. The normal distribution function is

$$p(y) = \frac{1}{\sqrt{2\pi}\,\sigma} \exp - \{(y - \mu)^2/2\sigma^2\}$$

It is symmetrical, bell-shaped, and extends from $-\infty$ to $+\infty$. It is commonly used to describe the result of the sum of several independent events, and hence frequently applies to noise. Without loss of generality, we can assume $\mu = 0$. Thus the mean absolute deviation is

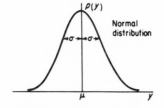

$$\Delta = \frac{2}{\sqrt{2\pi}\,\sigma} \int_0^\infty x e^{-x^2/2\sigma^2}\, dx = \frac{\sqrt{2}}{\sqrt{\pi}}\, \sigma$$

Exponential distribution. The exponential distribution can be written

$$p(y) = \frac{1}{\lambda} e^{-y/\lambda}$$

where $\mu = \sigma = \lambda$. The distribution is skewed, with the mode at $y = 0$. Furthermore, only $y \geqslant 0$ are allowed. The exponential distribution is characteristic of interarrival times. The mean absolute deviation is

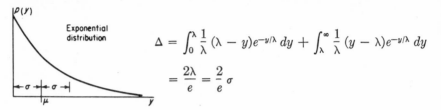

$$\Delta = \int_0^\lambda \frac{1}{\lambda} (\lambda - y)e^{-y/\lambda}\, dy + \int_\lambda^\infty \frac{1}{\lambda} (y - \lambda)e^{-y/\lambda}\, dy$$

$$= \frac{2\lambda}{e} = \frac{2}{e}\, \sigma$$

Uniform distribution. If all values of y, $A \leqslant y \leqslant B$, are equally likely, then

$$p(y) = \begin{cases} \dfrac{1}{B - A} & \text{if } A \leqslant y \leqslant B \\ 0 & \text{elsewhere} \end{cases}$$

and

$$\mu = \frac{B + A}{2}$$

$$\sigma = \frac{B - A}{2\sqrt{3}}$$

This distribution is artificial, but useful as an extreme case in testing whether some result is sensitive to the exact form of the distribution. Without loss of generality, we can let $-A = B = R/2$. Then the mean absolute deviation is

$$\Delta = \frac{2}{R} \int_0^{R/2} y\, dy = \frac{R}{4} = \sigma\sqrt{3}/2$$

Triangular distribution. The triangular distribution is included as an example of a skewed distribution. If the mode is at the lower end of the range A, and the other end of the range is B, then

$$p(y) = \begin{cases} \dfrac{2(B - y)}{(B - A)^2} & \text{if } A \leqslant y \leqslant B \\ 0 & \text{elsewhere} \end{cases}$$

$$\mu = \frac{B + 2A}{3}$$

$$\sigma = \frac{B - A}{3\sqrt{2}}$$

Triangular
distribution

It will simplify the computations to let $A = 0$. Then,

$$\Delta = \frac{2}{B^2} \int_0^{B/3} \left(\frac{B}{3} - y\right)(B - y)\, dy + \frac{2}{B^2} \int_{B/3}^B \left(y - \frac{B}{3}\right)(B - y)\, dy$$

$$= \frac{16B}{81} = \frac{16\sqrt{2}}{27}\, \sigma$$

Why are we interested in the distribution of forecast errors? We want to know the value of y that must be added to the forecast so that the chance of exceeding the sum is P. Let us use $P(z)$ to mean the probability that an observation will be larger than z. Then the problem is to find $y = z - \hat{x}$, where $\hat{x}$ is the current forecast and z is chosen so that, say, $P(z) = 0.93$.

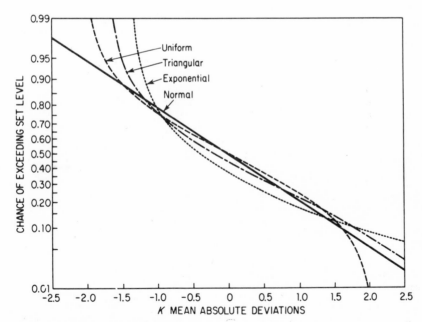

Fig. 19.2 Chances of exceeding a level set K mean absolute deviations above the mean.

(Section VII will deal with the problem of deciding what the particular value of this probability should be.)

It is most convenient to express the allowance for error y as a multiple of the mean absolute deviation

$$y = K \Delta$$

The chance that the observation will exceed the forecast by an amount y is the same as the chance that the forecast error will be larger than $K \Delta$. Table 19.6 gives representative values of the *safety factor* K for the four

Table 19.6 SAFETY FACTORS CORRESPONDING TO A GIVEN PROBABILITY THAT A SAMPLE WILL EXCEED SET LEVEL

Level = Mean + (K) Mean Absolute Deviations

Probability $P_r\{y \geqslant \bar{y} + K \Delta\}$	Normal K	Exponential K	Uniform K	Triangular K
0.00	∞	∞	2.00	3.376
0.01	2.915	4.900	1.96	2.869
0.05	2.062	2.713	1.80	2.243
0.10	1.607	1.771	1.60	1.770
0.15	1.298	1.219	1.40	1.414
0.20	1.055	0.8283	1.20	1.111
0.25	0.8454	0.5250	1.00	0.8439
0.30	0.6572	0.2773	0.80	0.6025
0.40	0.3176	−0.1138	0.40	0.1731
0.50	0.0000	−0.4171	0.00	−0.2045
0.60	−0.3176	−0.6649	−0.40	−0.5463
0.70	−0.6572	−0.8743	−0.80	−0.8606
0.75	−0.8454	−0.9681	−1.00	−1.009
0.80	−1.055	−1.056	−1.20	−1.153
0.85	−1.298	−1.138	−1.40	−1.292
0.90	−1.607	−1.216	−1.60	−1.427
0.95	−2.062	−1.289	−1.80	−1.560
0.99	−2.915	−1.346	−1.96	−1.662
1.00	−∞	−1.359	−2.00	−1.687

distributions we have discussed, for a range of values of the probability P. Figure 19.2 plots the four cumulative distributions on a normal probability scale. There are some differences among these distributions. The real question, of course, is whether the differences are significant in the actual application.

If one can estimate the mean absolute deviation of the forecast errors, it is quite simple to infer the probability that any given multiple of the estimated value will be exceeded. Conversely, if the probability that the level will be exceeded is given, the necessary margin for error can be established as a multiple of the mean absolute deviation.

TRACKING SIGNAL. The mean absolute deviation is a measure of the scatter of the errors around their mean. Theoretically, the average of the errors should be zero. If the future observations do in fact come from the same process as the model used to describe past data, then the average forecast error will be zero.

But there are many reasons why the model fitted to past observations will not be a good description of the future. In economic problems, the model is at best a superficial description of the process. A particular model is chosen because it seems to describe the type of systematic variation that has been observed. The underlying mechanism that generates the data is hardly ever well understood. Therefore, it is to be expected that some unforeseen change will change the pattern of the data. The change may appear as the result of an inadequate model of the process or of changes in the values of the parameters in the right model.

Sometimes the change is deliberate. A sales campaign may change the pattern of demand. If it's your own sales campaign, you can try to predict the effect; but if it's a competitor's campaign, you may not know about it in time for prediction. Sometimes, the change is caused by a change in the environment, such as a shift in the economy of the country that affects the consumer's willingness to buy. In the stock market, the professional investors watch price movement carefully. When a rising price gets too high, they start to sell to take a profit. The word gets around, and several other classes of investors gradually catch up and try to sell their holdings, too. Thus an excess supply is generated, and the prices start to drop, until the professional investors think that it's too low and start to buy again.

Even in a physical process, there are sudden unexpected changes. The equations of motion for a ballistic object are very well known, so that a very good model can be set up. Sometimes, however, wind gusts, or intentional modification of the flight path, can cause a change in the values of the coefficients in the model.

In Chapter 16, we discussed the analysis of significance for the terms in the model to be sure that the model is adequate. Now we shall concentrate on the random changes in the true values of the coefficients. If the changes are small, the adaptive estimates of the coefficients can keep up with the process. There may occasionally be very large changes, to which the smoothing process can't respond adequately.

The *tracking signal* is a measure of whether the sum of the forecast errors is reasonably close to zero. The rationale of this approach is that if the forecast is good, then the average forecast error will be zero. Further, if the average forecast error is zero, then the sum of the errors to date should be zero. Now obviously, unless each of the forecast errors is zero, the sum can't be exactly zero. There may be a positive error that increases the sum. It should be followed shortly by a negative error that decreases the sum. Thus, the sum of the errors will fluctuate around zero.

Now suppose there is a change in the process. As a very simple case, let's say that sales that used to fluctuate around a constant level suddenly start to grow. We observed (Chapter 8) that if we assumed a constant model, the estimate will start to lag consistently behind the growing sales. Thus, the errors will be much more likely to be positive than to be negative, and their sum will consequently grow and become very obviously different from zero.

The question is what departure from zero should be considered large. What is a reasonable fluctuation caused by random noise in the observations, as distinct from a significant departure caused by some systematic element in the observations not adequately represented by the forecast model?

Consider the case where the data can be represented by a constant model, and single exponential smoothing is used to estimate the current value of that constant. The impulse response of a system that produces the sum Y of the forecast errors is simply

$$h_Y(t) = \beta^t$$

We have proved that for any linear, discrete, time-invariant system, the variance of the output is equal to the variance σ_ϵ^2 of the input, multiplied by the sum of the squares of the impulse responses (if the input is random). Therefore, the variance of the sum of the forecast errors is

$$\sigma_Y^2 = \frac{1}{1 - \beta^2} \sigma_\epsilon^2$$

If a linear model were used, with the coefficients estimated by double exponential smoothing

$$\sigma_Y^2 = \left(\frac{2 - 2\alpha^3 + \alpha^4}{4 - \alpha - 4\alpha^2 + 2\alpha^3} \right) \frac{\sigma_\epsilon^2}{1 - \beta^2}$$

and if the coefficients in a quadratic model are estimated by triple smoothing*

$$\sigma_Y^2 = \left(\frac{6 - 4\alpha + 10\alpha^2 - 40\alpha^3 + 55\alpha^4 - 36\alpha^5 + 10\alpha^6}{16 - 7\alpha - 53\alpha^2 + 81\alpha^3 - 45\alpha^4 + 9\alpha^5} \right) \frac{\sigma_\epsilon^2}{1 - \beta^2}$$

It is impractical to carry through the analysis to obtain a formula for the variance of the sum of the errors when the data are described by other than

---

* G. J. Crook carried out the tedious algebra needed to obtain these results.

a low-order polynomial model. The results for first-order (linear) and second-order (quadratic) models above are approximated very closely by

$$\sigma_Y^2 = \frac{1}{1 - \beta^4} \sigma_\epsilon^2 \qquad \text{(linear)}$$

$$= \frac{1}{1 - \beta^6} \sigma_\epsilon^2 \qquad \text{(quadratic)}$$

This suggests the general relationship for a model with n degrees of freedom

$$\sigma_Y^2 = \frac{1}{1 - \beta^{2n}} \sigma_\epsilon^2$$

A number of simulations using the higher-order models of Chapter 12 have borne out this conjecture reasonably well.

Hence, if we knew the variance of σ_ϵ^2, the input, we could compute the variance of the sum of the errors that would be generated by random inputs, and hence establish confidence limits. The actual process used will be to estimate the variance of the noise from the mean absolute deviation of the forecast errors. If the errors are normally distributed, and the noise samples were serially independent, the mean absolute deviation

$$\Delta = \sqrt{2/\pi} \, \sqrt{2/(2 - \alpha)} \, \sigma_\epsilon$$

or

$$\sigma_\epsilon = \Delta \sqrt{\pi/2} \, \sqrt{(2 - \alpha)/2}$$

Therefore the standard deviation σ_Y of the sum of the forecast errors will be proportional to the mean absolute deviation, Δ. Figure 19.3 is a plot of

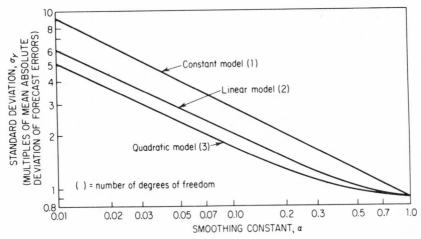

Fig. 19.3 The standard deviation of the sum of forecast errors.

the proportionality, as a function of the smoothing constant, for the three common polynomial models that might be used.

There is about a 5 percent chance that a normally distributed variable will fall outside the interval from $-2\sigma + \bar{x}$ to $\bar{x} + 2\sigma$. Substitution among the equations above yields

$$2\sigma_Y \doteq \frac{2\sigma_\epsilon}{\sqrt{1 - \beta^{2n}}} = \sqrt{\frac{\pi(1 + \beta)}{1 - \beta^{2n}}}\, \Delta$$

For $n = 3$, $\beta = 0.965$

$$2\sigma_Y = \sqrt{\frac{1.965\pi}{0.19}}\, \Delta = 5.7\, \Delta$$

If the sum of the forecast errors exceeds (in either direction) $5.7\, \Delta$, one would have 95 percent confidence that a non-random bias was present in the forecasts. The appropriate reaction to such a signal is discussed in the next chapter.

These confidence limits apply only when the noise is strictly random. Since the impulse response of a system that produces the sum of the forecast errors is $h(t) = \beta^t$ (assuming a constant model of the process), we can write the sum of the errors in terms of the past data as

$$Y(t) = \sum_{k=0}^{\infty} \beta^k x(t - k)$$

For a general lag τ in time, the autocovariance of the sum is

$$R_{YY}(\tau) = Y(t)Y(t + \tau)$$

$$= \sum_{k=0}^{\infty} \sum_{j=0}^{\infty} \beta^{j+k} R_{xx}(\tau - j + k)$$

Hence, the variance of the sum can be expressed in terms of the auto-covariance function of the noise

$$\sigma_Y^2 = R_{YY}(0) = \frac{\sigma_x^2}{1 - \beta^2} + \frac{2}{1 - \beta^2} \sum_{\tau=1}^{\infty} \beta^\tau R_{xx}(\tau)$$

Exercise. Suppose that the data have exponential autocorrelation

$$R_{xx}(\tau) = \sigma_x^2 a^{|\tau|}$$

Compute the standard deviation of the sum of the forecast errors for a smoothing constant $\alpha = 0.1$, as a function of a where $0 < a \leqslant 1$.

20 Forecasting the Allowance for Error

Let us briefly recapitulate the development so far. The problem is to estimate the distribution of forecast errors. The data are a sequence of observations of the forecast errors $e_\tau(t) = x(t) - \hat{x}_\tau(t - \tau)$, the difference between the actual observation and a prior forecast. Usually $\tau = 1$. These data are described by a probability distribution. In many, but not all cases, the distribution is normal. Therefore, we need estimates of two parameters from the data.

The mean of the distribution should be zero. We can use the tracking signal to determine whether it is zero or not, or we can check for significance the computed value of the high-order coefficients in a polynomial model (Chapter 16). Rather than estimate the variance of the distribution, we want to estimate the mean absolute deviation, which is proportional to the standard deviation.

In what follows now, we have the straightforward problem of smoothing, to estimate the current values of these two parameters. First, we'll consider the mean absolute deviation as a strict smoothing problem, estimating the values from the current data by exponential smoothing. Then, as an alternative, we'll discuss the use of information from a whole family of related time series to estimate the mean absolute deviation. The process of estimating the mean absolute deviation and the tracking signal will be illustrated by exercises that extend previous work sheets. Finally, we shall look at the way these two parameters respond to the standard test inputs considered in Chapter 10.

Mean Absolute Deviation

SMOOTHING. In most applications, the mean absolute deviation may change slowly with time, but the changes are slow enough that at any one time the value can be considered to be constant. That is, the absolute values of the forecast errors can be thought of as fluctuating around a constant level. Therefore, one should immediately think of using single exponential smoothing to estimate the value of that constant.

Exercise. Work Sheet 5a on page 300 is an extension of Work Sheet 5. In the first 13 weeks, the standard deviation of the data is 25.8. We can use the same smoothing constant $\alpha = 0.1$. Therefore, an initial estimate of the mean absolute deviation is

$$\Delta(0) = \sqrt{2/\pi} \sqrt{2/(2 - \alpha)} \, \sigma_x = (0.7979)\sqrt{1.053} \, (25.8) = 21.1$$

(We initially estimated the mean of the first 13 weeks to be 196.6. What is the average absolute difference between the actual demands in each of the first 13 weeks and 196.6?) The mean absolute deviation in any period is obtained by single exponential smoothing of the absolute errors.

Although a constant model is usually applicable, it is not necessarily so. A Middle Western manufacturer of batteries for automobiles has found that his sales follow a seasonal pattern, with a peak in demand in late summer and early fall. The pattern of demand then drops off through the winter and spring. The variability of demand increases in the winter. When demand is high, it's quite predictable. When it falls off in the winter, it varies tremendously. Severe unexpected cold snaps, or extra heavy snowfall, which doesn't occur often, can send the demand for batteries up when normally the driving pattern would cause a drop. Therefore in such a case one might want to construct a simple seasonal model of the absolute value of the forecast errors.

INITIAL CONDITIONS. When the estimate of the mean absolute deviation is to be revised recursively by exponential smoothing, it is necessary to have an initial estimate of the value. When there are historical data to be analyzed to provide the initial conditions for the forecasting computations, the same analysis can give the initial conditions for the mean absolute deviation.

Suppose that the data used in the analysis are $x(1), \ldots, x(T)$, and that the initial vector of coefficients is **a**. The residuals $x(T - j) - \mathbf{a}'\mathbf{f}(-j)$ for $j = 0, 1, \ldots, T - 1$ are estimates of the noise in the observations, so that their variance is an estimate of σ_ϵ^2. The variance of the forecasts will be proportional to the variance of the noise (Tables 12.1–12.10 give variance amplification factors in part 5 of the table for each model). The variance of the forecast error will be the sum of the variances of the forecasts and of the noise, and the standard deviation is the square root of the variance. Finally the mean absolute deviation will be very nearly 0.8 times the standard deviation.

Recall the example used in Work Sheet No. 9, with the Warmdot Filter sales data from Table C.14. The initial model (Chapter 12) was

$$\hat{x}(t) = 150 + 50 \sin \frac{2\pi(t - t_0)}{12}$$

where t is measured in months, and $t = t_0$ in September. The residuals $x(t) - \hat{x}(t)$ have variance 643.8. Part 5 of Table 12.4 (for $\beta = 0.96549$) gives the variance of the forecast error as $1.0530 \times 643.8 = 678.0$. The standard deviation of the errors in forecasting one month would be $\sqrt{678} = 26.1$. Therefore, the initial estimate of the mean absolute deviation is

$$\hat{\Delta}(0) = (0.8)(26.1) = 20.8$$

When this computation is carried out for a reasonably large sample of related time series, it may become apparent that there is a general relationship between the initial estimate of the mean absolute deviation $\hat{\Delta}$ and the forecast $\hat{x}$. Such a relationship can be used effectively to establish initial conditions for all related series without having to do the analysis on each one. The relationship is also very helpful as a guide to initial predictions in the case of new series where there are no historical data to be analyzed.

ESTIMATING THE STANDARD DEVIATION FROM THE POPULATION. In an inventory control system, forecasts will be computed for thousands of items that have similar demand patterns. It is possible to derive an estimate of the standard deviation of the forecast errors from the entire population of items. In some applications, such an estimate may be more appropriate than the estimates based solely on the data for one item at a time.

Figure 20.1 shows the apparent relationship between the standard deviation of forecast errors and the forecast rate for several thousand items stocked by a large Middle Western manufacturer of heavy equipment. (The data were plotted from a tabulation in sequence by the forecast rate of demand. The plot was continued far enough from each end of the list to make the pattern quite apparent—there were a great many items in the middle of the list for which it did not appear to be necessary to continue the detailed plotting.)

The standard deviation of the forecast errors for all items is approximately proportional to the 0.75 power of the forecast annual demand. In many other inventory control problems, it has been found that, for a large family of items, the standard deviation of the forecast errors is proportional to some power of the forecast, and that the power is frequently between 0.7 and 0.9 (occasionally higher or lower powers have been noticed).

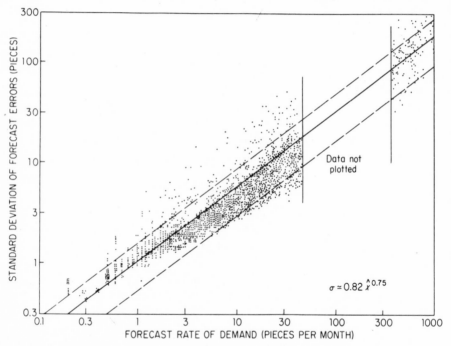

Fig. 20.1 Standard deviation of forecast errors versus forecast rate.

Note that the relationship is between the standard deviation of the forecast errors (for the relevant lead time) and the forecast, not the observations. In a going system, one can occasionally plot the recorded error variance for a sample of items against the corresponding forecasts. When the system is being set up there are no records of the forecast errors, and therefore one must use historical observations. If each time series in the family can be described by a simple polynomial (constant or at most linear in time), then the variance of the observations can be related to the variance of the forecast errors. If the processes involved are more complex, it is necessary to compute the residuals from the models established as initial conditions for further forecasting. In some cases, it may even be worthwhile to set up a simulation of the forecasting system to be applied to historical data.

The family of time series treated in this way should be homogeneous. In some inventories, all items can be treated together. One manufacturer has found consistent relationships among all items in each product line, but different relationships between different lines. Another manufacturer

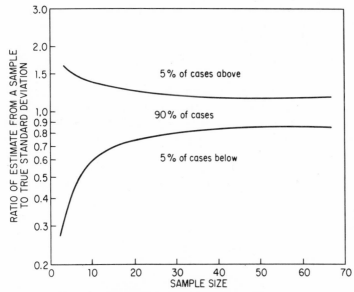

Fig. 20.2 Effect of sample size on the band containing 90 percent of the ratios of the estimated to true standard deviations for normal populations.

had to introduce the average quantity per demand transaction as well as the monthly rate of total demand.

The points plotted will not, of course, lie exactly along a straight line. Some of the scatter will be caused by factors not taken into account in the analysis—perhaps the total population of time series can be separated into more homogeneous populations according to some characteristic. Even in a truly homogeneous population, however, there will be scatter of the points resulting from sampling errors.

The standard deviation is computed from a finite sample of points (Table 8.1 is a guide to the approximate sample size for exponential smoothing.) The estimate computed from a sample will be distributed around the true value. If the true population is exactly normal, then the sample estimates of the variance will be distributed according to a χ^2 distribution. Figure 20.2 shows the 90 percent confidence limits as a function of sample size. These limits are shown only as a guide: even slight departures from normality can have very large effects on the distribution of the variance, which depends on the fourth moment of the distribution.

The best procedure is plotting the actual data in each case and establishing confidence bands on the evidence presented. At each sampling interval, when the forecast for each item is revised with new information, compute a new estimate for the mean absolute deviation, or for the standard deviation of forecast errors. Compare the revised estimate with the band established for all items in the same population. If the computed value lies within the band, use the median relationship for all items. If the computed value lies outside this band, seek to determine the cause and then use the estimate of the distribution of forecast errors that is appropriate.

For example, in the case plotted in Fig. 20.1, if the computed standard deviation of forecast errors for any item falls outside the range from $0.4\hat{x}^{0.75}$ to $1.2\hat{x}^{0.75}$ the average relationship $\sigma = 0.82\hat{x}^{0.75}$ would not be used.

Using the population estimate, where it is possible to do so, has the advantage of being much more stable. In any set of random data there are likely to be sequences when the noise is small, so that the mean absolute deviation will underestimate the allowance that should be made for error. There are other times when the noise is large, and the mean absolute deviation will overestimate the necessary allowance for error. Therefore, I suggest that where it is possible, use the population estimate, particularly for tests of significance (in the tracking signal, the size of extra coefficients in the model, and so on).

The Tracking Signal

The tracking signal computation has two steps. First, as the error is computed with each new observation, the result is added to the previous sum of the forecast errors $Y(t) = Y(t-1) + e(t)$. Note that only the sum to date is preserved, not the historical detail. Then the sum is compared with the current estimate of the spread of forecast errors (either an item estimate of the mean absolute deviation, or the estimate of the standard deviation derived from a consistency observed for a large population of similar items). Since the standard deviation of the sum of the forecast errors is proportional to either of these measures, the proper comparison is the ratio

$$\frac{Y(t)}{\Delta(t)} \quad \text{or} \quad \frac{Y(t)}{\sigma}$$

Some limit $K\,\Delta$ should be set to define the range within which variation in the sum of the forecast errors can reasonably be attributed to random noise in the observations. Suppose the forecasts are obtained from a linear mode, with double exponential smoothing, and a smoothing constant $\alpha = 0.1$. From Fig. 19.5, we see that $\sigma Y = 2\Delta$. Therefore, a limit of $K = \pm 4$ might reasonably be set.

There is approximately 1 chance in 20 that the sum will go outside these limits when the noise really is random. Therefore, it may be wise to provide for the first time the forecasts seem to go out of control: flag the item as a warning, but take no further action. If the forecasts go back into control at the time of the next observation, then the fluctuation was

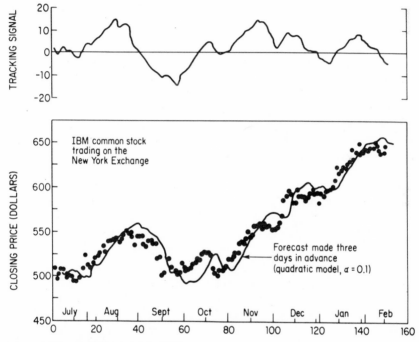

Fig. 20.3 The tracking signal in IBM stock price forecasts.

most probably due to chance. Figure 20.3 shows the tracking signal for the IBM stock prices, discussed previously in Chapter 9.

REACTION TO AN OUT-OF-CONTROL SIGNAL. If the forecast goes out of control on two successive observations, there is a very clear signal that something is wrong. The first step is to set the sum of the forecast errors back to zero. (Even if the process goes back into control itself, the sum will continue to fluctuate around its present level, generating further false alarms. Therefore, set the sum back to zero so that the variation is measured around zero, not its present level.)

Now look for the assignable cause. If you can find the reason for the sudden shift in the pattern of observations, you can reestimate the necessary coefficients for the forecast model—perhaps adding an extra term—and resume the smoothing process with new initial conditions. If you have included an extra term in the model all along, you will automatically have the correct conditions for the new pattern, and the extra terms will now appear to have values significantly different from zero.

In some cases, no amount of effort seems to reveal any assignable cause for the apparent bias in the forecasts. There is always the possibility that chance effects triggered the exception report. The pattern of demand is apparently changing rapidly. Therefore, older information should be discounted. This remark suggests an increase in the value of the smoothing constant.

In the discussion of alternative smoothing techniques (Section III), we stressed the conflicting objectives of stability and speed of response. In cases where the forecast model is an adequate representation of the actual sequence of observations and where the values of the coefficients are changing only very slowly, then the best results are obtained by averaging a great deal of information. When the smoothing constant α is very small (or, equivalently, the discount factor β near unity) the estimates of the values of these coefficients have small variance.

On the other hand, there may be cases when new terms are becoming significant in the forecast model, or where the values of one or more of the coefficients is changing rapidly. In those cases, it is not relevant to average a great deal of past history. The estimates of the coefficient values —and hence, the forecast—should be based on only the more recent information. Where speed of response to changing conditions is required, the value of the smoothing constant should be somewhat higher.

Therefore, especially in Chapter 12 where the necessary factors have been tabulated for each value of the discount factor β, we have chosen three values, from which two would be selected for a particular application. The high value is approximately equivalent to using $\beta^n = 0.95$, with one degree of freedom, for very stable situations. The middle value is equivalent to $\beta^n = 0.90$. The low value is approximately equivalent to using $\beta^n = 0.75$ for situations in which very rapid response is desired.

We now see that the tracking signal affords the necessary monitor to decide which of the two modes the system should operate in currently. So long as the sum of the forecast errors is small, relative to the natural noise in the system, use the higher value of β. If no assignable cause can be found for a significant departure from zero, then use the smaller value of β.

When the forecast process is started originally, one must estimate values of the coefficients in the model. If the tracking signal trips because of a radically new value for one coefficient, or even the addition of a new term in the model, then the appropriate coefficients should be estimated, just as though that were the point in time where the forecasting process was starting.

Sometimes it is more feasible to let the smoothing computations "learn" what the change is by rapidly discounting past information. That is, the effective discount factor may be decreased temporarily and later restored to the original value.

The values of the stored statistics $S^{[j]}(x)$ or $g_i(t)$ must be changed whenever the value of the smoothing constant is changed if one uses exponential smoothing or adaptive smoothing. Since exponential smoothing can be considered as a special case of adaptive forecasting, let us talk in terms of the component of the data vector $g_i(t)$. If the process has been going on for some time, the coefficients of the forecast model can be estimated by

$$\hat{\mathbf{a}}(t) = F^{-1}\mathbf{g}(t)$$

where F^{-1} is the inverse of the matrix of fitting functions. We assume that there's no basis for selecting some other set of values for these coefficients now. (We know that the values are apparently changing, but we don't know what the new values will be.) Therefore, we change from a discount factor β_1 to the discount factor β_2. There are different matrices associated with these two values, which we may as well denote by F_1^{-1} and F_2^{-1}. Since we start with the current estimates of the coefficients

$$F_1^{-1}\mathbf{g}_1(t) = \hat{\mathbf{a}}(t)$$

But by the same token, these same values of the coefficients should be obtained from the new matrix. Therefore,

$$\hat{\mathbf{a}}(t) = F_2^{-1}\mathbf{g}_2(t)$$

or, the initial conditions on the new data vector are

$$\hat{\mathbf{g}}_2(t) = F_2\hat{\mathbf{a}}(t) = F_2 F_1^{-1}\mathbf{g}_1(t)$$

If you expect that there will be any substantial volume of work in changing values of the discount factor (or smoothing constant) it may be well to precompute and tabulate the matrices $F_2 F_1^{-1}$, for the appropriate pairs of values for the discount factors that will be used. Remember that there must be *two* such transfer matrices: one to decrease the discount factor and another to use when it is time to raise the discount factor back to the original value.

Note that this change is not necessary when the computations are carried out directly on the coefficients themselves.

Exercise. Develop the correction matrices $F_2 F_1^{-1}$ to convert the statistics S and $S^{[2]}$ in double exponential smoothing from $\alpha = 0.1$ to $\alpha = 0.2$ and back.

In Fig. 8.2, we plotted the length of time for exponential smoothing to rise to 90 percent of a step. The increased value of the smoothing constant can be employed for that number of observations.

Exercise. Complete the computations for the tracking signal in Work Sheet 5a. If the sum of the forecast errors exceeds four times the mean absolute deviation twice in succession, reset the sum to zero. Plot the data to date on a graph and estimate the proper model and the coefficients. Reset the smoothed data to be consistent with your new estimate of these coefficients and continue the computations.

Work Sheet 5a DOUBLE EXPONENTIAL SMOOTHING

DATA: Warmdot Thermostat Weekly Sales, Table C.12
MODEL: Linear $\xi(T + t) = a_1 + a_2 t$
SMOOTHING: Double exponential smoothing, $\alpha = 0.1$
FORECAST: $\hat{x}_1(t) = \hat{a}_1(T) + \hat{a}_2(T)$
ERROR: $e(t) = x(t) - \hat{x}_1(t - 1)$
MEAN ABSOLUTE DEVIATION: $\Delta(t) = \alpha \, |e(t)| + \beta \, \Delta(t - 1)$

Date	Data	Coefficients		Forecast	Error	Mean Absolute Deviation	Sum of Errors	Tracking Signal
t	$x(t)$	$\hat{a}_1(T)$	$\hat{a}_2(T)$	$\hat{x}_1(t-1)$	$e(t)$	$\Delta(t)$	$y(t)$	$Y(t)/\Delta(t)$
13	·	196.6	0.0	·	·	21.1	0	0
14	189	195.2	0.2	196.6	−7.6	19.8	−7.6	−0.4
15	244	204.3	0.4	195.0	49.0	22.7	41.4	1.8
16	209	205.5	0.3	204.7	4.3	20.9	45.7	2.2
17	207	206.0	0.6	205.8	1.2	18.9	46.9	2.5
18	211	207.4	0.5	206.6	4.4	17.5	51.3	2.9
·	·	·	·	207.9	·	·	·	·
·	·	·	·	·	·	·	·	·
·	·	·	·	·	·	·	·	·

Before closing this chapter, we might comment on an interesting anomaly in the use of the tracking signal. Suppose that at time t the total forecast error isn't quite large enough to trip the exception report: $Y_t < 4\Delta_t$, but the difference is very small. Now at the next observation, it happens that $x(t + 1) = \hat{x}_1(t)$, so that the forecast error is $e_{t+1} = 0$. The total forecast

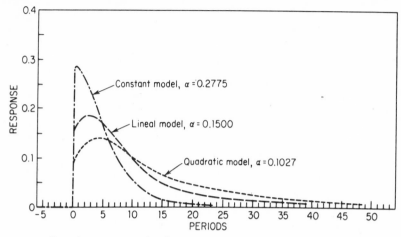

Fig. 20.4 Impulse responses—MAD.

error doesn't change. But the estimate of the mean absolute deviation will decrease. Therefore, the same total error as before will now appear to be larger than four times the new mean absolute deviation, triggering an exception report. This effect is very rare and applies only when $\Delta < (1/\beta)$. One organization that has a very large number of slow-moving items had 1000 such exception reports in one month.

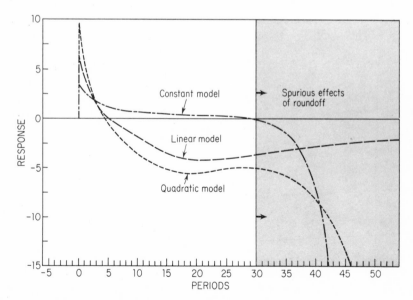

Fig. 20.5 Impulse responses—tracking signal.

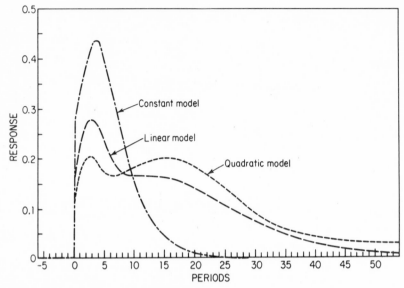

Fig. 20.6 Responses to a step—MAD.

Impulse Responses

Since the mean absolute deviation and the tracking signal are non-linear functions of the input noise, it is not possible to use the conventional methods of analyzing the response of these measures to standard input signals. Therefore, the standard signals, impulse, step, ramp, and parab-

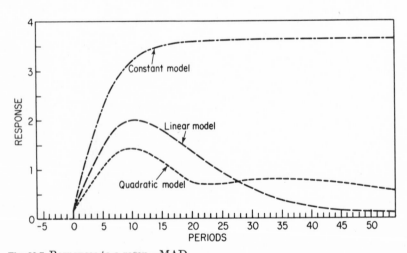

Fig. 20.7 Responses to a ramp—MAD.

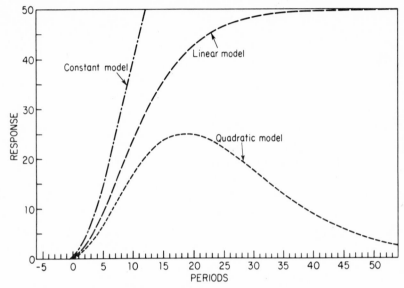

Fig. 20.8 Responses to a parabola—MAD.

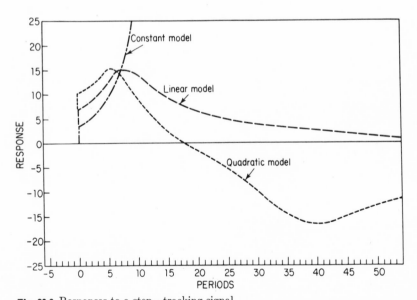

Fig. 20.9 Responses to a step—tracking signal.

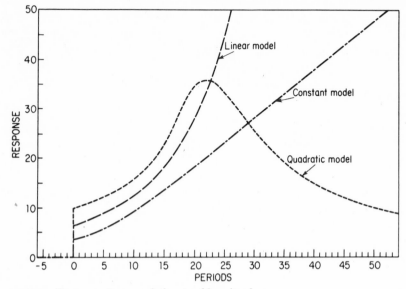

Fig. 20.10 Responses to a parabola—tracking signal.

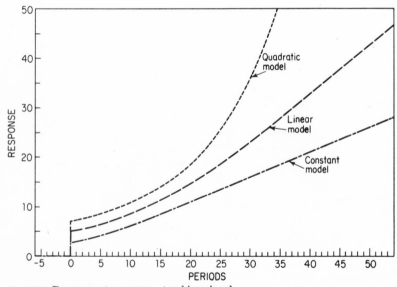

Fig. 20.11 Responses to a ramp—tracking signal.

ola, were used as inputs to a simulation* of the computations as in Work Sheet No. 5. Figure 20.4 shows that the mean absolute deviation rises sharply, and then decays steadily back to zero, when the observation is an impulse at time $t = 0$. The tracking signal also rises sharply and then decays slowly. Figure 20.5 shows the actual results obtained in the simulation. The changes after 30 periods are entirely spurious and due to the round-off of the data.

Figures 20.6–20.8 give the response of the mean absolute deviation to the other standard test inputs. In each case, the values of the smoothing constants were selected according to the definition of equivalence in Chapter 10. When the system is hit with a step input, the mean absolute deviation rises sharply and then decays. We noted before that a constant model will lag a ramp by a constant amount, and in Fig. 20.7, we see that when a constant model is used, the mean absolute deviation rises to a steady state value, whereas the linear and quadratic models ultimately die out to zero error.

Figure 20.8 illustrates a similar effect for a parabolic input. The quadratic model can ultimately forecast a parabola perfectly, so the mean absolute deviation drops back to zero. A linear model will have a constant error, and the mean absolute deviation settles down to a steady state value. The constant model blows up with a parabolic input, as would be expected.

Figures 20.10–20.11 show similar results for the tracking signal.

* See Chap. 24.

21   Optimum Linear Filters

In Section III, we started with time series that could be adequately described by a constant model, and we developed two smoothing techniques: the moving average and exponential smoothing. We also mentioned other possible weighted averages, but didn't go deeply into their characteristics. Now we want to return to the question of selecting these weights. Since there are so many alternatives, some must be better than others. In this chapter, we shall recapitulate the theoretical basis for finding the *best* set of weights, when the criterion of goodness is minimum mean square error in the forecast. The astute reader will, of course, realize that in many applications another criterion, such as maximum likelihood, is more appropriate.

The theoretical development does require that any trend be removed from the data, and it is helpful if we can think of the data as having zero mean. Furthermore, the design of the optimum weights depends on a knowledge of the autocorrelation function for the data. Therefore, this chapter is directed toward forecasting the forecast errors; these conditions do not always apply to the original data.*

---

* Much of the literature on the mathematical analysis of stochastic time series is written from this viewpoint. See, for example, Symposium on Time-Series Analysis, Brown University, June, 1962.

In most economic series, the original observations will have some trend, or even an elaborate pattern that must be represented by a model with several degrees of freedom. The forecasting process we have discussed so far is designed to measure the coefficients in the appropriate model, and in a sense, the forecast errors are the original data with all these knowable patterns removed. The noise in the original observations is quite typically uncorrelated. The process of smoothing and forecasting, however, introduces serial correlation, for successive values of T, in the forecast errors $e_\tau(T) = x(T) - \mathbf{a}'(T - \tau)\mathbf{f}(\tau)$, for fixed lead time τ. Since we know the design characteristics of the smoothing system—which we may refer to in this chapter as a *filter*—we can tell what the autocorrelation function is for the errors.

Forecast errors typically constitute the type of time series to which the theoretical development of this chapter applies: a sequence of data with mean zero and a known autocorrelation function. Of course, if the original observations of some process fulfill these requirements, an optimum filter can be designed to produce the basic forecast.

One can think of the observations themselves as autocorrelated samples from some distribution. For example, suppose the underlying process can be represented by a polynomial of degree $n - 1$.

$$\xi(t) = \sum_{i=0}^{n-1} a_i t^i$$

Then the nth successive difference of the series will be zero, and we could equally well represent the process by the autoregressive model

$$\xi(t) = \sum_{j=1}^{n} \binom{n}{j} \xi(t - j)$$

Alternatively, in a periodic model, such as

$$\xi(t) = A + B \cos \omega(t - t_0)$$

the process can be represented in terms of previous values

$$\xi(t) = (1 + 2 \cos \omega)[\xi(t - 1) - \xi(t - 2)] + \xi(t - 3)$$

In general, suppose that the process is

$$\xi(t) = \mathbf{a}'\mathbf{f}(t)$$

Then we can write n equations of the form

$$\xi(t - j) = \mathbf{a}'\mathbf{f}(t - j)$$

If the successive values of the fitting functions are generated by a transition matrix L such that $\mathbf{f}(t) = L\mathbf{f}(t - 1)$, then

$$\xi(t - j) = \mathbf{a}'L^{-j}\mathbf{f}(t)$$

This system of simultaneous linear equations can be written $\boldsymbol{\xi} = \Lambda \mathbf{f}(t)$.

Therefore, the current value of the process can be written in terms of the vector of the n previous values as

$$\xi(t) = \mathbf{a}'\Lambda^{-1}\boldsymbol{\xi}$$

When these special processes are cast into the autoregressive form, the methods of this chapter will yield the same procedures that were obtained by other methods in earlier chapters. The following discussion is more general than the cases covered in detail in Section III.

We shall first review the calculation of the serial correlation introduced by a linear filter for which we know the impulse response, using exponential smoothing as an example. Then we shall very briefly sketch the development of Wiener's optimum weights in a weighted moving average. Another attack, the Bode-Shannon design of linear filters, is less accessible in the literature and will be carried through in slightly more detail. One result of this analysis is showing that exponential smoothing is the optimum smoothing technique when the data can be represented as an exponentially correlated process buried in random noise. The results of this chapter can be summarized in an example that compares four possible filters applied to a particular time series.

Many readers, especially those not thoroughly at home in mathematical analysis, will find that they can, without loss, skip this chapter.

Serial Correlation of Forecast Errors

In order to provide some motivation for the study of correlated signals, let us look at the correlation of successive errors produced by some smooth-

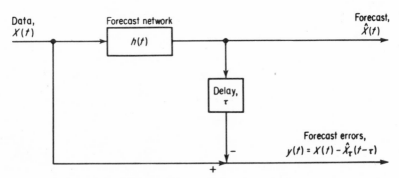

Fig. 21.1 The network that produces forecast errors.

ing system. The block diagram of the process is shown in Fig. 21.1. The data $x(t)$ are fed into a forecast system, which we can characterize completely by its impulse response $h(t)$ (see Appendix B). The output is the forecast $\hat{x}(t)$ made as of time t. The forecast is delayed τ periods and then compared with the current observation. The forecast error is

$$e_\tau(t) = x(t) - \hat{x}_\tau(t - \tau)$$

The forecast $\hat{x}(t)$ can be expressed in terms of the original data by the convolution

$$\hat{x}(t) = \sum_{n=0}^{\infty} h(n)x(t - n)$$

so that the forecast error, for a forecast τ periods ahead, is

$$e_\tau(t) = x(t) - \sum_{n=0}^{\infty} h(n)x(t - \tau - n)$$

We shall assume here that the forecast network does a reasonable job of forecasting, that is, that $\mathcal{E}(e) = 0$.

All the information that is relevant to forecasting future errors is contained in the autocorrelation function, or more properly, the autocovariance $R_{ee}(k) = \overline{e(t)e(t + k)}$ where the bar over the lagged product indicates the average of all such products over the time t. (Appendix A gives a general review of the concept of autocorrelation.) By direct substitution, then we obtain

$$R_{ee}(k) = R_{xx}(k) - \sum_{n=0}^{\infty} h(n)[R_{xx}(k + \tau + n) + R_{xx}(k - \tau - n)]$$
$$+ \sum_{n=0}^{\infty} \sum_{m=0}^{\infty} h(m)h(n)R_{xx}(k + n - m)$$

where $R_{xx}(k)$ is the autocovariance for the original data, sampled k periods apart in the sequence.

Now let us assume that the input data are merely random noise, so that $R_{xx}(0) = \sigma_x^2$ and $R_{xx}(k) = 0$ for $k \neq 0$. There is no correlation between any pairs of noise samples. When we substitute this assumption into the preceding equation, we find that the autocovariance of the errors in forecasting for a lead time of τ sampling intervals is

$$R_{ee}(0) = \sigma_x^2 \left[1 + \sum_{n}^{\infty} h^2(n) \right]$$

$$R_{ee}(k) = \sigma_x^2 \sum_{n=0}^{\infty} h(n)h(k + n) \qquad 0 < k < \tau$$

$$R_{ee}(h) = \sigma_x^2 \left[\sum_{n=0}^{\infty} h(n)h(k + n) - h(k - \tau) \right] \qquad k \geqslant \tau$$

In particular, think of a single exponential smoothing filter for which the impulse response is $h(t) = \alpha\beta^t$. Then,

$$R_{ee}(0) = \frac{2}{2-\alpha} \sigma_x^2$$

$$R_{ee}(k) = \frac{\alpha\beta^k}{2-\alpha} \sigma_x^2 \qquad 0 < k < \tau$$

$$= \frac{\alpha\beta^k}{2-\alpha} \sigma_x^2[1 - (2-\alpha)\beta^{-\tau}] \quad k \geqslant \tau$$

Suppose the data were random noise. The forecast is obtained by single exponential smoothing, with $\alpha = 0.1$. The forecast errors are measured

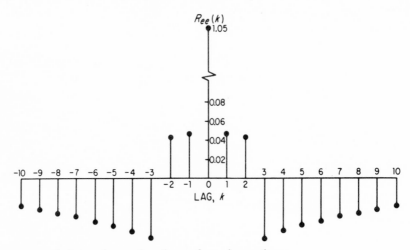

Fig. 21.2 Autocovariance function when forecasting random noise three sampling intervals ahead by single smoothing.

after a delay of $\tau = 3$ observations. The autocorrelation function for these errors is plotted in Fig. 21.2.

Exercise. Verify this theory experimentally. The table of random numbers in Appendix D can serve as the data.

Wiener Weighted Moving Averages

Suppose now that we want a forecast that is a linear combination of the n most recent observations.

$$\hat{x}_T(t) = \omega_1 x(t-T) + \omega_2 x(t-T-1) + \ldots + \omega_n x(t-T-n+1)$$

where the n weights $w_j = h(j)$ are to be determined in some optimum way. Furthermore, the weights might conceivably depend on the length of the lead time for which the forecast is desired, $w_i = w_i(T)$.

The criterion used by Wiener* in finding these weights was minimizing the average square error. That is, values of the weights w_i are to be found so that

$$\lim_{N \to \infty} \frac{1}{N+1} \sum_{t=0}^{N} [\hat{x}_T(t) - x(t)]^2$$

is a minimum. It is easy to see that this problem is simply one of multiple regression, where the independent variables are previous values in the same sequence. Let the matrix $\mathbf{R}$ be a square matrix where the element in the ith column and the jth row is the autocovariance $\mathbf{R}_{ij} = R_{xx}(i-j)$. Since the autocorrelation function is symmetrical, the matrix $\mathbf{R}$ is also symmetrical. The matrix is positive definite, and has an inverse $\mathbf{R}^{-1}$.

Let the vector $\mathbf{P}(T)$ have elements $P_i(T) = R_{xx}(i+T)$. Then the vector of weights $\mathbf{w}$ that minimizes the average square forecast error is given by the system of simultaneous equations whose solution is

$$\mathbf{w}(T) = \mathbf{R}^{-1}\mathbf{P}(T)$$

The optimum weights, in the least-squares sense, are completely determined by the autocorrelation function of the data.

Exercise. Assume that

$$R_{xx}(k) = \sigma_x^2 a^{|k|}$$

where $0 < a < 1$, and that $\bar{x} = 0$. Show that the optimum forecast is

$$\hat{x}(t+T) = x(t)a^T$$

Bode-Shannon Optimum Linear Filters

The communications engineers are concerned with the design of networks that will filter noise from a message in order to recover a signal. In some applications, such as the design of automatic fire control systems, it is also necessary to forecast future values of the message, which may be the position of a target, for example. The z-transform (Appendix B) is a powerful analytical tool for determining the characteristics of a filter. Much of the work has been done in the context of communications engineering, where the filter may be a network of resistors, capacitors, and inductors. The results are relevant to problems where numerical data are to be "filtered" by calculations in a digital computer. The forecast systems we have discussed are, in this sense, filters.

These principles of filter design are quite new, and not readily accessible

---

* N. Wiener, *Extrapolation, Interpolation and Smoothing of Stationary Time Series* (New York: Wiley, 1949).

in the literature. The following discussion is based on Sittler's lectures*
and should serve to illustrate how the approach works.

The communications engineer's problem of filtering—strictly the problem of recovering a message from the noise—is not of direct interest to us
in designing a forecast system. We shall go through such a design problem
first, however, to illustrate the techniques. Next, we shall consider forecasts when the data contain no noise at all. The system is designed just
to anticipate the exact future observation. The final step will be to combine these techniques into the design of a network that will both filter
and forecast. The network will be entirely specified by its impulse response:
the actual realization could be an electrical network or a set of equations
governing digital computations.

The observed data at time t is $x(t)$, the input to the system.

$$x(t) = \xi(t) + \epsilon(t)$$

where $\xi(t)$ is a "message," and $\epsilon(t)$ is noise superimposed on the message.
We shall assume, for an example of using the techniques, that the message
is a stochastic time series with mean zero (for convenience) and autocovariance $R_{\xi\xi}(k) = \sigma_1^2 a^{|k|}$, where $a < 1$. The superimposed noise also has
mean zero, and has no serial correlation with itself or with the message

$$R_{\epsilon\epsilon}(0) = \sigma_2^2$$

$$R_{\epsilon\epsilon}(k) = 0, \quad k \neq 0$$

$$R_{\epsilon\xi}(k) = 0$$

THE FILTERING PROBLEM. The first problem that we want to consider
is the design of a network that will accept the noisy observations $x(t)$
and produce, as well as possible, only the message $\xi(t)$. The *desired output*
of the system is $d(t) = \xi(t)$, and the actual output $g(t)$ is to be produced†
so that $\overline{[g(t) - d(t)]^2}$ is a minimum. Sittler proves that the transfer function (z-transform of the impulse response) for the filter that does minimize
the average square error is

$$H_0(z) = \frac{P_{xd}(z)}{P_{xx}(z)}$$

where $P_{xd}(z)$ is the z-transform of the covariance function between the two
sequences $x(t)$ and $d(t)$

---

* R. W. Sittler, "Lectures on Sampled Data Systems Analysis," M.I.T. Lincoln
Laboratory Memorandum 2M-0671, 22 Aug., 1957, chap. 10–12. Those who are interested in a more thorough treatment should consult Y. W. Lee, *Statistical Theory of Communication* (New York: Wiley, 1960) or D. Middleton, *An Introduction to Statistical
Communication Theory* (New York: McGraw-Hill, 1960).

† Here, as elsewhere, the horizontal bar indicates an average over time t.

$$P_{xd}(z) = \sum_{j=-\infty}^{\infty} R_{xd}(k)z^k$$

The transform $P_{xx}(z)$ is similarly defined for the autocovariance $R_{xx}(k)$. This transform can be called (by analogy with continuous signals) the *power spectrum* (see Appendix A).

Since the noise is not correlated with the message, the power spectrum of the input signal is simply

$$P_{xx}(z) = P_{\xi\xi}(z) + P_{\epsilon\epsilon}(z)$$

From the assumptions regarding the statistics of the message, its power spectrum is

$$P_{\xi\xi}(z) = \frac{\sigma_1^2(1 - a^2)}{(1 - az)(1 - az^{-1})}$$

and the power spectrum of the random noise is simply

$$P_{\epsilon\epsilon}(z) = \sigma_2^2$$

The power spectrum for the total input signal can be manipulated into a symmetrical form, with one factor in terms of z and the other factor in terms of z^{-1}

$$P_{xx}(z) = \frac{(A - Bz)(A - Bz^{-1})}{(1 - az)(1 - az^{-1})}$$

where

$$A = \tfrac{1}{2}[\sqrt{b + 2a\sigma_2^2} + \sqrt{b - 2a\sigma_2^2}]$$

$$B = \tfrac{1}{2}[\sqrt{b + 2a\sigma_2^2} - \sqrt{b - 2a\sigma_2^2}]$$

$$b = \sigma_1^2(1 - a^2) + \sigma_2^2(1 + a^2)$$

The noise has no correlation with the message, so that the cross correlation between the input and the desired output is

$$R_{xd}(k) = R_{xx}(k)$$

and hence the power spectrum $P_{xd}(z)$ is the same as given above, $P_{xx}(z)$. When these power spectra are substituted in the equation for the transfer function of the optimum filter, we obtain

$$H_0(z) = \left[\frac{1}{1 - (B/A)z} + \frac{(B/A)z^{-1}}{1 - (B/A)z^{-1}} \right] \frac{\sigma_1^2(1 - a^2)}{A^2 - B^2}$$

The corresponding impulse response is

$$h_0(t) = UV^{|t|}$$

where

$$U = \frac{\sigma_1^2(1 - a^2)}{\sqrt{b^2 - 4a^2}} \quad \text{and} \quad V = \frac{b - \sqrt{b^2 - 4a^2}}{2a}$$

Figure 21.3 is a plot of these two factors as a function of the exponential base in the message correlation function. For simplicity, we have assumed that $\sigma_2^2 = 1$, so that σ_1^2 is effectively the signal-to-noise variance ratio. Two cases are shown: one where the noise is high relative to the message; the other where it is low.

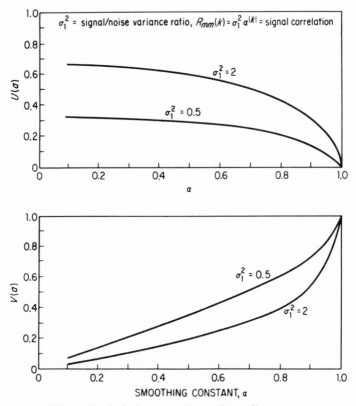

Fig. 21.3 Factors for designing an optimum linear filter.

Notice that this filter has an impulse response that is the same as exponential smoothing, except for the constant coefficient. This process is not physically realizable, since it has non-zero impulse response for negative time. This consideration is not important for strictly filtering problems that can be carried out at leisure after the entire sequence has been recorded, as for example in finding echoes in a seismographic record.

THE SIMPLE FORECASTING PROBLEM. Now we shall change our objectives and seek to design a network that will forecast. In this simple case, we shall take the input signal to be the process itself, $x(t) = \xi(t)$, where the process has the same statistical properties as those considered in the previous problem, and there is no noise. The desired output is a forecast τ periods into the future, $d(t) = x(t + \tau)$.

The linear filter that will minimize the mean square difference between the actual output and the desired output will have an impulse response defined by

$$\sum_{j=-\infty}^{\infty} h_0(j)R_{xx}(n-j) = R_{xd}(n)$$

Now we must introduce the concept of physical realizability: a real forecast system cannot be expected to react *before* any signal is introduced. That is to say, the impulse response must be zero for negative time, $h_0(n) = 0$, for $n < 0$.

It is easy to verify that, in this case, the cross correlation between the input signal and the desired output is

$$R_{xd}(k) = R_{xx}(k + \tau) = \sigma_1^2 a^{|k+\tau|}$$

Sittler goes through a development of the Bode-Shannon design of optimum realizable filters that can be summarized as follows:

(1) Pass the signals $x(t)$ through a filter that converts them into uncorrelated samples. The transfer function for such a "whitening" filter is

$$H'(z) = \frac{1}{\psi_{xx}(z)}$$

The transform $\psi_{xx}(z)$ is a factor of the power spectrum $P_{xx}(z)$ such that all poles and zeros of ψ are outside the unit circle, and such that

$$\psi_{xx}(z)\psi_{xx}(z^{-1}) = P_{xx}(z)$$

(These are the symmetrical factors encountered above.)

(2) Now pass the uncorrelated result $x'(t)$ through a second filter to obtain a least-squares approximation to the desired result $d(n)$. The transfer function of the second filter is similar to the one encountered before

$$H_0''(z) = \frac{P_{xd}(z)}{\psi_{xx}(z^{-1})}$$

(3) Retransform the transfer function into the time domain to obtain the impulse response $h_0''(n)$. In general, the result will include some response for negative time. In a physically realizable filter, the impulse response for negative time must be zero, so these responses are set to zero. Transform this result back into the transform domain and call the result $H_0'''(z)$.

(4) Finally, the transfer function for the over-all, physically realizable filter will be

$$H_0(z) = \frac{H_0'''(z)}{\psi_{xx}(z)}$$

When one carries through these steps for the simple forecasting problem with an exponentially correlated message and no noise, the impulse response for the optimum filter turns out to be $h(0) = a^\tau$, $h(k) = 0$ for $k \neq 0$.

For exponentially correlated signals, the least-squares forecast τ periods into the future is just a^T times the current observation. (Recall that it is a particular assumption in this derivation that the mean of the signal is zero.)

FILTERING AND FORECASTING. Now let us go back to our original noisy data $x(t) = \xi(t) + \epsilon(t)$, where the message has zero mean and exponential autocorrelation, and the noise has zero mean and no correlation, either with itself or with the message. The desired output of the system is a forecast τ periods ahead, $d(t) = \xi(t + \tau)$, and the filter must be physically realizable.

We have already written the power spectrum of the signal in symmetrical factors, so

$$\psi_{xx}(z) = \frac{A - Bz}{1 - az}$$

The transform of the cross correlation between the input and the desired output is

$$P_{xd}(z) = z^{-\tau} P_{xx}(z)$$

The transfer function of the second filter, that makes the uncorrelated input match the desired output as well as possible, is

$$H_0''(z) = z^{-\tau} \frac{A - Bz}{1 - az}$$

In the time domain, this network has a response that starts at time $n = -T$, with a jump to height A. This response decays by a factor a for each time period. From time $n = -\tau + 1$, a second response (initially of height B) is subtracted from the first. When we throw out the terms for negative time and return to the transform domain, the transfer function is

$$H_0'''(z) = \frac{a^\tau(A - B/a)}{1 - az}$$

Therefore the optimum over-all transfer function is

$$H_0(z) = \frac{a^\tau(1 - B/Aa)}{1 - Bz/A}$$

and the corresponding impulse response is

$$h_0(n) = a^\tau \left(1 - \frac{B}{aA}\right) \left(\frac{B}{A}\right)^n \quad \text{for } n \leqslant 0$$

Again, we have an exponentially decaying response, similar to exponential smoothing. The factor $B/A = V(a)$ was plotted in Fig. 21.3.

The constant coefficient $W(\tau) = a^\tau(1 - B/aA)$ is plotted in Fig. 21.4, for forecasts $\tau = 3$ periods ahead. Note that considerably less weight is given current errors when they are to be forecast than was the case when

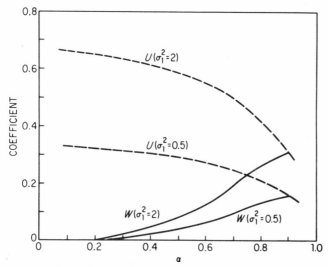

Fig. 21.4 Comparison of the filter coefficients with the filter-and-forecast coefficients.

it was simply a matter of filtering the correlated message out of the random noise.*

An Experimental Trial of the Theory

An interesting case on which to try these theories is Warmdot's total sales (Fig. 21.5). The actual figures are given in Table C.16 if you want to verify the computations. Note the sharp rise in 1948 after the wartime shortages started to ease up. The effect of the Korean War didn't hit Warmdot until 1952, when there was a substantial upturn in government business. The recession started in 1957, but the effects weren't apparent until the end of the year.

---

* See also J. F. Muth, "Optimal Properties of Exponentially Weighted Forecasts," *Journal of American Statistical Association*, Vol. 55, No. 290 (June, 1960), 299–306; R. F. Meyer, "An Adaptive Method of Short-term Forecasting," International Federation of Operational Research Societies, Oslo, July, 1963; and L. R. Saunders, "The Prediction of a Random Time Series Affected by a Prescribed Time Function," *Australian Journal of Statistics*, Vol. 4, No. 1 (April, 1962), 11–24.

Now, of course, in a case like this, we don't know exactly what the autocorrelation function really is. The autocorrelation coefficients (see

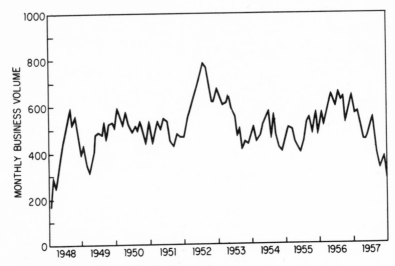

Fig. 21.5 Warmdot's monthly business volume.

Appendix A) were computed for lags up to twenty-four months, with the following results:

Table 21.1 AUTOCORRELATION COEFFICIENTS FOR WARMDOT'S TOTAL SALES

Lag	Computed Autocorrelation Coefficient	Lag	Computed Autocorrelation Coefficient
0	1.0000	13	−0.0424
1	0.7743	14	−0.0685
2	0.6566	15	−0.1539
3	0.4997	16	−0.1997
4	0.3390	17	−0.2339
5	0.2463	18	−0.2289
6	0.1855	19	−0.2380
7	0.1266	20	−0.1829
8	0.1266	21	−0.1453
9	0.0415	22	−0.1014
10	0.0300	23	−0.0695
11	0.0008	24	−0.0910
12	−0.0332		

These coefficients are plotted in Fig. 21.6. Since there were 120 points form which to calculate these coefficients, their standard deviation is on the order of 0.1, so we can ignore values for lags greater than eight periods.

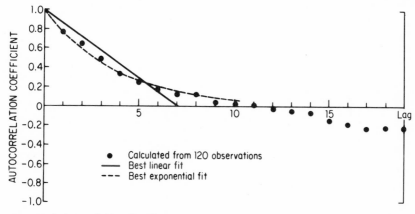

Fig. 21.6 Autocorrelation functions.

We shall compare two hypotheses about this function. One is a straight line for the first seven coefficients, and the other an exponential function similar to the type just discussed for stochastic messages. We shall forecast over lead times of one, two, three, and four months into the future. These alternatives are to be compared by the standard deviation of forecast errors. (For comparison, the standard deviation of the data is 101.6.)

In the first forecast, we naively assume a constant model (initially estimated at an average of 500) and each month revise this estimate by simple exponential smoothing, $\alpha = 0.1$. The standard deviation of the forecast errors was somewhat better than just holding to the forecast of 500 for each month, especially for lead times of only one or two months.

In the next forecast, we first estimate the average of the data by taking the total to date and dividing by the total number of elapsed months. At each sampling interval, the residual between the actual observation and the average is an estimate of the noise. Since the noise was assumed to have an exponential autocorrelation function, future residuals are forecast by a^r times the current residual.

In the third forecast, the procedure was the same, except that the noise was assumed to have a linear autocorrelation function. Figure 21.7 shows how the accuracy of these three forecasts compared for lead times of from one to four months. Note that when the autocorrelation of the noise is taken into account, the forecasts are significantly more accurate than those obtained by simple exponential smoothing. The difference diminishes for longer lead times.

There is a fourth curve in Fig. 21.7. The data in Table C.16 are taken from my previous book,* where they were presented as a sequence of numbers generated to have exponential correlation. Hence, we know the mean of the entire series exactly, and also the exact form of the autocorrelation

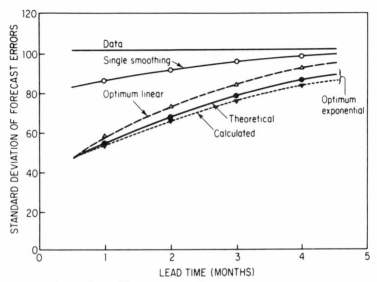

Fig. 21.7 Comparison of forecast accuracies.

function. (The preceding narrative about wars and recessions was pointed out to me by an economist who didn't know where the numbers had come from.) The fourth curve in Fig. 21.7 shows that we can do just about as well by the experimentally determined autocorrelation functions as with the exact theoretical one.

* *Statistical Forecasting for Inventory Control* (New York: McGraw-Hill, 1959), p. 173.

Section VI Exploration of Alternatives

"All my instincts are one way, and all the facts are the
other, and I very much fear that British juries have not
yet attained that pitch of intelligence when they will
give preference to my theories over Lestrade's facts."

Adventure of The Norwood Builder

I frankly admit to a very definite view about the use of statistical fore-casting systems. It's quite natural that the arguments put forth in this book should be persuasive toward that point of view. At many junctures, I have suggested alternatives, even when I firmly believe in only one among the many cited. My purpose is not to confuse the issue, but to stimulate you, as you design a system for your own particular needs, to think through these alternatives carefully. Henry David Thoreau said, "Where is this division of labor to end? and what object does it finally serve? No doubt another *may* also think for me; but it is not therefore desirable that he should do so to the exclusion of my thinking for myself."*

This section deals with some practical problems of evaluating alterna-tives. Some of the questions that need to be resolved are procedural; others relate to the numerical values of some parameter; neither type should be overlooked. For example, at what point do you record demand data: deal-er's orders on the plant, or retail sales to consumers? Should the original ob-servations be transformed, and if so how? Over what lead times are fore-casts required, and should the forecasts refer to the single observation at the end or to the cumulative total during the entire time? Should the data be represented by a time-series model or by a probability model, and which one? What action do you take if the tracking signal indicates that the forecasts are likely to be biased? These are very important procedural questions.

On the other hand, there are such questions as: What terms should be

* Walden, 1845.

included in the model? Should the coefficients be estimated by an ordinary moving average, by a discounting process, or by some optimum set of weights? What should the values of the weights be? At what level of confidence does one accept the significance of a high-order term in the model or the significance of bias indicated by the tracking signal?

Answers to the procedural questions require a thorough understanding of the environment in which the forecast system will be required to work. What are the real opportunities for getting different kinds of data, and how much would each cost? Who is going to use the forecast and for what purposes?

Answers to the questions of internal technical operation can be answered by theoretical analysis and by numerical test examples. There is a greater scope for exploration, but unfortunately the effects tend to be minor. A practical look at the environment may suggest a feasible alternative source of data that will lead to a significant improvement in the forecasts. The optimum choice of the weights in the smoothing process will have little discernible effect in the over-all operation of the control system in which the forecasts are embedded.

Throughout this book we have discussed alternatives. The exercises were intended to enhance the reader's understanding of the choice. Where possible, the theoretical consequences of the alternatives have been explored mathematically. We have now toured five of the six floors in the department store, looking at the possibilities on each floor. It is time to think of putting some set of alternatives together into a tentative system, to see how everything might work together.

Chapter 22 deals with hand computations. With a desk calculator, work out an example for each alternative that you want to explore. You'll get to know exactly what the computations are; you'll find any major flaws; and you'll have an example against which to check later examples worked out by clerks or on an electronic computer. You'll also have an excellent opportunity to think about the consequences of alternatives, and some basis for determining which combinations are really worth exploring in detail.

Chapter 23 discusses the organization of the program for thorough exploration of the principal alternatives. Why are particular alternatives being considered at all? How will you decide which is the better? Will your criteria convince other people who have a particular interest in the system?

Finally, Chapter 24 discusses the design of computer simulation programs. Most of the necessary calculations are discussed in connection with the work sheets in this book. Chapter 24 includes directions for generating synthetic data (Monte Carlo) for test problems and for finding the inverse of a symmetrical, positive definite, matrix.

22 Work Sheets for Hand Computations

How would you buy a hi-fi system for your own home? Some people want a very elaborate system, designed to order; others want only a simple prepackaged set. The set may be able to play records (in various speeds), magnetic tape, or to receive radio broadcasts in FM or AM, in various bands. The amplifier may be separate from the preamp, or combined with it. There may be provision for recording and a wide variety of speakers through which the result is to be produced either stereophonically or monaurally.

Some big cities have department stores that deal solely in hi-fi systems; a department for each component. One department is designed to give the prospective buyer a chance to listen to various popular combinations in order to help him to make the best compromise between quality and the money available. There are several turntables, several amplifiers, and several speakers. A switchboard makes it possible to hook almost any combination together into a system. There is even a wide variety of records to be played.

Sometimes a major difference is noticeable when one component is substituted for another; sometimes only a person with a highly trained ear (or a highly trained imagination) can tell the difference. At best, such samples illustrate only a portion of the possible performance. Many systems are modified regularly, as new components come on the market, or

325

as the owner becomes thoroughly familiar with the original system at home, or as he gets the motivation or the money for something more elaborate.

The design of a forecasting system can be approached in the same way. There are a variety of components that can be plugged together. Some systems are simple; some are elaborate. A great degree of refinement is possible, where it will be appreciated. But in other cases, a simple system can be just as effective, and a good deal cheaper. One key point in this analogy is the notion of pluggable components. At any time, it should be possible to remove one component and install a newer model in its place, either just for test, or for actual operation.

Work sheets can be something like the test of a high-fidelity system in ·the store. Instead of physical equipment with a switchboard, the system is represented on paper. Various sections of the work sheet correspond to alternative components that can be hooked together to see how they work. In a well-designed system, it should be easy to replace any section by an alternative.

Later, when you have a pretty good idea of the principal types of components to be included in the system, you can set up a thorough trial, probably using an electronic computer, to be able to carry out a complete range of tests. But it is a waste of time to start using the computer immediately, before you have any real idea of what to expect.

One does not have unlimited freedom to substitute components even in a well-designed modular system. The over-all systems design specifies the format and content of the information that is transmitted from one stage to the next, and that information cannot be changed without substantial alterations to the basic skeleton. For example, if a control system is designed to incorporate a forecasting subsystem that requires only current observations of the process, one *can* change the model, or the smoothing constant; one *cannot* easily go to a multiple regression on several independent time series. Such a change would be similar to a change from a monaural hi-fi system to a stereophonic system.

Within the forecast system itself, it is quite easy to change the model and the smoothing constant, and only slightly more difficult to change from a time series model to a probability model.

There is probably a temptation to carry out hand computations on any old piece of paper available. Resist that temptation. A little extra work at the start can save a great deal of grief later on. Three aspects of the work sheet merit more attention than most people are naturally inclined to give:

(1) Think through the sequence of calculations and lay out the sections of the work sheet in an orderly manner. It is not a bad idea to provide extra columns in case extra steps turn up.

(2) Record exactly the steps that are taken in the computation. If the instruction is short, it can be included in the heading of the column. If it is a longer equation, make a note of it on a separate sheet. If you could give the sheet with the instructions you have written down to a girl and know that she will produce the correct answers, you will have no trouble in programming the same problem on a computer. Furthermore, anyone (including yourself) who later looks over the sheet, will know exactly what was done.

(3) Have lots of room at the top of the sheet in which to make a careful note of the exact conditions: source of data, model, smoothing technique, way of obtaining initial conditions, values of weights, lead times, and confidence limits, and so on. When you have a new idea to try out, it's frustrating to have to work an example all over again because you can't tell whether an old work sheet is appropriate to this case or not.

Throughout this book there have been work sheets, with step-by-step instructions for carrying out the computations, for individual components of the forecasting system. Now design your own work sheet for an entire system. A form with 30 to 50 lines and about 20 columns will be handy to work with. There are standard commercial forms, but if you print one of your own, leave five inches of blank space at the top of the page in which to record the conditions of this particular calculation.

Some of the information in the heading will be standard for all examples:

TITLE: What system is being explored?

DATA: Where did the data come from?

MODEL: How are you representing the process? What is the transition matrix L and the vector $\mathbf{f}(0)$ of initial values of the fitting functions?

SMOOTHING: What technique of smoothing are you using, and what are the values of the necessary parameters, such as smoothing constant, discount factor, number of periods in a moving average, smoothing vector, and so on. (Initial conditions and recursive equations for revising the information can be in the heading or on a separate sheet.)

FORECAST: How long is the lead time? Do you use all terms in the forecast model? If not, what is the test of significance? Is the forecast cumulative or discrete?

ERROR MEASUREMENT: How is the forecast error to be measured?

CRITERIA: How will you judge the relative merits of this alternative among others?

There should also be space in the heading for other notes, including any remarks that occur to you as you go through the calculations. In a large organization, it is worthwhile to have a space for the name of the person actually doing the arithmetic, and the date the work was done. I know—all this is a lot of extra work. You know what you're doing, and there's no need to be so formal about it all. I have seen so many cases of real trouble and frustration in large-scale systems design projects, that I say unequivocally that there *is* need.

Generally, one line of the work sheet will refer to a single observation and all the calculations that derive from that observation. When there is a long sequence of observations, you will probably need several sheets. Number the sheets—since the sequence of the data may be very important —and include some key that will relate a particular sheet to its problem if it gets lost from the set. It isn't necessary to copy all the detailed heading data.

Now, as to the organization of the columns. For a complete system there may be up to seven sets of columns, as in Fig. 22.1. There may be

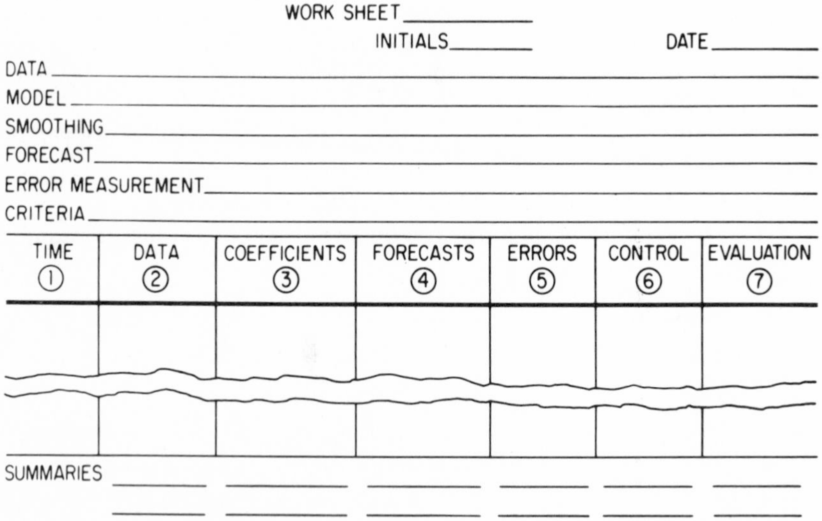

WORK SHEET _____

INITIALS _____   DATE _____

DATA _____

MODEL _____

SMOOTHING _____

FORECAST _____

ERROR MEASUREMENT _____

CRITERIA _____

TIME ①	DATA ②	COEFFICIENTS ③	FORECASTS ④	ERRORS ⑤	CONTROL ⑥	EVALUATION ⑦

SUMMARIES

Fig. 22.1 Outline of a system work sheet.

only one column in some sets; others will have several columns. For some problems, a complete set of columns can be dropped.

(1) *Time:* The observations should be numbered in sequence. A column for t can have $t = 1, 2, 3, \ldots, T$. It is frequently helpful to have another column that keys the observations to the original time scale: the date of the observation, or the clock time, for every tenth observation or so.

(2) *Data:* The first column in this section should record the actual observation $x(t)$. If the data are to be transformed in some way before being processed further, additional columns will be required for (a) the basis of the transformation and (b) the transformed results. For example, if usage of left-hand refrigerator doors is related to total production, there should be a column for production and one for the ratio. Be sure to record the basis of the transformation in the heading. If the dependent observations are to be related to several independent time series, there should be a column for the current value of each of the independent series.

(3) *Model coefficients:* There is a group of n columns, with one column in which to record the current value of each of the n coefficients in the model (or equivalently the n components of the vector of probabilities in a probability model). The first line for this group of columns records the initial values used to start the computations.

NOTE: In the case of exponential smoothing one stores the statistics $S_t^{[j]}$ instead of the coefficients, so that an extra set of columns should be provided for these statistics. The same is true of general exponential smoothing, where one stores from one sampling interval to the next the values of the components of the data vector $\mathbf{g}(t)$. An auxiliary slip of paper with

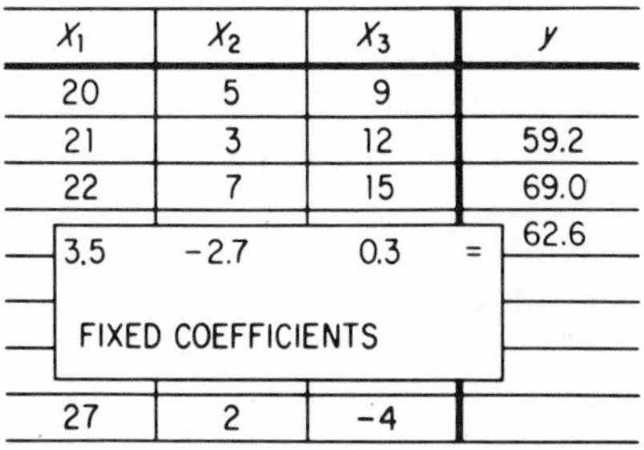

x_1	x_2	x_3	y
20	5	9	
21	3	12	59.2
22	7	15	69.0
3.5	−2.7	0.3 =	62.6
FIXED COEFFICIENTS			
27	2	−4	

Fig. 22.2 Auxiliary slip with constant coefficients.

constant coefficients (Fig. 22.2) can be of considerable help in carrying out the computations of linear combinations.

(4) *Forecasts:* There should be one column for each period in the lead time. For example, if the lead time is three days with daily observations, there would be three columns. The forecasts made one day ahead are recorded in the first column, and the forecasts made three days ahead, in the third column.

You have a choice as to the line on which you record the forecast. Some people like to record all the forecasts on the line that corresponds to the observation used in the computations. It is somewhat more natural, however, to record the forecast $\hat{x}_\tau(t - \tau)$ on the line t corresponding to the period being forecast. The forecast for two periods ahead would be recorded on the second line down.

If the original observations were transformed, it will be necessary to retransform the forecasts in order to get them into the terms of the original observations. This reverse transformation will require additional columns.

(5) *Errors:* The first column can be used to record the error in forecasting one period ahead: the difference between the current observation and the forecast made one observation earlier.

$$e(t) = x(t) - \hat{x}_1(t - 1)$$

Other columns can be used to compute the errors in forecasting for other lead times, if desired. An additional column is used to record the current estimate of the mean absolute deviation. If a relative, rather than absolute error is used, an additional column will be required for the computation.

(6) *Control:* One important aspect of the types of system described in this book is the opportunity to change the mode of operation between one designed for stability and one intended for response. The sum of the forecast errors can be used as a monitor to decide which mode to use currently. Another alternative is to include or omit higher-order terms in the model, depending on whether they appear to be significant or not.

Columns in the control field should be provided for the sum of the errors, the ratio to the mean absolute deviation, and a code designating the mode currently used.

(7) *Evaluation:* For some purposes a particular system can be evaluated in terms of the forecast errors, perhaps the mean and variance. In other cases the final evaluation should be in terms of the operational use. If the forecasts are to be used for inventory control, for example, it may be a good idea in some examples to include columns on the work sheet in which you can compute the inventory levels at the end of each lead time.

Summary. When the example has been worked out, it may be necessary to summarize the results. For example, you will probably want the mean and standard deviation of some of the results. Therefore, at the foot of the column provide space to record a count of the number of entries, the sum of the entries, and the sum of squares of the entries. In other cases, you may want a count of the number of positive entries and of the number of negative entries. (Ending inventories are a case in point.)

The work sheets provided in the various sections of this book give an example of the use in each of these alternative sections of the system work sheet. Note that this organization makes it possible to replace the columns and instructions for one component, and thus investigate the effect of making any kind of a change. You will want to investigate alternative types of systems during the design change. You will also find that, after the final system is designed and installed, you will later want to modify some section of it. The habits learned in the layout of these work sheets for hand computation will carry over into the organization of a computer program, and it will be very easy to keep the system up-to-date with new improvements.

When looking at one component at a time, as in the earlier sections, the calculations are most easily carried out by going down one column (or set of interrelated columns) at a time. Fill in all the times. Then fill in all the data with any necessary transformations. Then go back to the beginning and work out all the coefficients, and so on. This method of computation is the fastest, since you will get into the proper rhythm of the sequence of operations.

When you want to explore the entire system, however, it is better to work completely across each row. Then advance in time to the next observation and work completely across that row. That is the sequence of computations that an operating program would follow. It may turn out that there is some peculiarity to the instructions that you would not have encountered in going down one column at a time. Going across each row emphasizes the exact information that is actually available to you in doing the calculation.

For example, when it comes to exploring the tracking signal, you will have to work across the row. If the tracking signal becomes large, some steps must be taken to bring the forecast back into control, and those steps will affect the numbers in several of the columns.

You'll get a good understanding of the system, just by laying out the necessary work sheets and the instructions for filling in the spaces. The number of cases you actually carry through depends on the resources available to you and on other demands upon your attention. At a bare minimum, work out ten lines for one case in each type of system you will later want to explore thoroughly. That amount of work will check out your instructions and provide a test case against which to test a computer program.

If you are going to evaluate the difference between two alternatives, then you must carry through much longer examples. In general, you can be badly misled if you try to select one of two alternatives on the results from less than 50 observations. Even if it is necessary to use synthetic data (see Chapter 24) use a long enough series to provide a real test. If there are several degrees of freedom in the model, an even longer series will be required. As a rule of thumb, the number of observations in the test sequence should be at least 20 to 50 times the number of degrees of freedom in the model. When the discount factor is large (near one), an even longer sequence is required.

Finally, if you want to develop a real understanding of the system, so that you will instinctively know what to do to make it better, several examples, each with many observations, will be required. It's usually hard to get that much real data. That's why Appendix C includes tables of several time series, representing a wide variety of the problems encountered in practice.

23 Planning the Exploration Program

The systems designer can expect to progress through three phases of understanding with imperceptible boundaries, but with vital distinctions between them. During the first phase he should seek to get an understanding of what the alternative *is*. Can he reproduce the examples given in this book? Does he know what the difference between the available alternatives is? In this stage the work sheets given for each alternative component can be a great help. There is no question of deciding whether an alternative is good or bad. The question is merely: does he understand it well enough to be able to explain it to someone else?

In the second stage the systems designer seeks to find out what some particular alternative will *do*. Component work sheets can still be used to investigate step responses, or perhaps to watch the effect of a choice of the smoothing constant on the balance between stability and speed of response. The answers are given theoretically, of course, but there's nothing like actually working out a case and finding that the results do conform quite closely to the theory. Several such examples will serve to illustrate what is meant by "quite closely." Later on, the designer's attention will begin to shift from the characteristics of various components to the characteristics of several components in one system. Here, the work sheets for total systems described in Chapter 22 will be of help.

In neither of the first two stages is it important what cases are tested, nor the sequence in which they are tested. The designer should follow any lead that intrigues him. The results may suggest any kind of modification at all. Keep careful records of what you do explore, of course. Even though the cases weren't part of a carefully thought-out plan, they may later turn out to be important parts of such a plan, and you won't have to do them over.

This chapter is concerned with the third stage in the development. The designer honestly knows what the alternatives are, and has a good appreciation—both theoretical and empirical—for what the alternatives are likely to do. Now he wants to make a serious evaluation of the alternatives in order to select that which is best for the particular application.

Exercise. If the systems designer does not know what the available alternatives are, how can he be sure that he has, in fact, selected the best system?

In order to make a thorough evaluation, it is usually advisable to have recourse to an internally programmed electronic computer. Even if the ultimate system is to be put into operation on simple punched card machines, the speed and flexibility of the high-speed computers usually makes their use advantageous for at least the earlier stages of the evaluation. There are many service bureaus that have time available.

The plan for the evaluation program will depend on the objectives. I don't intend to lay out a *pro forma* program here. I do want to get you to think through carefully some of the important factors. Then you're on your own. In particular, let's discuss the needs of programs that are designed for

Research into better methods

Evaluation of alternatives

Training operating personnel

Selling those affected

Research

This book is only a progress report on continuing research in the field of statistical forecasting. Some of the novel techniques discussed are given with complete formal mathematical proofs. The original source of the idea was not a mathematical derivation. In almost every case, the mathematics followed laboratory experiments. That is, a great many examples were carried out, both by hand, with the aid of a desk calculator, and on large electronic computers. A careful analysis of the results of these runs—or a peculiar phenomenon in the development—occasionally led to an idea: "What would happen if we tried . . . ?" Some of these conjectures led to results that were qualitatively expected; others did not.

The next question was, why didn't the results behave as expected? A search for an understanding of that phenomenon led to further trials until the process was well enough known that one could give a good guess as to what would happen on the next trial. The next step was to try to formalize that understanding: can someone else be taught to make an equally good guess as to the results?

It is only at this stage of understanding that the mathematical theorem can be stated.* It is usually stated in a form that is almost certain to be true—and that makes a big difference. Some of the theorems are very difficult to prove. Several attempts would have faltered and died had it not been for the conviction that the theorem actually was true. Sometimes additional trials of special cases helped suggest a line of proof. When the theorem is proved,† it generally leads to much deeper insight as to how the results could be extended.

The computer is a very useful laboratory tool for this sort of mathematical research. The programs should be "quick and dirty." The aim in designing a research simulation should be to get an idea on Monday, write and debug the program on Tuesday, and have some results to look at by Wednesday. Niceties of format or of internal arithmetic should be sacrificed in the interest of getting some results before you've forgotten what the idea was. FORTRAN is a very useful language in which to design such simulations.‡ (The only major drawback that I've encountered is that it's hard to write a random-number routine, and the library program has some disadvantages.)

A slow computer is also a great boon, if it is one where you can sit at the console and modify the program on the spot in response to the output you see. It's the worst possible way of writing computer programs and highly inefficient use of an expensive computer. But at this stage the total emphasis is on getting results quickly for research into newer and better ways of forecasting, not on efficient use of the computer.

Thus the analyst who can write his own computer programs, and even operate the machine, will have a distinct advantage over someone who must rely on help from some other part of the organization. Ideas in research are ephemeral and can easily wither unless acted upon promptly.

* See G. Polya, *Induction and Analogy in Mathematics* (Princeton, N.J.: Princeton University Press, 1954), especially chap. I.

† Dr. Ronald Howard, Dr. Richard Meyer, and Dr. Robert Barringer all played important roles in discovering the formal lines of analysis that ultimately led to the major proofs discussed in this book.

‡ D. D. McCracken, *A Guide to FORTRAN Programming* (New York: Wiley, 1961).

A great many areas are still open for this sort of research. One might start by trying to verify the effect of the choice for a smoothing constant on forecast accuracy with highly correlated noise,* and get into the whole area of the difference among correlation functions. The transient responses of adaptive smoothing techniques have not been worked out. The criteria for selection of the proper class limits in a probability model could be strengthened, and so can the techniques for interpolating the results between limits.

We have considered processes $\xi(t) = \mathbf{a}'\mathbf{f}(t)$ where the values of the coefficients $\mathbf{a}$ go through a slow random walk. The optimum choice of a discount factor β is related to the statistics of the changes in these coefficients and to their joint distribution with the noise $\epsilon(t)$. Someday, someone will extend Meyer's proof for the simple case $\mathbf{f} = 1$ to more complex processes and show how to measure the required statistics from data.

Evaluation

Probably not everyone will want to carry through research of this nature. The research that has been done to date has provided alternative answers to some problems that the user may not know he has. Therefore, the problem is one of evaluation and selection among these alternatives.

The first step is designing a work sheet for the entire system. Include space and instructions for each of the alternatives that is worth considering. Carry through enough steps by hand to be very sure that the instructions are accurate and complete and to have a test problem against which to check the computer results. Those instructions will become the computer program. Therefore, if you find that you have to do the computations a different way, record the change in the instructions as well.

The computer program is seldom more than a translation of the instructions you have written on your work sheet. Don't worry too much about elegance of format or of internal arithmetic. The first program won't work and will have to be rewritten. Later programs will work, but will be unsatisfactory. The program can be changed by patchwork. If you have designed the program in segments, it may be very easy to replace one subroutine by another, without disturbing the rest of the program. It seems trivial to mention it, but no one seems to write down what the changes are when they're made. It saves so much time to make a careful clear record of what you do, when you do it. There never has been a case

---

* W. Freiberger, M. Rosenblatt, and J. Van Ness, "Regression Analysis of Vector-Valued Random Processes," *Journal of the Society for Industrial and Applied Mathematics*, Vol. 10, No. 1 (March, 1962), 89–102.

yet where someone didn't want to go back later and trace through the program. It takes an enormous amount of time to try to decipher machine-language instructions, or even a listing of FORTRAN statements.

The program should be rewritten from scratch several times. After a while, the patchwork—even in a segmented program—becomes unwieldy. It's surprisingly easy to write the second program and trivial to write the third. Bear that in mind when you write the first one, and don't waste too much time on non-essentials.

The program can have a variety of uses. Theoretical results have been presented here, for example, on the effect of the smoothing constant, or the length of the lead time. Make enough runs to verify these results. Once you believe in the theory you won't have to make further extensive runs to test that sort of alternative.

Try alternative kinds of data in the program. Usually you won't have available data from alternative sources, such as dealer orders and consumer sales. The characteristics of the missing alternative can be simulated. In fact, it is probably a good idea to have a set of subroutines available (see Chapter 24) that can generate time series with any characteristics you like: underlying model, probability distribution of the noise, and serial correlation of noise samples. The standard test inputs should also be considered as data: impulse, step, ramp, and sine wave.

Usually, the chronic need is a long enough sequence of observations. Industrial organizations seem to have about 50 observations of any time series: two months by days, or one year by weeks, or five years by months. Fifty observations is a bare minimum sample on which to make any effective distinction between alternative forecast systems.

Organizations that have mechanized their records tend to have even less historical information. The methods of forecasting developed here were designed to minimize the number of past observations required in the record. The older information is lost forever.

Therefore, many companies have found it necessary to select a test sample of 100 (or 500) items, on which a complete detailed history is maintained for continuing analysis. It doesn't take much space or money to record everything that is known about these items in some permanent, but machine-legible form. A very wide variety of problems can be investigated with such data.

The program can also be used to explore the effect of representing the data by different kinds of models. At some point the increased effort in using a more sophisticated model overbalances the increase in accuracy achieved.

When you carry through runs with alternative data, models, smoothing techniques, and the like, you must have some basis for choosing the best. It isn't enough to print out a replica of the work sheet and scan the columns.

There is just too much data, and the differences will often be small. Therefore, plan in advance exactly what measures are to be used as a figure of merit and get the computer program to calculate the appropriate summaries for you. Frequently, when a large array of alternatives is to be explored, all the detail should be suppressed, and only the summary tables printed for each case.

Also plan how the results are to be displayed. Sometimes a table of alternatives is useful; in others, a graph of the figure of merit against a parameter value is better. Usually it is worthwhile first to plan a pilot run that finds only the areas worthy of more intensive investigation.

For example, three or four runs can usually serve to show where a curve is changing rapidly, and where it is relatively flat. Additional runs in the area of fast change will provide more information. This sequential approach usually gives more information for the effort involved than planning in advance to make one set of runs at equally spaced intervals.

The systems engineer will know some criteria that are valid for judging among alternatives. Sometimes the interests of the operating people are overlooked. Bring into the design group one or two representatives of the operating group whose jobs are being affected by the new improvements. Get them to state what criteria they think are valid as a basis for comparison. And, by all means, write down and distribute the consensus of such discussions. Otherwise a man may later find that his job is at stake, and he will find it hard to remember what he agreed to earlier.

Some of the criteria worth considering in such an evaluation are

Forecasting accuracy

Stability

Computing time

Record length required

These measures have been discussed in Section III. It is important to decide whether mean error or error variance is a better measure of accuracy. Should the variance of the forecasts be used as a measure of stability?

Plan these criteria in advance and get them summarized in the course of the other calculations. I have found it helpful to have a subroutine that will compute the mean, the standard deviation, and a few autocorrelation coefficients for any time series. Part of the instructions for assembling a particular evaluation program is designating those series for which these summaries are to be prepared.

Beyond the questions of accuracy, stability, and simplicity, several operational criteria should be considered. For example, if the forecasts are to be used in an inventory control system, then it may be relevant to ask how much total inventory would be required to give a predetermined level of service for a sample of 100 items. In a fire-control system, the probability of kill, given something about the lethal radius of the weapon, may be a valid measure. At some point, the forecast system must be embedded in the over-all control system, for rigorous evaluation.

Selling and Training

The problem of evaluation (including the selection of values for the various parameters) is properly one for a small systems design group. It is highly unlikely that the group as such will actually operate the system when it is installed. It is a very good idea to include on the design team one or two representatives of the operating department, who, when the study is over, will have direct responsibility for operating the new system.

There are the very real problems of selling the new system to the operating people and of training them to use it effectively. Usually, the design of the training program presents no great difficulty. The most recent version of the evaluation program can be used as a very effective selling tool, to convince the skeptics. In the selling stage, one is not concerned about alternative techniques, but in testing the system against a variety of problems imposed by the external environment. One of the best tests to distinguish among similar techniques is to use synthetic input data. Synthetic data can be devised to give a very much longer test run than is usually possible with actual data. Pure examples of the significant characteristics (underlying models, noise distributions, serial correlation, and so on) can be explored thoroughly. The system can be shocked by step and impulse inputs. The responses to such shocks can be very revealing, and the shock is so much worse than anything that can happen in practice that the designer will have a great deal of confidence in his work.

Now bring in the operating people and ask them to try out any problems they like. Everyone can remember some case that was a particular problem to him at the time—and therefore should be a problem for a new system. Run the problem through your evaluation program and let him watch the output as it is printed. If you are a natural showman, and understand your system well enough, you can rapidly scan his problem and tell him what to expect. You can also suggest how to modify the problem (or the system) to produce other results.

Encourage all operating people to try just as many different problems as they can think up. Someone may indeed find a problem that the system can't handle. If the problem arises only rarely, make a non-routine provision for it outside the normal functioning of the system. If it does occur frequently, treat the problem as one of evaluating alternatives. Consider whether some modification of the system you've designed will handle the problem.

At any rate, if it's a real problem, it is far better to find out about it at this stage than when the system has gone on stream.

24   Computer Simulation Programs

In this chapter, we shall discuss the design of a computer program that might be used for research, evaluation, or demonstration. Many such programs are in existence and have been used extensively. We shall not, however, present even a complete flow chart for any one program, much less a set of specific instructions that have been thoroughly checked. This is deliberate. A very large part of the value of a computer simulation is in the act of designing it. If you had a prepackaged simulation, you could get on with your analysis, but you wouldn't learn nearly as much as if you had had to sweat through the details of organizing the simulation yourself.

The discussion is centered around simulations rather than operating programs. This book deals only with forecasts, which are a small part of a total operating control system. The design of the forecast system for regular operation will depend a great deal on the nature of the rest of the control system, and on the kind of data-processing equipment (anything from people to STRETCH computers) that will be used.

If you will write several forecast simulations (or modify the first one you write out of all recognition), you'll find that it will be obvious how to write the operating program quickly and accurately. You should want to explore more different forecast subsystems than can possibly be used in the operating program.

Therefore, for the purposes of this chapter, we assume that you have access to a moderately fast, internally programmed, digital computer, and that you can design the simulation in one of the languages, such as FORTRAN, COBOL, GECOM, TABSOL, or ALGOL. We shall go through the same sequence of major blocks that we discussed for the manual work sheets and comment briefly on the principal alternatives that you might want to consider in the design of a simulation. Where the calculations have already been illustrated on a work sheet elsewhere in this book, we shan't go into any detail of how to program the same computations for a computer. There are three principal subroutines that are required in some simulations which we shall go into more thoroughly.

The first two subroutines can be used to generate a sequence of synthetic data to use in testing alternatives. One makes it possible to generate any desired (and known) underlying pattern in the data, so that you can see whether the smoothing calculations do, in fact, recover the true model coefficients. The other subroutine is a noise generator, including a random number routine, and means for obtaining samples from any desired distribution (with zero mean) and with known serial correlation.

These two subroutines make it possible to have an ample set of data on which to test alternatives. Furthermore, the data can be designed to be a much more rigorous test than real data usually are.

The third subroutine is a special program for inverting symmetrical positive definite matrices, developed by P. F. Strong and not generally known in the literature.

Outline of a Forecast Simulation

The first step in designing a forecast simulation is laying out a general block diagram with boxes for time, data, model coefficients, forecasts, errors, control, evaluation, recycling, and summary. In addition, it is necessary to keep careful check of all the conditions in the simulation that require initial conditions. Although the initial conditions are the first block that the simulation runs through, it will generally be the last block filled in, in detail. In discussing each of the other blocks, we shall comment on the calculations that are necessary at the start of the program to get things running.

Time: The time block is a simple indexing procedure. Initially, you'll have to specify when time starts (usually $t = 0$, or $t = 1$), and how long the program is to run. If the data are to be provided from an external source, then the data can be counted as they are read in, and the count indicates when the run will be finished. If the data are generated synthetically as part of the simulation, then the total number of observations must be specified as an initial condition.

Data: At some point, you will want to use actual historical data from your own records as an input to the simulation. It is far better to have very long records for a few items than to have only short records for many items. In some cases, it will also be necessary to write a subroutine to transform the original observations, with respect to some other independent function of time.

Initially, however, I strongly urge the use of synthetic data, which can provide much longer sequences and much more exacting tests of the alternatives. A sequence of between 100 and 200 observations will be sufficient to make any significant differences clear. The results will be different from run to run. Some differences, even though small, should properly be attributed to real differences between the alternative procedures. Other differences, sometimes large ones, will be the result of the particular set of data. The objective is to find the former and ignore the latter. The chances of doing so are better with very long sequences.

The subroutines for generating synthetic data are given later in this chapter.

Model coefficients: The first choice in this block is among the alternative smoothing techniques that you may want to explore: probability vector smoothing, exponential smoothing, general adaptive smoothing, general exponential smoothing, or moving averages.

The next specification is the number of degrees of freedom to be used in the model (to be used as a check that all the initial conditions are properly set up, to provide an index for the number of equations required to revise these statistics, and so on). The transition matrix L and the vector $\mathbf{f}(0)$ of initial values of the fitting functions define the model exactly.

For any of the techniques except moving averages, either the smoothing constant α must be specified, or its complement β, the discount factor. It is well to provide for two values: one for stable forecasts and one for a system that responds more rapidly to change.

For exponential smoothing, or adaptive forecasting under steady state conditions, initial values for the model coefficients must be provided. Where the data are generated synthetically, the correct initial values are easily obtained. You may want to provide for these initial values externally, however, to explore the effect of poor initial estimates.

Finally, specify the rules for revising the stored coefficients recursively with each new observation. Remember that there may be two modes of operation: the stable mode, and the rapidly responding mode. Rules for revision must be provided for both modes.

Forecasts: You can design the simulation either to compute cumulative forecasts through each of the next τ periods, or the actual forecast in each of the next τ periods. The choice depends on the application of the forecasts and is not usually a matter of testing alternatives. Provide for a specification of what the maximum lead time τ is, and whether you want all the forecasts for lead times $1, 2, 3, \ldots, \tau$, or just the one forecast at time τ.

At some point, you will want to explore the possibility of testing higher-order terms in the model for significance, so that the forecast will be based only on these terms for which the model coefficient is significantly different from zero.

Errors: The forecast error is the difference between the current observation $x(t)$ and the forecast $\hat{x}_1(t-1)$ made one sampling interval ago. You may also want to provide for keeping track of other forecast errors defined similarly, but for other lead times. Decide whether the error should be cumulative through the lead time or specific to a particular observation.

The mean absolute deviation is obtained as the result of single exponential smoothing of the absolute value of the forecast errors. You will have to specify an initial value, since it is computed recursively, and a value for the smoothing constant. It is quite convenient to use the same smoothing constant that is used for smoothing the stored statistics, but you will have great flexibility in your simulation if you allow for a separate specification. An alternative is to recompute the mean and variance of the errors at each sampling interval.

Do you have problems for which it may be appropriate to represent the variability of the noise by other than a constant model?

Control: The primary control is the algebraic sum of the errors. It was shown that this sum should not exceed K times the mean absolute deviation, where K depends on the smoothing constant used, the number of degrees of freedom in the model, and the probability that chance effects will trigger the tracking signal. Therefore, you must specify the value of K to be used in each run.

One use of your simulation will be deciding what to do about the smoothing process when the tracking signal does indicate a reasonable chance of systematic bias. Therefore, it may be well to design three possible steps, of which only one will be chosen for any particular run.

The simplest course of action is just to compute the ratio of the sum of the errors to the mean absolute deviation and print that ratio at each observation interval. For example, that was done for the IBM stock price data, Fig. 20.3.

The next possibility is printing a distinctive symbol whenever the ratio has exceeded K twice in succession, and then automatically setting the sum of the errors back to zero. In practice, of course, some competent person outside the system would review the facts of the case whenever such a signal occurred and decide whether any change in the model was warranted and, if so, what change.

The final possibility is letting the simulation automatically make a change. First, set the sum of the errors back to zero. Second, set a counter which will automatically be reduced by one with each successive observation. Third, switch the smoothing computations to a higher value of the smoothing constant (which is to be dropped back to the lower value when the counter reaches zero). Be sure that the print-out indicates when such an automatic correction is made.

Evaluation: At first the alternative forecast systems will probably be compared on their own merits. One measure that I have frequently used on forecasts that are to be used for production planning, or for inventory control, is comparing the actual total of the next τ observations with the forecast for the total of the same periods. In Section VII, we shall discuss the safety factors that allow a reasonable margin for forecast errors. At each observation compute

$$\text{excess} = \text{actual total} - \text{forecast} - k(\text{MAD})$$

where k is the safety factor of interest. If the excess is positive, then add 1 to a counter C1, and the value of the excess to a total E1. If the excess is zero or negative, then add 1 to a counter C2, and the value of the negative of the excess to a total E2.

NOTE: These counters and totals must be set to zero at the beginning of the run.

At the end of the run, these summaries give a fair indication of the number of times (and the amount) when actual demand would have exceeded the supply or fallen short of it. These statistics provide a rough estimate of the average inventory required because of the forecast errors and because of the service routinely rendered to customers.

An alternative is provision for an exit to some other control program, of which this simulation is treated as just a subroutine. The forecasts can then be evaluated in the proper context of the over-all control system. The reentry point on the next cycle will be in the Time block of this simulation.

There are some very tricky problems of comparing the forecast with actual data near the end of the run. By far the best way of being sure that the bookkeeping is done correctly is to carry out the computations on a work sheet by hand. Write down exact instructions as to what you have done. Ask someone who knows nothing of what you are trying to do to follow your instructions as to what you have done. If he gets the correct answer, program those instructions into the computer.

There is also the question of what results you want to count in a summary. Generally speaking, for a simulation, one does not count the results at the beginning in a comparative evaluation of alternative techniques. There may be a severe initial transient in the use of general adaptive smoothing on noisy data. Other techniques would have different effects, because of the way that the initial conditions were set.

Therefore, provide for the specification of a time T^* when all sums of statistics used for summary evaluation of the run are set to zero. The value of T^* can be 1, of course, if you want to count from the beginning of the run. Usually it is well to allow ample time for the initial transients to die out. For this reason, too, it is important to have very long sequences of data to be able to determine real differences among alternatives.

Recycle: At first, you will want the simulation to print out all the information that would appear on a line of the work sheet after processing each observation. Later on, a good deal of time can be saved if only the detail in which you are interested is printed. I usually like to provide that all initial conditions be printed, as well as the summary statistics, automatically, on every run. Then there is a separate control on each of the seven principal blocks, so that any set of them can be printed or suppressed, as desired.

When the necessary data have been printed, then check to see whether there are any more observations to be processed. If there are, increase the time index by one (and decrease the special control counters by one) and return to the next observation. If there are no more observations, process any summary information, such as means and standard deviations of any measures that you're interested in. On small computers, it is sometimes necessary to provide for accumulating a count, sum, and sum of squares, for each item to be measured. On a large computer, like the IBM 7090, where everything is in core anyhow, you can write the statistical summary instruction at the end of the program. It's much less efficient use of the memory space, and it may occasionally lead to trouble on very large problems. But it's faster to write, with less chance of error, and, hence, probably better strategy on the first simulations.

Initial conditions: When you have written fairly detailed instructions for each of the operating blocks in the simulation, go back over them with a fine-toothed comb and check off everything that requires some previous value in the computation. Now write the block that provides the necessary initial conditions.

On the first simulation program you write, make the analyst work. Require him to specify the numerical values of the coefficients for the various linear combinations required. Later on, refine the program so that he can specify more general initial conditions and let the computer make the necessary adjustments for him.

General remark: Some people easily learn to write simulations and other computer programs. Others have a very hard time. There seems to be a general characteristic that separates the two groups: those who get programs written and running quickly take more time in the writing.

First write down a very general block diagram with short prose notes on what each block is supposed to accomplish. Now take one block at a time and write out the instructions in plain English (the plainer the better) or as mathematical equations. Follow these instructions with an actual numerical example or, better yet, ask someone else to follow the instructions. Now rewrite the instructions so that they are accurate and complete. Get a hand solution to a fairly large problem to be used as a check.

Now, and only at this time, worry about the niceties of computer instructions: fixed versus floating point, nomenclature, format statements, and the like.

This detailed rewriting of the simulation can be very time-consuming. It may take as much as a week for a large, complex problem. But after the inevitable two or three diagnostic passes, the program will assemble and run, and what is more, it will give reliable answers.

The people who try to short-cut that work get their first diagnostic several days earlier. Unfortunately, they also get a running program considerably later with considerably more expense for machine time.

Now, about the week that such a process should take. If you find that it takes more than a week to get a running program, you've bitten off too large a problem. Back up and take something much simpler. Get a data-generating program written and running. Then get a statistical summary program written and running. Now try just smoothing and model coefficients, with no optional changes to be specified for each run. And so on. As you build up your own little library of subroutines and your skill at writing simulations, you will ultimately find that you can write a gigantic simulation, including everything in this chapter, and get it running in a week.

Data Pattern Generator

You will want to explore the consequences of using each of several alternative forecast systems on a variety of time series. The kind of data used in any particular study depends a great deal on the purposes of that study. Actual historical data of the same kind that would be used in the operating program will be required for some purposes. Frequently, the available record is too short for other types of study. Recall the discussion in Chapter 2 regarding the historical data used in studies and the current data used in actual operations.

In what follows we shall discuss the generation of a deterministic process $\xi(t)$ that underlies a sequence of observations $x(t)$ according to the model

$$\xi(t) = a_1 f_1(t) + a_2 f_2(t) + \ldots + a_n f_n(t)$$

where the $f_i(t)$ are specified mathematical functions of time, and the a_i are coefficients whose values are to be specified at the start of the run.

First, specify n the number of degrees of freedom in the model. Next, specify an n-component column vector of values $\mathbf{a}$. If you want to explore transient responses to changes in the pattern, or the test of significance for higher-order terms in the model, specify a second vector $\mathbf{b}$ and a time t_1.

The functions of time can also be thought of as a vector $\mathbf{f}(t)$ with components $f_i(t)$. You need only specify a set of initial values $\mathbf{f}(0)$ and a transition matrix L.

The type of functions included in the model depends on the specification of the transition matrix L. They may include: polynomials in time, trigonometric functions of time, exponential functions of time, or sums and products of these functions. A complete list of such transition matrices is given in Chapter 11.

After the initial conditions are specified, the basic cycle is as follows: Let t be the index of time in the general simulation. It is increased by one unit at each sampling interval

(1) $\mathbf{f}(t) = L\mathbf{f}(t - 1)$: multiply the previous vector of functional values by the transition matrix.

(2) IF $t < t_1$, go to 3, otherwise go to 4.

(3) $\xi(t) = \mathbf{a}'\mathbf{f}(t)$: the scalar product of the functional values and the constant coefficients for the first part of the program.

(4) $\xi(t) = \mathbf{b}'\mathbf{f}(t)$: the scalar product for the second set of constant coefficients.

In some simulations, the estimates used in setting the initial values of the coefficients will be the actual values of the coefficients used to generate the data pattern, and the forecast model will be the same as the model used to generate the data. It is worthwhile, however, to explore the consequences of initial conditions different from the actual pattern being generated.

As an example, suppose you want to study the detection of a change in the trend, when the forecast is being based on a linear model of the observations. The number of degrees of freedom is $n = 2$. Initially the data process might be based on

$$\mathbf{a} = \begin{bmatrix} 100 \\ 0 \end{bmatrix}$$

After $t_1 = 50$ observations, a trend is to be introduced, so that

$$\mathbf{b} = \begin{bmatrix} -400 \\ 10 \end{bmatrix}$$

The initial values of the function vector are

$$\mathbf{f}(0) = \begin{bmatrix} 1 \\ 0 \end{bmatrix}$$

and the transition matrix for a first-degree polynomial is

$$L = \begin{bmatrix} 1 & 0 \\ 1 & 1 \end{bmatrix}$$

Noise Generator

In problems of general interest, the process cannot be observed directly, but will be buried in superimposed noise

$$x(t) = \xi(t) + \epsilon(t)$$

Let us now discuss ways of generating successive noise samples $\epsilon(t)$. The first step is generating the next sample in a sequence that has a uniform distribution between zero and one, with no serial correlation between successive samples. This is our random-number generator.

The second step is using successive random numbers to select samples from some specified distribution. The standard deviation of the distribution can be specified as one of the values chosen at the beginning of each run; the mean of the distribution will always be zero.

The final step is introducing specific autocorrelation between successive noise samples. Frequently, of course, this step will be omitted, so that the noise samples are random.

The noise generator and the process generator programs will usually be used together to provide the actual observation

$$x(t) = a_1 f_1(t) + \ldots + a_n f_n(t) + \epsilon(t)$$

RANDOM-NUMBER GENERATORS. Strictly speaking, there isn't any really random sequence of numbers.* It is quite easy, however, to generate a sequence that has all the essential properties of a random sequence:

(1) The numbers generated should be uniformly distributed on the unit interval $(0, 1)$.

(2) There should be no serial correlation between successive samples in the sequence.

(3) Although any practical means of generating such samples will eventually start producing the same sequence over again, the length of the period should be as long as possible.

* The RAND Corporation, *A Million Random Digits* (Glencoe, Ill.: Free Press, 1955).

To these requirements may be added a fourth: that the arithmetic for generating successive samples be simple.

In the last ten years attention has focused on the formidably titled "multiplicative-congruential" method of generating a quasi-random sequence of numbers. The process requires the specification of three numbers: R_o, the initial random number; K, a fixed multiplier; and M, a fixed modulus. Successive samples are computed by

$$R(t) \equiv K \cdot R(t - 1)(\bmod M)$$

On a decimal machine with 10 digits per word, two schemes have been widely used. In the first, R_o is any number of the form $xyz0000001$, $K = 7^{11} = 1,977,326,743$, and the modulus is $M = 10^{10}$. The process generates about 50 million different numbers before it repeats.

The second scheme is even more attractive. The starting random number may be any odd number. The fixed multiplier is $10^5 + 11 = 100,011$, and the modulus is again 10^{10}. This process generates all the odd 10-decimal digit numbers between 0 and 1–500 million of them before it repeats.

On a 35-bit binary computer, Greenberger* has developed a similar scheme, where the starting number is any odd number, the fixed multiplier is $K = 2^{18} + 3$, and the modulus is 2^{35}. That is, one uses the low-order 35 bits of the 70-bit product.

The principal disadvantage of these routines is that the present versions of FORTRAN, which is so useful for writing other parts of the simulation, are not adapted to the necessary modular arithmetic in fixed-point notation.

The apparent disadvantage, that they are all odd numbers, is trivial. Any of these systems produces numbers with about ten decimal digits, which can be treated as a decimal fraction between zero and one. The random characteristics are exhibited by the five high-order positions of these numbers—the low-order positions don't matter.

IBM has a rather comprehensive manual† on random-number generators that also gives references to library programs that can be assembled into FORTRAN programs. For hand computations a table of random numbers is given in Appendix D. The mean of 1000 five-digit numbers is 47,867.9 (theoretically 49,999.5) and their standard deviation is 29,118.2 (theoretically 28,867.5). The correlation between all pairs of numbers is less than 0.05.

The entries in Table D.11 are arranged as 1000 five-digit words. If the distribution of digits were exactly uniform, there would be 100 of each of

---

* G. H. Orcutt, M. Greenberger, *et al.*, *Microanalysis of Socioeconomic Systems* (New York: Harper, 1961).

† IBM Reference Manual, "Random Number Generation and Testing," International Business Machines Corporation, 1959. See also A. Rotenberg, "A Pseudo-random Number Generator," *Journal of the Association of Computer Machines*, 1959.

the 10 digits in each column. Actually, the digits are random selections from a uniform distribution so that the probability of getting a digit is $p = 0.1$. The expected value is $1000p = 100$, and the variance should be $1000pq = 90$. Hence, there should be between 81 and 119 of each digit in each column. Table 24.1 gives the actual counts.

Table 24.1 COUNT OF DIGITS BY COLUMN IN TABLE D.11

Digit	Column 1	2	3	4	5	Total
0	107	107	86	85	103	488
1	121	104	95	106	89	515
2	108	100	104	90	118	520
3	92	101	115	92	110	510
4	95	100	104	103	88	490
5	107	101	103	104	99	514
6	94	107	119	99	107	526
7	91	84	85	108	93	461
8	97	108	100	101	104	510
9	88	88	89	112	89	466

Samples from particular distributions: Since the cumulative probability function $P(\epsilon)$ has values between zero and one, it is very easy to find a random sample, once one has a random number: the nth samples from that population is just the value ϵ_n such that $P(\epsilon_n) = R_n$. This method of sampling requires that the probability function be stored as a table, which takes up space, time, and worst of all, programming effort.

There are schemes for sampling from the uniform, exponential, triangular, and normal distributions, in which the mean is zero, and the standard deviation is specified for the particular run. The current sample from the random sequence is $R = R(t)$ throughout.

Uniform distribution: The simplest type of probability distribution is the uniform, in which the samples are equally likely at any point in some finite range. The random sample R is uniformly distributed between zero and one. Therefore to get a uniform distribution of samples with mean 0 and standard deviation σ take $\epsilon(t) = \sqrt{3}\, \sigma(2R - 1)$.

Exponential distribution: The exponential distribution is usually considered only for positive values of the variable, and the standard deviation is equal to the mean. It is sometimes convenient as an example of a skewed distribution. Since we want it to represent noise superimposed on the data pattern, we shall subtract the mean from the final result to reduce it to zero mean. (The proof for this scheme is due to John von Neumann.) The flow chart for this program is given in Fig. 24.1.

Triangular distribution: The triangular distribution is another skewed distribution. The time taken to generate a sample from the exponential distribution, using Fig. 24.1, is proportional to the size of the number,

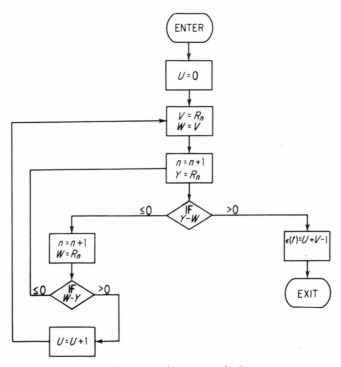

Fig. 24.1 Flow chart for generating a sample from an exponential distribution with unit variance and zero mean.

whereas a sample from a triangular distribution can be obtained immediately as

$$\epsilon(t) = \sqrt{3}\, \sigma(2 - 3\sqrt{1 - R})$$

The proof of this assertion is left as an exercise for the reader.

Normal distribution: In Chapter 19, we discussed the practical application of the central-limit theorem, to develop the normal distribution as the sum of samples from independent uniform distributions. We shall use the fact that the sum of 12 such samples has mean 6.0 and, in particular, unit variance. These samples will be described by a distribution that has no essential difference from the normal (gaussian) distribution. Therefore, in order to get a noise sample from a distribution with zero mean and standard deviation σ use

$$\epsilon(t) = (N_t - 6)\sigma$$

where N_t is the sum of 12 successive numbers generated by the random-number generator.

Correlated samples: Most of the theoretical work on the nature of the forecasts and forecast errors begins by assuming that the noise in the original observations has a zero mean, constant variance, and no serial correlation. Some simulation studies should be undertaken to see whether serial correlation in the noise has any significant effect on the relative usefulness of alternative ways of forecasting.

Votaw and Rafferty* have shown how to produce a sequence of samples from any distribution, with autocovariance

$$R_{\epsilon\epsilon}(k) = \sigma_\epsilon^2 a^{|k|}$$

where the exponential base is a number $0 < a < 1$.

First, generate a sample $y(t)$ from the appropriate distribution with standard deviation $\sigma_\epsilon(1 + a)/(1 - a)$. Let the first noise sample be

$$\epsilon(0) = (1 - a)y(0)$$

Thereafter, the successive noise samples are produced by exponential smoothing

$$\epsilon(t) = (1 - a)y(t) + a\epsilon(t - 1)$$

[This process, with $a = 0.8$, was used to generate the Warmdot total business volume data, Table C.16. The samples $y(t)$ were uniformly distributed noise, with a standard deviation of $500/\sqrt{3} = 288.7$.]

Since the samples from a normal distribution were generated as sums of twelve successive uniform random variables, it is possible to introduce a linear autocorrelation function by having some of the samples in one sum in common with samples in the succeeding sum.†

Matrix Inversion

Most computer libraries have a routine for finding the inverse of a non-singular square matrix. In this book we have made repeated use of a special type of matrix: symmetrical, positive definite. P. F. Strong, in a private

* D. F. Votaw and J. A. Rafferty, "High-Speed Sampling," *Mathematical Tables and Other Aids to Computation,* Vol. V, No. 33 (January, 1951), 1–8.

† See R. G. Brown, *Statistical Forecasting for Inventory Control* (New York: McGraw-Hill, 1959), pp. 169–72.

communication, has suggested the following simple program for finding the inverse of such a matrix:

Given the matrix A (elements $a_{ij} = a_{ji}$) construct the matrix B (elements b_{ij}) as follows:

(1) Find the largest diagonal element, say a_{kk}

(2) $b_{kk} = -\dfrac{1}{a_{kk}}$

(3) $b_{kj} = -a_{kj}b_{kk}$ for $k \neq j$

(4) $b_{jk} = b_{kj}$

(5) $b_{ij} = a_{ij} - b_{ik}a_{jk}$ $i \neq k,$ $j \neq k,$ $j \geqslant i$

(6) $b_{ji} = b_{ij},$ $j < i$

The matrix B may now be regarded as a new matrix A and the operation repeated on it, and so on, until the inversion has been completed after a number of repetitions equal to the size of the matrix. When the inversion is complete, all the diagonal elements of B will be negative. In a computer matters may easily be arranged so that the elements of the matrix B replace the elements of the matrix A one by one as the b_{ij} are formed.

AT THE END, CHANGE ALL SIGNS! The result is $-B = A^{-1}$.

It is usual in matrix operations to do a bit of checking. In the present case if row sums, say a_i are known for A, the corresponding row sums b_i for matrix B should satisfy the identities

$$b_k = \frac{a_k - 1}{a_{kk}} - 1$$

$$b_i = a_i - b_{ik}(a_k - 1) \qquad i \neq k$$

Note that the diagonal element a_{jj} becomes $a_{jj} - (a_{jk}a_{kj})/a_{kk}$, which is a smaller number. The amount of decrease is a measure of the loss of significance.

Applications

"The path of our investigation is at present obscure, but
I shall be very much interested if before evening we have
not cleared it up, or made a considerable advance along
it."

The Missing Three-Quarter

As you commute day after day between home and office, your wife notes the times when you get home and plans when to have dinner ready. In a chemical plant the operators watch the yield and purity of the product, and then adjust temperatures, flow rates, or the quantity of a catalyst. A professional investor watches the movement of stock prices and the trading volumes, and then decides whether to buy, sell, or wait. The Warmdot Corporation continually watches the demand for its products, and then decides whether to replenish stocks, how much to make, and where to keep it.

In each of these situations some sort of *process* goes on regularly. Some characteristic of the process is *observed* (for the purposes of this book, we assume that it is observed at discrete intervals). Finally, some *action* is taken to *control* the process. Section I discussed some of the general principles to be considered in deciding what to observe, where to observe it, and how often to make the observations. The data represent one connection between the forecasting system and the environment of which it is a part. Now in Section VII, we come to the other bridge connecting the forecast system back to the environment, the control system.

A long string of observations isn't, by itself, much use. We want a formal, compact description. There is a large branch of statistics, called *statistical inference*, that has to do with finding good descriptions for a set of observations. The textbooks in this field seem to go heavily in for drawing colored balls from urns: on the basis of 27 draws, we conclude that there are 20 percent red balls and 80 percent black balls in the urn. Or, on the basis of demand in the last two years we conclude that the demand in any one month can be described as a random sample from a poisson distribution with mean 82.

Now why would someone want a description like that? Presumably there is the tacit belief that future events will be similarly described. In this book, we have been quite explicit in the analysis of past observations in such a way as to project apparent changes into the future. The forecasting subsystem provides a description of what future observations can be. Remember that one can't forecast a specific event, but he can forecast very well the relative chances of several events. The forecast, including some estimate of the errors, should be viewed as a probability distribution over all possible values of the observation at some time in the future. In the probability vector models the probability distribution is explicit. In the time-series models, the model gives the mean of the future distribution, the mean absolute deviation determines the variance, and the form of the distribution is often normal.

But the description of future observations is not an end in itself. What are you going to do with the description? The entire development of this book has implied that the description is important in selecting among alternative courses of action. It is not our intent to go deeply into statistical decision theory. The bibliography has a long list of references in this field. Nevertheless, the decisions that lead to some sort of control action can have an important bearing on the design of the forecasting subsystem. Therefore, this section is intended to serve as a bridge, relating the forecast (to be thought of as a probability distribution) to the control decisions.

Your wife could pick any of a great many times when dinner is to be ready. She has to pick only one. The operator of a chemical plant could set the flow rate anywhere between 20 and 50 cubic feet per minute. He has to pick only one. The trader could "buy" any quantity of a stock, ranging from the maximum his resources will support down to selling short—if we think of selling as merely buying a negative quantity. He has to decide on one quantity, which may be positive, negative, or zero. Warmdot could start to manufacture more thermostats when the present supply gets down to 1, . . . , 50, . . . , 517, . . . pieces. The reorder point is set at one particular number.

At another time in the light of more information which may change the forecast probability distribution, any of these actions can be changed to some other number. But, at the moment one number must be picked somewhere in the feasible range.

The basis for picking this number is usually like the rubber stamp of operations research (Fig. 3.1). Think of the action as an independent variable that can take on any value in some range of numbers. Associated with each possible number there is some risk, gain, cost, or utility. The aim is to select the one number that should give the best results.

One clearly can't forecast the next observation—or any future observation—exactly. Therefore, the decision cannot be the correct one for a single event. We are dealing with continuing processes, and the decision must be evaluated on the average result over many events. There is a body of theory* for making a single decision in some best way; we shall not be concerned with that here. We have not been concerned with the "one-shot" type of economic forecast that sometimes must be made for a single particular project. The forecasts are progressively revised in the light of continuing information. Similarly, the decisions about the control process are based on these forecasts and evaluated on the long-run expectation of the results.

If your wife has dinner ready at 6:00, you may get home earlier, or later. When you're home earlier, you must wait, which probably has only a small imputed "cost." If you're late, the dinner may be spoilt, which will have a larger cost. Only one cost is incurred in a particular evening. The dinner hour can be picked so that in the long run the sum of the averages of each cost is a minimum.

The professional trader buys stocks with the hope that the market price will rise. If he buys early in a cycle, there is an opportunity for a very large rise, but the information about market trends is poor so that there may be a drop. If he waits until the movement is much clearer, then the possibility of a loss through a market drop is cut, but so is the possibility for gain. Somehow he must try to find the time to buy that will over a long time yield the best average profit.

Warmdot keeps thermostats in stock to be able to fill customers' demand. If the shop starts to make a new lot too early, there will be some left in stock when the new lot arrives in the warehouse, and it costs something to carry the inventory. If the shop starts to make the new lot too late, then either production must be expedited (at a cost), or some customers must wait (which has an imputed cost), or customers will go elsewhere (which loses profits). Warmdot must set its order points at a level that, in the long run, balances the expected costs of having too much on hand against the costs of not having enough.

In Chapter 25 we deal with some of the theoretical bases for making the decisions required in inventory control and production planning systems. We shall start with the simple problem of estimating the probability that present stocks will be exhausted before the end of the production

---

* Howard Raiffa and Robert Schlaifer, *Applied Statistical Decision Theory* (Boston: Harvard University Press, 1961).

lead time, and then go on to the estimate of the average quantity that would be short by the end of the lead time. Finally, we shall consider the formal problem of finding a safety factor that minimizes the sum of the expected costs of being overstocked, or of being short. Both linear and quadratic cost functions will be explored briefly.

Chapter 26, by way of contrast, considers the question of setting a fair handicap for sports car rallies. To those who are thoroughly familiar with the basic underlying principles of these analyses, it will be clear that a wide variety of other decision problems can be treated by analysis similar to these examples. This book does not intend to be definitive on the whole subject of statistical control systems design. These chapters merely suggest lines of thought in order to indicate how the forecast subsystem can be related to the general environment.

Please treat this theory with a little common sense. You select a safety factor that governs the control action. In making that selection, you considered the probabilities that future observations would be larger than the value selected, and the probabilities that they would be smaller. There is generally a long chain of theoretical reasoning that leads to that selection. Some links in the chain are very strong; others are likely to be quite weak. On the whole, you should find that most of the time the theory leads to good results. Either the theory was correct, or the errors counterbalanced each other. It is typical, for example, to find that, for about 80 percent of the items in an inventory, the theoretical order points lead to the anticipated probability of being short. Perhaps 10 percent of the items don't conform: the shortages are appreciably more severe than had been planned. For such items ignore the theory and increase the safety factor. Base the actual decision on the results observed. For the other 10 percent of the items, there may be considerably more stock than had been planned. Again, ignore the theory and decrease the safety factor.

You'll have to provide for some data collection and for some feedback. Plan the control system so that you know in advance what you expect to happen so that you measure what actually does happen and so that you can correct the control system. Thus, the entire control system becomes an adaptive network, gradually modifying the initial theoretical assumptions so that the end result is the result actually desired.

The temperature in a room should feel comfortable. The initial theory says that 70°F is a comfortable temperature, so you set the thermostat to 70°. In many cases the room will feel comfortable. But the thermostat may have been incorrectly calibrated. The thermostat may be mounted over a hot air duct, and you're on the opposite side of the room. Perhaps even 72° is really the comfortable temperature for you. It doesn't really matter what the cause is. If the room feels cool, you turn the thermostat up until the temperature is comfortable.

There is a time lag, of course. It takes a while for the furnace to come on and warm the air and for the blower to distribute the warm air to you. So you move the thermostat a little and wait a reasonable time. If it's still too cool, you can make another adjustment. But if the natural response time of the heating system is much longer than you thought it was, you may suddenly find the room much too hot and have to turn the thermostat down.

Make small changes in the safety factor. Wait long enough for the control system to respond to that change. Don't be trapped into overcompensating for changes that are in the process of taking effect.

25 Safety Factors for Inventory Control

Inventory systems have been studied very intensively, from the point of statistical decision theory. We do not intend to try to review all of a host of alternative control systems or the assumptions under which various theoretical problems have been solved. There are control systems, such as a max-min system, a two-bin system, an order-point, order-quantity system, a fixed-interval system, a base-stock system, and so on. Each of them has its own characteristics and areas of successful application. In each system, however, there is some number, used in the control of stock replenishment, that is related to the probability distribution governing demand in the immediate future.

Many articles and books* have been written on the optimum choice of the value for such a number, under assumptions of no lead time, fixed lead times, variable lead times; demand from poisson, gamma, and negative binomial distributions; single items and joint replenishment and multi-echelon control. The possibilities seem endless.

In this chapter, we discuss just three topics to illustrate the line that the analysis may take. First, we shall estimate the chance that a definite quantity of stock will be exhausted by the end of a lead time τ, given the

* A recent one is M. K. Starr and D. W. Miller, *Inventory Control: Theory and Practice* (Englewood Cliffs, N.J.: Prentice-Hall, Inc., 1962).

forecast distribution of demand. This is a very elementary problem, but in many real cases the only consideration necessary for the design of an effective inventory control system.

Next, we shall estimate the average quantity of unsatisfied demand as it is affected by the frequency with which orders for resupply are placed. There may be a very high chance that stock will be exhausted before the end of a replenishment lead time; if stock is replenished only occasionally, but in large quantities, on the average almost all the demand will be satisfied directly from stock on hand.

Again, this is a fairly simple approach to the problem, but effective in many real situations. If management can specify the level of service that is desirable for the firm, in terms of the chance that a customer will get what he wants immediately, then a sound inventory control system can be designed on this basis.

Finally, we shall consider the case where it is possible to assign actual costs to the inventory that results when demand falls short of supply, and to the shortages that materialize when demand exceeds supply. We shall consider both linear and quadratic cost functions.

To fix ideas, we shall consider only an order-point system. The same sort of analysis can be carried through for other types of systems as well, and even to situations that, at first blush, would not appear to be inventory problems at all: a bank's policy regarding the amount of cash to have at the teller's windows, the design of a dam for flood control,* and so on.

In this type of system, there is a number called the *order point*. The *available stock* in the system is the stock currently on hand, less any customer orders that haven't been filled, plus any stock that has already been ordered. After each transaction that affects the inventory, the available stock is compared with the order point. If the available stock is less than, or equal to, the order point, additional stock is ordered for replenishment.

Customers appear from time to time with demand on the inventory. If there is stock on hand, their demand is filled immediately. If there isn't any stock on hand, the customer's demand waits in backorder until the next receipt of material. It is mathematically convenient to regard the accumulated quantity backordered at any time as negative inventory.

Now it is quite apparent that if the order point is a large number, then the replenishment orders will be issued soon enough so that there always is stock on hand to meet customers' demand. If the order point is a smaller number, then customers may deplete the stock on hand before a new shipment arrives, and backorders can accumulate.

The order point can be related to the forecast of future demand. Remem-

---

* P. A. P. Moran, *The Theory of Storage* (London: Methuen, 1959).

ber that the forecast says, in effect, that future observations of demand x are samples from a probability distribution $P(x)$. The probability distribution can be represented by a vector of probabilities. (The observations, in this case, should be demand during a lead time, see Chapter 18.) Then the order point would correspond to the Pth percentile. If the order point corresponds to the ninety-third percentile, then 93 percent of the time, demand would be less than the available stock, and 7 percent of the time there would be backorders. Hence, if you want that chance that a backorder will occur, set the order point equal to the ninety-third percentile.

In general, however, the forecast $\hat{X}_\tau$ is derived from a time-series model. The errors in the forecast are normally distributed with standard deviation σ_τ. The order point M will be set according to the formula

$$M = \hat{X}_\tau + k\sigma_\tau$$

and it corresponds to some percentile of the distribution from which future demand will be observed. We shall call k the *safety factor*. Its value can be selected to

Set the chance that a stockout will occur

Set the average quantity in backorder

Minimize the expected costs of being short and of carrying stock

The Standard Deviation σ_τ

Throughout this chapter σ_τ is used to represent the standard deviation of the errors in forecasting the total demand in a lead time of τ sampling intervals. When the lead time over which the protection is required is known exactly there are several ways to obtain an estimate of σ_τ.

(1) *Direct measurement:* Maintain a record of the forecasts $\hat{X}_\tau$ and of the actual demand in each sampling interval. Compare the total forecast with the total actual demand in successive groups of τ sampling intervals. At each sampling interval recompute the variance of these differences. The square root of the variance is the required value of σ_τ.

This procedure requires considerable data-processing effort. The storage space for the history of forecasts and demand will require longer files. The computation of the square root of the variance takes machine time.

(2) *Error for one sampling interval:* The requirement for file space can be reduced. At each sampling interval compare the current observation of demand $x(t)$ with the previous forecast $\hat{x}_1(t-1)$ and recompute the variance of the differences. Then the appropriate factor

from part 6 of the table in Chapter 12 will give an estimate of σ_τ, provided that the noise in the observations has no serial correlation. The machine time for computing the variance and its square root is the same as in direct measurement.

(3) *Mean absolute deviation:* The mean absolute deviation can be re-computed at each sampling interval with less machine time than the square root of the variance. The factors in Table 19.5 can then be used to convert the mean absolute deviation into the standard deviation σ_1. Finally, part 6 of the appropriate table from Chapter 12 will convert σ_1 to σ_τ.

Suppose that the current value of the mean absolute deviation is $\Delta(T) = 20.4$ and that the normal distribution is a reasonable representation of the distribution of forecast errors. From Table 19.5, we see that the standard deviation $\sigma_1 = 20.4/0.8 = 25.5$. Further, suppose that the lead time is $\tau = 6$ sampling intervals and that the forecasts have been computed with the simple sinusoidal model Table 12.4, with $\beta = 0.965$. Then the standard deviation $\sigma_6 = 2.6473 \times 25.5 = 67.6$.

(4) *Population estimates:* The items in an inventory may be classified into one of a few homogeneous groups. For each group there will be a general relationship (Fig. 20.1) between the forecast $\hat{X}_\tau$ and the standard deviation σ_τ of the general form $\sigma_\tau \simeq a\hat{X}_\tau^b$ where the constants a and b are characteristic of the class. When this method is used, some current estimate of σ_1 should be maintained from the historical behavior of each item, to make sure that the item still belongs to the class to which it was originally assigned.

These four methods can be used whenever the lead time is known to be exactly τ sampling intervals. There are important cases where the lead time is a stochastic variable itself. The most reliable way of estimating σ_τ in such cases is measuring the demand during a lead time directly, as described in Chapter 18. Then the sampling interval becomes the interval between successive receipts of material, rather than a specific calendar time. The mean absolute deviation, together with Table 19.5, estimates σ_τ directly.

In the special case where the demand can be represented by a constant model $\hat{x}(t) = \hat{a}$, and where the distribution of demand about its average is independent of the distribution of lead times about their averages, it is possible to estimate the variance of the demand during a lead time. We shall need four factors:

$\hat{a}$ is the current estimate of the average demand in one sampling interval, for example, as the result of single exponential smoothing or a simple moving average of demand.

σ_1^2 is the current estimate of the variance of the forecast errors around the forecast $\hat{a}$. For example, if one uses the mean absolute deviation Δ, then $\sigma_1^2 = (\Delta/0.8)^2$.

$\bar{\tau}$ is the average lead time, perhaps obtained by single smoothing of past observations of lead times.

s^2 is the variance of the lead times about the average, which can be computed in the same way that the variance of the forecast errors is computed.

Then the variance of demand during a lead time is

$$\sigma_\tau^2 = \bar{\tau}\sigma_1^2 + \hat{a}^2 s^2$$

To prove this result, consider a fixed lead time τ. The expected sum of demands in exactly τ sampling intervals is $\hat{a}\tau$. Because *the noise in the demand is serially independent*, the variance of the total is just $\tau\sigma_1^2$. Therefore, the second moment of the total is

$$\mathcal{E}(X^2|\tau) = \tau\sigma_1^2 + (\hat{a}\tau)^2$$

Now suppose that, in one particular trial the actual lead time is a number chosen from the probability distribution $p(\tau)$. The expected value of the total demand is

$$\mathcal{E}(X) = \sum_{\tau=0}^{\infty} \mathcal{E}(X|\tau)p(\tau)$$

$$= \hat{a}\bar{\tau}$$

In a similar way, we can get the second moment of the total as

$$\mathcal{E}(X^2) = \sum_{\tau=0}^{\infty} \mathcal{E}(X^2|\tau)p(\tau)$$

$$= \sigma_1^2\bar{\tau} + \hat{a}^2 \sum_{\tau=0}^{\infty} \tau^2 p(\tau)$$

from which the desired result follows immediately. Note that the estimate of the first and second moments of X depends on the assumption that the demand and the lead time vary independently.

Probability that a Stockout Occurs

The expected demand during a lead time is the sum of the forecasts for each of the sampling intervals in the lead time

$$\hat{X}_\tau(T) = \sum_{t=1}^{\tau} \hat{x}_t(T)$$

When the lead time is at least three times as long as the sampling interval, the distribution of the forecast errors is normal, with standard deviation σ_τ proportional to the mean absolute deviation $\Delta(T)$. The constant of proportionality is the product of a factor from Table 19.5 and a factor from one of the tables in Chapter 12.

The order point is to be

$$M(T) = \hat{X}_\tau(T) + k\sigma_\tau$$

The chance that a stockout occurs is the chance that the total demand in a lead time exceeds $M(T)$, which can be obtained from a table of the normal distribution. Suppose, for example, that it is practical to run short of stock in 7 percent of the replenishment cycles. There is a 7 percent chance that a sample from a normal distribution will be more than 1.48 standard deviations above the mean; therefore, $k = 1.48$.

We see that the order point can be expressed directly in terms of the mean absolute deviation as

$$M(T) = \hat{X}_\tau(T) + K\,\Delta(T)$$

where the composite safety factor K is the product of three factors:

1.25 from Table 19.5 (mean absolute deviation to standard deviation)

2.6473 from Table 12.4 (lead time of one to lead time of six sampling intervals)

1.48 from Table D.6 (7 percent chance of being exceeded in a normal distribution)

Hence, $K = 4.90$.

These theoretical results can be checked by a simulation. Recall from Chapter 4 the discussion of Company B's monthly imports (Table C.9 and Fig. 4.7). The original data were transformed to a four-week basis for each month, so that a simple sinusoidal model (Table 12.4) could be used to represent the imports. The forecasting process was simulated, keeping track of the forecast errors for lead times of 1, 2, . . . , 12 months, for each of the 107 months starting with February, 1951. The standard deviation of these errors is plotted in Fig. 25.1 against the lead time, with a solid line corresponding to the factors in part 6 of Table 12.4. These errors are smaller than those resulting from a similar trial with a more elaborate model of the original data. Note that some correlation of the residuals causes the simulated points to lie appreciably above the theoretical curve, which was based on the assumption of random residuals.

The simulation was repeated several times, with values of the safety factor ranging from $k = 0.25\tau$ to $k = 2.00\tau$, and for lead times ranging from $\tau = 1$ month to $\tau = 12$ months. On each run, a count was kept of the number of times when the actual demand during the lead time exceeded the order point. Table 25.1 shows a very good agreement (for a

Table 25.1 A SIMULATION OF COMPANY B'S IMPORTS NUMBER
OF STOCKOUTS IN 107 MONTHS

Lead Time τ	Safety Factor k	Equivalent Number of Standard Deviations	Number of Stockouts	
			Actual	Theoretical
1	0.25	0.2	36	42
	0.50	0.4	30	35
	0.75	0.6	22	27
	1.00	0.8	20	21
	1.50	1.2	12	11
	2.00	1.6	6	5
3	0.75	0.22	35	41
	2.25	0.66	21	25
	3.75	1.11	10	13
	6.00	1.77	1	3
6	1.50	0.27	24	40
	4.50	0.82	13	21
	7.50	1.36	3	9
	12.00	2.18	0	1
9	2.25	0.35	22	36
	6.75	1.04	5	15
	11.25	1.73	2	4
12	3	0.39	17	35
	6	0.78	14	22
	9	1.10	1	12

small sample) between the number of times the stock would have run short in the simulation compared with the expected number of occasions, based on the number of standard deviations of protection afforded.

The criterion of a preset probability that a stockout will occur by the end of a replenishment lead time has a great deal of merit in many inventory control systems. The basis for selecting the appropriate safety factor is straightforward. Items that are replenished more frequently have more opportunities per year to run short. But in most inventory systems, items that are ordered more frequently are also the vast-moving items that represent the bulk of the money involved. If some sort of expediting effort is going to be spent whenever there is a potential shortage, it seems rational to spend that effort on those items where the greatest amount of investment can be saved. This criterion automatically allocates effort in proportion to the item's importance (if any of the usual square root formulas for reorder frequency is used).

Furthermore, it is very simple to determine whether the system is behaving as planned. If the safety factor was selected so that there is a 7 percent chance of a stockout by the end of the lead time, then in each month

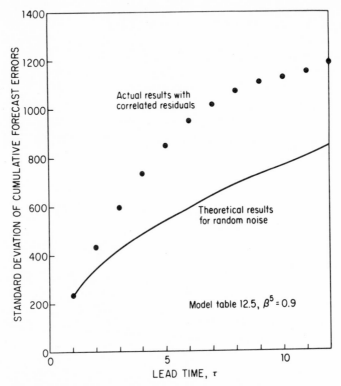

Fig. 25.1 Errors in forecasting Company B's imports.

(or any other period of time), very nearly 7 percent of the items received that month should have backorders or have had expedited deliveries. It is possible to measure the system performance directly, in the same terms that the design criterion was measured.

Expected Quantity Short

The next possibility to consider is the average quantity short, rather than the mere probability that there will be a shortage (or that special action was required to avert it). The actual demand during the next lead time is a sample X from a population that we can describe reasonably well by the normal distribution with mean $\hat{X}$ and standard deviation σ_τ.

The order point, as before, is written

$$M = \hat{X}_\tau + K\Delta = \hat{X}_\tau + k\sigma_\tau$$

and the demand sample is

$$X = \hat{X}_\tau + t\sigma_\tau$$

If the demand is small, $t \leqslant k$, there is no shortage. If the demand is large, $t > k$ then the quantity short is $(t - k)\sigma$.

Let the probability that the demand $X = \hat{X} + t\sigma$ be characterized by the density function $p(t)$. Then the average quantity short, over all such replenishment cycles is

$$\bar{U} = \sigma \int_k^\infty (t - k)p(t)\, dt$$

Raiffa* has extensive tables of these averages of one tail for several forms of the distribution $p(t)$. In particular, for the normal distribution

$$p(t) = \frac{1}{\sqrt{2\pi}}\, e^{-t^2/2}$$

and $\quad E(t > k) = f(k) = \displaystyle\int_k^\infty (t - k)p(t)\, dt = p(k) - k\int_k^\infty p(t)\, dt$

The expected quantity short at the end of a reorder cycle is $\sigma_\tau f(k)$. The total quantity sold during a reorder cycle is the order quantity Q. Therefore, the fraction of total demand short is

$$R = \frac{\sigma_\tau f(k)}{Q}$$

The policy is usually stated in terms of the fraction $P = 1 - R$ of demand that is to be satisfied from stock "off the shelf." The required safety factor satisfies

$$f(k) = \frac{QR}{\sigma_\tau} = \frac{Q(1 - P)}{\sigma_\tau}$$

where $f(k)$ is the partial expectation $E(t > k)$ given in the table of the normal distribution (D.6).

Exercise. Demand data have been sampled once a month, and can be described by a linear model (double exponential smoothing, $\beta = 0.94868$). The mean absolute deviation is $\Delta = 58$, and the lead time is five months. What is the standard deviation of the forecast errors? What is the average quantity short at the end of the lead time if the safety factor is $k = 1.4$? The average annual demand is 1500 pieces. If the average order quantity lasts three months, what safety factor K would you use to satisfy 93 percent of the demand from stock? What is the corresponding chance that a stockout will occur?

These two cases serve to illustrate what would happen—in terms of the frequency and the quantity of shortages—as affected by the choice of a safety factor. When the safety factor is large, then there is a small chance of a stockout, and a small average quantity short. When the safety

---

* H. Raiffa and R. Schlaifer, *Applied Statistical Decision Theory* (Boston: Harvard University Press, 1961), p. 198.

factor is smaller the chances of shortage increase. Therefore, these results give us one of the curves in the "rubber stamp" of operations research: the costs that decrease with an increase in the safety factor, which is the independent variable here. Let us now consider both the ascending and descending curves to see what the minimum cost can be.

Safety Factors to Balance Costs

Throughout this section we assume that the actual demand during the next lead time is a sample from a (normal) distribution, with mean $\hat{X}_r$, and standard deviation σ_r. The mean is a cumulative forecast, and the standard deviation is proportional to the mean absolute deviation (Chapter 16).

We might note in passing that here at the end of this book we are looking very briefly at the question of how to select a safety factor for an inventory system, knowing that demand will be a sample from a particular distribution. Most books on the theory of inventory control *start* with the assumption that demand will be such a sample. This chapter, then, is a bridge between the two streams of theoretical development.

We shall now explore two elementary models for selecting a value of the safety factor that minimizes the total cost function. The first example considered might be for an item like automotive antifreeze. The selling season is very short. Any demand not filled from stock is lost, and it seems reasonable to assign the loss of gross profit per unit of demand not filled as the cost of being short. Any stock left in inventory at the end of the season is carried over to the next year. Again, it is not too difficult to assign a cost per extra unit for keeping it in inventory. The two costs are proportional to the number of units, but the cost per unit of lost sales may be quite different from the cost per unit carried over to the next year.

In the other example we shall consider an optional feature of the product, such as left-hand doors for refrigerators. The refrigerator model has a definite end date when it will be supplanted by a new model. If the necessary doors are not in stock toward the end of the model year, extra supplies are expedited, and the cost is taken to be proportional to the square of the number of units to be procured. On the other hand, if some doors are left over at the end of the model year, they can be gradually sold for repairs, or for salvage value. The cost of holding the units in a steadily decreasing inventory will be seen to be proportional to the square of the initial number of units carried over.

EXAMPLE 1. LINEAR COSTS. Let us first consider an item such as antifreeze. The selling season is quite short; there is no chance to revise the production schedule during the season. If the schedule is too low, there will be some demand that cannot be filled, and the risk can be taken as C_1 dollars per unit of demand not filled. The cost C_1 can be thought of as the lost profit on the sales. On the other hand, if the schedule is set too high, there will be an inventory at the end of the selling season that will be carried over until the next year. We shall assume that it costs C_2 dollars per unit to carry this inventory.

The number of units scheduled will be

$$M = \hat{X}_\tau + k\sigma_\tau$$

The actual demand that materializes can be written in a similar form as

$$X = \hat{X}_\tau + t\sigma_\tau$$

The risks that will be incurred can then be written as

$$C = \begin{matrix} C_1(t - k)\sigma & t \geqslant k \\ C_2(k - t)\sigma & t \leqslant k \end{matrix}$$

The basic cost model: The expected cost associated with using a value k for the safety factor is

$$\mathcal{E}(C) = C_2\sigma \int_{-\infty}^{k} (k - t)p(t)\, dt + C_1\sigma \int_{k}^{\infty} (t - k)p(t)\, dt$$

We can write the total cost, in normalized form, as

$$\frac{\mathcal{E}(C)}{C_1\sigma} = \lambda f(-k) + f(k)$$

where

$$\lambda = \frac{C_2}{C_1} \quad \text{and} \quad f(k) = \int_{k}^{\infty} (t - k)p(t)\, dt$$

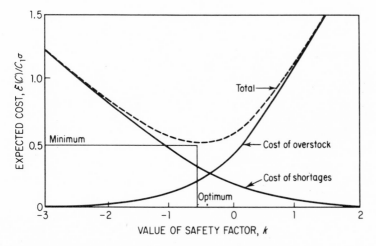

Fig. 25.2 The balance between costs of overstock and shortages.

is the partial expectation given in Table D.6. Figure 25.2 is the corresponding rubber stamp. When the safety factor k has a low value, there is a large risk of being short. When the value of k is high, there is a high risk of having an overstock. Between these extremes is a value that minimizes the total expected cost.

The optimum safety stock: The next step is finding an expression for the value for the safety factor k that makes the expected cost a minimum. If we differentiate with respect to k and solve $d\mathcal{E}(C)/dk = 0$, we find that the optimum safety factor is defined by

$$\int_{-\infty}^{k} p(t)\, dt = \frac{C_1}{C_1 + C_2} = \frac{1}{1 + \lambda}$$

The total probability that demand should be less than the level allowed for in the schedule depends on the ratio $\lambda = C_2/C_1$ of the cost of being overstocked to the cost of being understocked.

Table 25.2 lists values of the ratio $1/(1 + \lambda)$ for a sequence of values of the cost ratio λ. The third column lists the corresponding values for the safety factor.

Table 25.2   SAFETY FACTORS TO MINIMIZE TOTAL LINEAR COSTS

Cost Ratio $\lambda = \dfrac{\text{cost of excess}}{\text{cost of shortage}}$	Probability of Filling All Demand $P = \dfrac{1}{1 + \lambda}$	Safety Factor k $\int_{-\infty}^{k} p(t)\, dt = P$
0.01	0.9901	2.33
0.05	0.9524	1.67
0.1	0.9091	1.34
0.5	0.6667	0.43
1.0	0.5000	0.00
2.0	0.3333	−0.43
10	0.0909	−1.34
20	0.0476	−1.67
100	0.0099	−2.33

Minimum achievable costs: Since the expected cost for any safety factor can be written in terms of the service function as

$$\frac{\mathcal{E}(C)}{C_1} = \lambda f(-k) + f(k)$$

we can find the value of the minimum expected cost (for the optimum value of the safety factor) as a function of the cost ratio λ.

From the plot of the results in Fig. 25.3, we see that the minimum achievable costs are low for small cost ratios; that is, when the cost of an excess is small compared with the cost of a shortage. There is a minimum

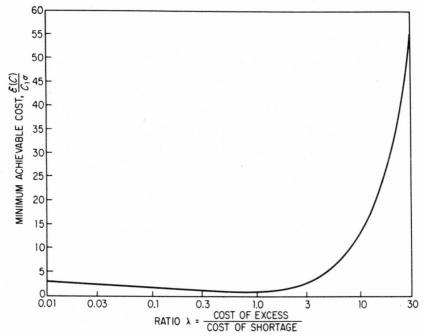

Fig. 25.3 Expected total costs with optimum safety factor.

when the ratio is about 0.5. For large cost ratios, the minimum costs become very large.

A numerical example: Now let us apply these results to our antifreeze. For example, suppose the gross margin is 50 percent, and it costs 24 percent to carry the inventory for a year. We would actually carry a surplus for only ten months, so that the cost of being overstocked is 20 percent of cost. The cost ratio is

$$\frac{C_2}{C_1} = \frac{0.20}{0.50} = 0.4 = \lambda$$

The best value for the safety factor is $k = 0.57$. That is, for the best balance of risks, one should aim to produce 0.57σ more than the forecast of expected demand. There is a 71 percent chance that this level will satisfy all the demand. (Note that if it costs a great deal to carry over the surplus, a negative safety factor is best.)

Routine stock replenishment: The same sort of linear cost equation may apply in the case of an inventory item that is replenished in lots of Q pieces each, every time the available stock (on hand plus on order less commitments) falls to the order point

$$M = \hat{X}_\tau + k\sigma_\tau$$

The actual demand during a lead time can be written

$$X_\tau = X + t\sigma_\tau$$

where the distribution of t is some function (likely to be the normal distribution function) with zero mean and unit variance.

When the demand during a lead time is greater than the order point ($t > k$) there will be a shortage. The expected number of pieces short is

$$\sigma_\tau \int_k^\infty (t - k)p(t)\, dt = \sigma_\tau f(k)$$

When the demand is less than the order point ($t \leqslant k$), there is stock left on hand that must be carried for the next reorder cycle. The expected number of pieces left over is

$$\sigma_\tau \int_{-\infty}^k (k - t)p(t)\, dt$$

Consider first the case when a shortage occurs. We shall assume that a penalty cost C_1 is incurred per unit short. The value of C_1 may depend on unit price or be set as an arbitrary policy variable. The expected cost per reorder cycle for being short is

$$C_1\sigma_\tau \int_k^\infty (t - k)p(t)\, dt$$

Suppose we sell S pieces per year and order Q at one time, then there will be S/Q reorder cycles per year, giving the expected *annual* cost of shortages as

$$D_1 = \frac{C_1\sigma_\tau}{Q} \int_k^\infty (t - k)p(t)\, dt$$

Now consider the other cycles, in which there is some safety stock left on hand. The annual cost of carrying that portion of the inventory investment will be

$$D_2 = rv\sigma_\tau \int_{-\infty}^k (k - t)p(t)\, dt$$

where r is the annual carrying charge and v is the unit cost of the item.

If it is the practice to accumulate backorders when there is a shortage and fill them from the next shipment, then the stock level will be reduced by the average quantity of the shortage, so that the annual cost to carry the cycle stock would be

$$D_2' = rv\sigma_\tau \left[\int_{-\infty}^k (k - t)p(t)\, dt - \int_k^\infty (t - k)p(t)\, dt \right]$$

$$= rv\sigma_\tau k$$

Hence there are two possible models of total annual cost:

(1) When shortages represent lost business

$$D = D_1 + D_2 = \frac{SC_1\sigma_r}{Q} \int_k^\infty (t - k)p(t) \, dt + rv\sigma_r \int_{-\infty}^k (k - t)p(t) \, dt$$

(2) When shortages are backordered

$$D' = D_1 + D_2' = \frac{SC_1\sigma_r}{Q} \int_k^\infty (t - k)p(t) \, dt + rv\sigma_r k$$

In either case, we can think of the total annual cost as a function $D(k)$ of the safety factor selected. For very low safety factors there is a high cost of shortage, but a low cost to carry stock. For a very high safety factor, the shortage costs become negligible, but there is a high carrying cost. Perhaps at some intermediate level the total cost has a minimum. We can check first to see whether the first derivative dD/dk has a zero value, where the second derivative d^2D/dk^2 is positive.

Case (1)

$$\frac{dD}{dk} = \frac{SC_1\sigma_r}{Q}\left[-\int_k^\infty p(t) \, dt\right] + rv\sigma_r\left[1 - \int_k^\infty p(t) \, dt\right]$$

The derivative is zero when the probability that there will be a shortage is

$$1 - F(k) = \int_k^\infty p(t) \, dt = \frac{1}{1 + (SC_1/rvQ)}$$

The second derivative is always positive, so this result must yield a minimum total cost. If the unit penalty of being short C_1 is large, the probability of a shortage is small. If there are many opportunities for a shortage (S/Q large), then the shortage chance is small. On the other hand, if it costs a great deal to carry the stock (rv large), a larger chance of shortage is economical.

Case (2)

$$\frac{dD'}{dk} = \frac{SC_1\sigma_r}{Q}\left[-\int_k^\infty p(t) \, dt\right] + rv\sigma_r$$

The derivative is zero when the chance of a shortage is

$$1 - F(k) = \int_k^\infty p(t) \, dt = \frac{rvQ}{SC_1}$$

Again the second derivative is positive, so the solution is a minimum total cost, *if* the ratio on the right of the equation is less than unity, so that there is a probability equal to that ratio.

It is interesting to consider the case where (rvQ/SC_1) is small. Then in Case (1) we have

$$\frac{rvQ}{SC_1}\left[\frac{1}{1 + (rvQ/SC)_1}\right] = \frac{rvQ}{SC_1}\left[1 - \frac{rvQ}{SC_1} + \left(\frac{rvQ}{SC_1}\right)^2 - \cdots\right]$$

If the ratio is small enough to neglect the square $(rvQ/SC_1)^2$, then both cases yield the same results. This result is not surprising, since the expected shortage will be very small and it doesn't matter whether the backorders are carried over or lost.

Note that nowhere in the derivation so far have we assumed anything about the nature of the unit shortage penalty C_1, or about the probability distribution $p(x)$. Furthermore, the final formulas used to determine $F(k)$ do not depend on the standard deviation σ_r.

EXAMPLE 2. QUADRATIC COSTS. Now let us turn our attention to an assembly which may be sold as an optional extra on a major piece of equipment. The equipment is scheduled to go out of production at the end of the year, and the new model cannot use this particular assembly. We must plan how many assemblies to have available between now and the end of the year.

We shall still plan in terms of the expected demand plus a safety factor times the standard deviation of forecast errors, and our policy can be specified by selecting a value for the safety factor. If we use a high value, we will have enough to meet all demand that materializes, but run the risk of being stuck with stock at the end of the year. We can sell off any excess for repair parts.

If we come to the end of the model year with N pieces in inventory, they will gradually be used up; let's say at the rate of S pieces per year. The average inventory will then be $N/2$ pieces, and it will take N/S years before they are all gone. Therefore, if it costs I dollars per piece per year to carry the assembly in inventory, the total cost penalty for having too many is $IN^2/2S$—proportional to the *square* of the excess. We can let $C_3 = I/2S$ be the constant of proportionality.

We could still use the assumption of lost profits on demand for any units we are short, but let us take an alternative model. We assume that somehow we will furnish enough assemblies to meet the demand. If there is a small shortage, we can get the extra units at low cost, but if the shortage is large, the costs of expediting additional material can become very large indeed. For mathematical convenience, let us assume that the costs of expediting for a shortage are proportional to the square of the size of the shortage, with the constant of C_4.

Basic cost model: Now, if we plan for $\hat{X} + k\sigma$ and get a demand for $\hat{X} + t\sigma$, the costs incurred will be

$$C_4[(t - k)\sigma]^2 \qquad t \geqslant k$$

or

$$C_3[(k - t)\sigma]^2 \qquad t \leqslant k$$

Assuming, as we did before, a probability distribution of the forecast errors, the expected costs associated with the policy of using a value k for the safety factor will be

$$\mathcal{E}(C) = C_3\sigma^2 \int_{-\infty}^{k} (k - t)^2 p(t)\, dt + C_4\sigma^2 \int_{k}^{\infty} (t - k)^2 p(t)\, dt$$

We can normalize the expected cost, as we did in the earlier model, and get

$$\frac{\mathcal{E}(C)}{C_4\sigma^2} = \lambda \int_{-\infty}^{k} (k - t)^2 p(t)\, dt + \int_{k}^{\infty} (t - k)^2 p(t)\, dt$$

For the normal probability distribution,

$$p(t) = \frac{1}{\sqrt{2\pi}} e^{-t^2/2}$$

the cost equation can be written

$$\frac{\mathcal{E}(C)}{C_4\sigma^2} = \lambda \left[kp(k) + (1 + k^2) \int_{-\infty}^{k} p(t)\, dt \right] - kp(k) + (1 + k^2) \int_{k}^{\infty} p(t)\, dt$$

$$= \lambda g(-k) + g(k)$$

Table 25.3 gives typical values of the function

$$g(k) = -kp(k) + (1 + k^2) \int_{k}^{\infty} p(t)\, dt$$

When we plot the costs (Fig. 25.4) we see that, again, a high safety factor leads to appreciable costs of overstock, whereas a low value leads

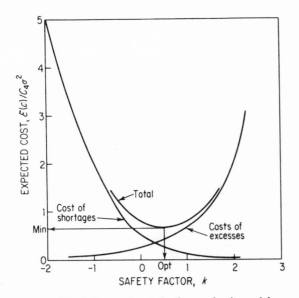

Fig. 25.4 The balance of costs in the quadratic model.

to costs of shortages. There is a value of the safety factor that minimizes the total cost.

Table 25.3   SECOND MOMENT OF THE UPPER TAIL
OF THE NORMAL DISTRIBUTION

Safety Factor k	Second Moment $-kp(k) + (1 + k^2) \int_k^\infty p(t)\, dt$
−3.0	9.99989
−2.5	7.24878
−2.0	4.99423
−1.5	3.22714
−1.0	1.92465
−0.5	1.04037
0.0	0.50000
0.5	0.20964
1.0	0.07535
1.5	0.02286
2.0	0.00577
2.5	0.00122
3.0	0.00011

Safety factor for minimum cost: The derivative with respect to k is

$$\frac{d\mathcal{E}(C)}{dk} = 2kC_3\sigma^2 + (C_4 - C_3)\sigma^2 \int_k^\infty -2(t - k)p(t)\, dt = 0$$

Hence, the optimum value of the safety factor is the solution to

$$\frac{k}{f(k)} = \frac{C_4' - C_3}{C_3} = \frac{1 - \lambda}{\lambda}$$

where now $\lambda = C_3/C_4$ (cost of excess divided by the cost of a shortage). The solution to this equation is approximately $k = -0.874 \log \lambda$.

Sensitivity

In any development of objective rules and equations for selecting the value of some policy variable, such as the safety factor, we come to the question: "How important is it to know the costs exactly?" The equations developed here do not lend themselves to easy manipulation for finding the sensitivity, but we may gain some insight from a study of the various graphs.

The value of the safety factor: In Fig. 25.2 for the linear-cost model, we see that the optimum value of the safety factor (for a cost ratio $\lambda = 2.5$) is $k = -0.57$. If we went down to $k = -1.0$, or up to $k = -0.25$, however, the total costs would remain almost the same as they are at the absolute minimum. Thus we might conclude that we are seeking a value of the safety factor within a factor of 2 from the optimum; that is, between double and half the true value.

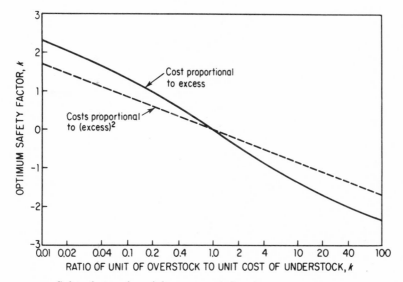

Fig. 25.5 Safety factors for minimum expected costs.

In Fig. 25.4, for the quadratic-cost model, the optimum is $k = 0.35$. Again, the graph appears to show that between double and half the optimum value will give costs that are essentially the same as the minimum. When the cost of an excess is less than the cost of a shortage, there is very little difference in the final results between different values of the cost ratio.

Therefore, one might conclude that if each of the components of the cost ratio is known to within a factor of 2 from its "true" value, the resulting safety factor will give a reasonable balance in costs. Extra labor, necessary to get more precise estimates, would probably not be justified by additional savings.

Cost models: We have discussed two models. In the first, the costs are proportional to the size of the differences between the actual demand and the level planned on. In the second, the costs are proportional to the squares of these differences. In each case, the optimum safety factor was found to depend on the ratio of the cost coefficients.

Figure 25.5 reveals that the safety factor used for a given cost ratio is about the same with either model. Certainly, the maximum difference is well within the range of double-to-half that seems to give the minimum attainable costs. Therefore, it does not seem to be vital to establish whether one or the other (or some intermediate model) is the exact representation of the facts.

26 Rally Handicaps

A great many decision problems fall in the class of trying to minimize the sum of two counter-varying costs. The policy is stated, ultimately, in terms of some percentile on the probability distribution from which future observations will be drawn. If an observable current state exceeds that percentile, one type of action is taken; if the state is below that percentile, another action is taken. The costs actually incurred depend on whether the future event also exceeds or falls short of the estimated level. The particular percentile chosen is determined, either explicitly or implicitly, in terms of those costs.

Let us turn, for variety, to another kind of problem that also uses the forecast distribution of future observations, but in quite a different way. In Chapter 3, we examined the scores earned on successive sports car rallies (see Fig. 3.4). When the scores are expressed in standard units, they can be compared from rally to rally. An average rallyist will get a standard score of zero. A better than average rallyist (like Ted Patton) will, on the average, get a standard score below zero. Each rallyist's performance can be represented by a constant model of past standard scores, and the current value of that constant can be estimated by single exponential smoothing. These average scores, for full members of the Touring Club of New England who participated in at least three rallies during

1959, ranged from −1.56 for Pete Sachs down to 1.33 for Earl Spaulding.

Some members have a fairly consistent pattern. Bill Frye, for example, had a mean absolute deviation of his standard scores of only 0.10 during 1959. Ted Patton, by way of contrast, is a fairly good rallyist, on the average, but erratic. The mean absolute deviation of his 1959 scores was 1.27. Figure 26.1 is a scatter diagram for 74 members of the club, with

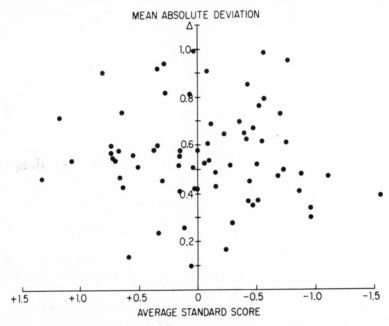

Fig. 26.1 Average and MAD of members' rally scores.

the mean absolute deviation plotted against average score. The variability of performance does not seem to be related to average performance. It is necessary to keep a current estimate of the variability, in terms of the mean absolute deviation. (For the items in an inventory, we'd expect some qualitative correlation between the average sales and the variability.)

The typical rally has from 45 to 50 entries. It is usual to award a trophy to each of the first five teams in the rally. From the way that the standard scores are computed (Fig. 3.5), we see that the fifth-place team will earn a standard score of approximately −1.25. If every team had an equal chance at these trophies, then each team should earn a score of −1.25 or better, with probability 5/50 = 0.1. Actually, each team has a probability 0.1 of exceeding its average score by 1.6 mean absolute deviations. For some teams, this score is better than −1.25; for others, it is far worse.

For example, consider Earl Spaulding. His average score was 1.33, and the mean absolute deviation 0.47, based on his 1959 rally experience. He has a 10 percent chance of getting a score of $1.33 - 1.6 \times 0.47 = 0.58$ or better. That score corresponds to thirty-second place in a 45-car rally. To get a trophy, he'd have to do 5.5 mean absolute deviations better than his average score. In a normal distribution, there's a chance of 1 in 10,000 of being that far from the mean!

That's an extreme case, to be sure. But the club had noticed a consistency with which the trophies seemed to go to a few members and therefore thought of establishing handicaps. In horse racing, a perfect handicap would lead to all horses tying for first place in the race. In rallying, as in golf, the handicap should be designed to reduce the marked disparity between different performers, but still have the better performers retain a slight edge.

Since every team has a chance of 0.1 of exceeding its average score by 1.6 mean absolute deviations, the handicap that would equalize everyone's chances of winning one of five trophies is H' such that

$$\bar{x} + H' - 1.6\Delta = -1.25$$

where $\bar{x}$ is the average score, and Δ is the mean absolute deviation. This handicap is a linear function of the two parameters that describe a member's past performance.

$$H'(\bar{x}, \Delta) = -1.25 + 1.6\Delta - \bar{x}$$

The actual handicap, however, is $H = 0.75H'$, which gives a slight bias in favor of those members who were more likely to win a trophy anyhow.

$$H(\bar{x}, \Delta) = -0.9375 + 1.2\Delta - 0.75\bar{x}$$

Spaulding's handicap would be

$$-0.9375 + (1.2)(0.47) - (0.75)(1.33) = -1.37$$

His effective mean score now becomes $1.33 - 1.37 = -0.04$. The fifth-place score is now only 2.6 mean absolute deviations better than the effective average score. He has a probability of 0.02 of exceeding that score. Still only one chance in 50 rallies, but appreciably better than one chance in 10,000 rallies!

By way of contrast, consider Pete Sachs. His average score is -1.56, and the mean absolute deviation is 0.38. Without a handicap, he has probability 0.81 of getting a fifth-place score or better. With a handicap of $+0.69$, his effective average score becomes -0.87, and the chances of getting fifth place have dropped to 0.16.

Exercise. Ted Patton's average score was -0.60, and his mean absolute deviation was 1.27. Compute his chances at getting a trophy, both with, and without, a handicap.

This system was tested during 1960 in twelve rallies where a total of 120 trophies were distributed.* Table 26.1 shows the number of members

Table 26.1 TROPHY AWARDS

Number of Trophies Won	Raw Scores	Number of People Handicap	Random Draw
1	51	68	66
2	12	12	24
3	3	7	2
4	5	0	0
5	2	1	0
6	1	0	0
	74	90	92

receiving N trophies during the year ($N = 1, 2, \ldots, 6$) both as they were actually awarded and as they would have been awarded if every member had carried a handicap. (Five cars were also picked at random in each rally. The last column shows the way trophies would have been awarded on such a random draw.)

---

* Each team has a driver and navigator, but the same people don't necessarily compete together on every rally.

Regression, Autocorrelation, and Spectral Analysis

"I have no data yet. It is a capital mistake to theorize before one has data. Insensibly one begins to twist facts to suit theories, instead of theories to suit facts."

A Scandal in Bohemia

This book presumes that the reader has a reasonable background in mathematical statistics. In several places the text uses three topics, usually treated in separate parts of the literature, regression, autocorrelation, and spectral analysis. Highlights of these topics are reviewed in this appendix.

At each time t, $t = 1, 2, \ldots, T$, we observe x_t and a corresponding vector of values

$$\mathbf{f}(t) = \begin{bmatrix} f_1(t) \\ f_2(t) \\ \cdot \\ \cdot \\ \cdot \\ f_n(t) \end{bmatrix}$$

We may suspect that the data can be represented as a linear combination of these function values

$$x_t = \sum_{i=1}^{n} a_i f_i(t) + e_t = \mathbf{a}'\mathbf{f}(t) + e_t = \hat{x}_t + e_t$$

where the residuals e_t are caused by two principal elements. The first is the noise in the observations: the observed values may be equal to some true value plus a random stochastic variation. The second is errors in the model. In physical processes there may be a priori reasons for knowing what functions $f_i(t)$ are required to describe the data; in economics problems, the description is at best superficial. Therefore, the model can be wrong in that it includes the wrong set of fitting functions. Even when the correct set of functions is used, there will be errors in estimating the coefficients because of the noise in the observations. All these factors contribute to the residuals e_t.

Regression deals with the problem of estimating values for the vector

$$\hat{\mathbf{a}} = \begin{bmatrix} \hat{a}_1 \\ \hat{a}_2 \\ \cdot \\ \cdot \\ \cdot \\ \cdot \\ \hat{a}_n \end{bmatrix}$$

of coefficients in the model. The estimate is computed from a finite set of data in such a way that the weighted sum of the squared residuals

$$\sum_{t=1}^{T} w_1^2 (x_t - \hat{x}_t)^2 = \sum (w_t e_t)^2$$

is a minimum. The computation will always lead formally to a set of values for the coefficient vector $\hat{\mathbf{a}}$ if there are more observations than there are components to that vector.

The fitting functions $f_i(t)$ must be linearly independent. That is, one cannot use any function that can be expressed as a linear combination of other functions in the set. Otherwise, no restriction is placed on the independent variables. They may be empirical variables. For example, if the data x_t represent the Danish birth rate in the year t, then $f_1(t)$ can be a census of the storks' nests in Copenhagen. The independent variables can be mathematical functions of time, such as 1, t, $\sin \omega t$, $te^{-\lambda t}$, and so on. The independent variables can even be past values of the dependent variable itself, for example, $f_i(t) = x_{t-i}$.

If the process can be best represented in terms of previous values of the dependent variable, it is said to be *autoregressive*. The *autocovariance* of the data, or the mean, variance, and autocorrelation coefficients contain all the information necessary for the estimation of the vector of coefficients that minimize the sum of the squared residuals (least squares) in an autoregressive model. The *power spectrum* is a cosine transformation of the autocovariance function, which can be used to design the optimum linear forecast filter for an autoregressive process. The power spectrum is also of great help in detecting the frequencies ω_i that should be included in a periodic model:

$$\hat{x}_t = \sum_{i=1}^{m} (a_i \sin \omega_i t + b_i \cos \omega_i t) + \sum_{j=m+1}^{n} c_j f_j(t)$$

Each of these three topics has been developed for a variety of other uses that are not of direct concern in this text. The bibliography contains a long list of references in which such extensions may be found.

Regression

The tth observation of the data, or the dependent variable, is designated x_t, and the corresponding value of the ith independent fitting function is called* $f_i(t)$. The index of time at which these observations is made is $t = 1, 2, \ldots, T$, and the index of the independent fitting functions is $i = 1, 2, \ldots, n$. It is formally necessary that there be at least as many observations as there are fitting functions, and if there is noise in the data, there should be a great many more $T \gg n$.

We shall represent the data by a linear model

$$x_t = \sum_{i=1}^{n} a_i f_i(t) = \mathbf{a}' \mathbf{f}(t)$$

(Section II discusses at some length the problem of selecting the necessary and sufficient set of functions **f**. In physical processes there may be good theoretical grounds for the selection, such as Kepler's laws for describing the orbit of a ballistic object. In economic processes, the descriptions are almost always *ad hoc*.) Both **a** and **f** are n-component column vectors.

It will simplify the notation in what follows to think of the time sequences as T-component row vectors:

x is the sequence $(x_1, x_2, \ldots, x_T)$ of actual observations, which may sometimes be thought of as a true process ξ plus random noise ϵ.

$\mathfrak{F}$ is the $n \times T$ matrix of fitting functions, with element $f_i(t)$ in the ith row and the tth column.

$\hat{\mathbf{x}}$ is the sequence $(\hat{x}_1, \hat{x}_2, \ldots, \hat{x}_T)$ of values given by the model $\mathbf{a}'\mathfrak{F}$. In the text, we are particularly concerned with the recursive estimates of the coefficients with each new observation, so $\mathbf{a} = \mathbf{a}(T)$. In this appendix, we shall consider only one such calculation; hence the time index is omitted.

e is the sequence $(e_1, e_2, \ldots, e_T)$ of residuals, where

$$e_t = x_t - \hat{x}_t = x_t - \mathbf{a}'(T)\mathbf{f}(t)$$

The model can be expressed $\mathbf{x} = \mathbf{a}'\mathfrak{F}$. The central problem of regression is finding the values of the coefficient vector **a** so as to minimize the weighted sum of the squared residuals. We shall let W be a $T \times T$ matrix in which W_{ii} is the square root of the weight given the residual for time i; all off-diagonal elements of W are zero.

* Do you see why they are called *fit*ting functions?

The general procedure is as follows. By definition the model $\mathbf{a}'\mathfrak{F} = \hat{\mathbf{x}} - \mathbf{e}$. Therefore, we can write the residuals as $\mathbf{e} = \mathbf{x} - \mathbf{a}'\mathfrak{F}$, and the sum of squares for a particular choice of $\mathbf{a}$ is

$$S_\mathbf{a} = \mathbf{e}\mathbf{e}' = (\mathbf{x}W - \mathbf{a}'\mathfrak{F}W)(\mathbf{x}W - \mathbf{a}'\mathfrak{F}W)'$$

The particular set of coefficients that minimizes this sum is the solution to the system of n simultaneous linear equations

$$\frac{\partial S_\mathbf{a}}{\partial \mathbf{a}} = -\mathbf{x}WW'\mathfrak{F}' + \mathbf{a}'\mathfrak{F}W(\mathfrak{F}W)' = 0$$

or
$$\mathbf{x}WW'\mathfrak{F}' = \mathbf{a}'\mathfrak{F}WW'\mathfrak{F}'$$

Let us call the $n \times n$ symmetrical matrix

$$\mathfrak{F}W(\mathfrak{F}W)' = \sum_{t=1}^{T} w_t^2 \mathbf{f}(t)\mathbf{f}'(t) = F$$

Then
$$\mathbf{x}WW'\mathfrak{F}' = \mathbf{a}'F$$

If, as we suppose, there are many more observations than there are degrees of freedom in the model $(T \gg n)$ and the fitting functions are linearly independent, then F will have an inverse F^{-1}. Therefore,

$$\mathbf{a}' = \mathbf{x}W^2\mathfrak{F}'F^{-1}$$

is the general expression for the vector of coefficients that minimize the weighed sum of squared residuals. The vector $\mathbf{x}W^2\mathfrak{F}'$ is the data vector $\mathbf{g}$ discussed in Chapter 11.

Exercise. Derive the explicit expressions for $\mathbf{a}$ when $f_1(t) = 1$, $f_2(t) = t$, and W is the unit matrix.

Suppose that the observations are composed of a true process plus noise, $\mathbf{x} = \boldsymbol{\xi} + \boldsymbol{\epsilon}$, and that the true process is exactly represented by some (unknown) linear combination of the chosen fitting functions

$$\boldsymbol{\xi} = \tilde{\mathbf{a}}'\mathfrak{F}$$

where the vector $\tilde{\mathbf{a}}$ is the true set of coefficients. Then the expected value of the tth observation is

$$\mathcal{E}(x_t) = \tilde{\mathbf{a}}'\mathbf{f}(t)$$

The expected value of the coefficients estimated by the least-squares procedure is an unbiased estimate of the true values.

$$\mathcal{E}(\mathbf{a}') = \mathcal{E}(\mathbf{x}W^2\mathfrak{F}'F^{-1}) = \boldsymbol{\xi}W^2\mathfrak{F}'F^{-1} = \tilde{\mathbf{a}}'\mathfrak{F}W^2\mathfrak{F}'F^{-1} = \tilde{\mathbf{a}}'$$

Let us now look at the variation in the estimated coefficients caused by the noise $\epsilon_t = x_t - \xi_t$ in the observed data. The $n \times n$ matrix of variances and covariances of the least-squares estimates of the coefficients $\mathbf{a}$ is

$$\mathcal{E}(\hat{\mathbf{a}} - \tilde{\mathbf{a}})(\hat{\mathbf{a}} - \tilde{\mathbf{a}})' = F^{-1}\mathfrak{F}W'^2\mathcal{E}(\mathbf{x} - \boldsymbol{\xi})'(\mathbf{x} - \boldsymbol{\xi})W^2\mathfrak{F}'F^{-1}$$

REGRESSION **393**

In particular, if the noise has no serial correlation,* and all samples have the same variance σ^2, then $\mathcal{E}(\mathbf{x} - \boldsymbol{\xi})'(\mathbf{x} - \boldsymbol{\xi}) = I\sigma^2$. Then the covariance matrix for the coefficients reduces to

$$F^{-1}\mathfrak{F}W^2(\mathfrak{F}W^2)'F^{-1}\sigma^2 = F^{-1}KF^{-1}\sigma^2 \quad \text{where } K = (\mathfrak{F}W^2)(\mathfrak{F}W^2)'$$

The covariance between the jth coefficient and the kth coefficient is the (j, k) element of $V = F^{-1}KF^{-1}$, and the variance of the ith coefficient is

$$\text{var } \{\hat{a}_i\} = \text{cov } \{\hat{a}_i, \hat{a}_i\} = V_{ii}\sigma^2$$

In particular, if W is the unit matrix (all data receiving the same weight) $K = F$, so that $V = F^{-1}$.

We can use these results to obtain the variance of the forecast obtained by using the model $x_t = a'(T)f(t)$.

$$\text{var } \{\hat{x}_t\} = \sum_j \sum_k f_j(t)f_k(t) \text{ cov } \{\hat{a}_j, \hat{a}_k\}$$

$$= \sigma^2 \mathbf{f}'(t) V \mathbf{f}(t)$$

If the variance σ^2 is unknown and if the model can be assumed an adequate description of the true process, then the variance can be estimated satisfactorily by the sum of squares of the residuals $\hat{\sigma}^2 = \mathbf{e}\mathbf{e}'$. We have shown above that, under these conditions, the expected value of the residual is $\mathcal{E}(e) = 0$. Therefore, we can write $\mathcal{E}(\mathbf{e}\mathbf{e}') = \mathcal{E}(\mathbf{e} - 0)(\mathbf{e} - 0)'$ as

$$\mathcal{E}(\mathbf{e}\mathbf{e}') = \mathcal{E}\{(\mathbf{x} - \boldsymbol{\xi}) - (\mathbf{a}' - \tilde{\mathbf{a}}')\mathfrak{F}\}\{(\mathbf{x} - \boldsymbol{\xi}) - (\mathbf{a}' - \tilde{\mathbf{a}}')\mathfrak{F}\}'$$

$$= \mathcal{E}(\mathbf{x} - \boldsymbol{\xi})(\mathbf{x} - \boldsymbol{\xi})' - \mathcal{E}(\mathbf{a}' - \tilde{\mathbf{a}}')\mathfrak{F}\mathfrak{F}'(\mathbf{a}' - \tilde{\mathbf{a}}')$$

$$= (T - n)\sigma^2$$

Hence the sum

$$\frac{\sum_t (x_t - \hat{x}_t)^2}{T - n} = \frac{\mathbf{e}\mathbf{e}'}{T - n}$$

can be used as an unbiased estimate of the variance σ^2.

Autocorrelation

Now let us consider the special case where the fitting functions are past values of the dependent variable. We could, for example, let $f_i(t) = x_{t-i}$. Then the $\mathfrak{F}$ matrix of fitting functions consists of rows of the past observations, with each row shifted one observation from the one above it. (It will be noted, of course, that the sequence must extend back at least to time $t = -n$, so that in any one row we deal with only a total of T observations.)

---

* Otherwise one introduces the covariance matrix Φ for the noise samples (see Chapter 21).

The elements of the matrix $F = \mathfrak{F}\mathfrak{F}'$ will be the sums of the cross products between observations

$$F_{jk} = \sum_t x_{t-j} x_{t-k}$$

Note that the terms of this sum are always $(k - j)$ observations apart in the sequence. The expected value of this term $\mathcal{E}(F_{jk})$ is called the *average lagged product*. In particular, if the sequence has been adjusted so that the average value $\mathcal{E}(x) = 0$, then the average lagged product is the *auto-covariance*, represented in this book by $R_{xx}(k - j)$.

The expected value of the data vector $\mathbf{x}\mathfrak{F}'$ will have components $[R_{xx}(1), R_{xx}(2), \ldots, R_{xx}(n)]$. Therefore, the coefficients that result from solving the ordinary regression equation, with expected values on both sides, is just the Wiener optimum linear filter discussed in Chapter 21.

The variance of a sequence of numbers that has zero mean is just the expected value of the square $\mathcal{E}(x^2)$, which is $R_{xx}(0)$. The autocovariance is obviously symmetrical $R_{xx}(-k) = R_{xx}(k)$, so that many graphical representations (such as Fig. 4.8, Fig. 4.9, and Fig. 5.2) show only the values for non-negative lags. The set of values for the autocovariance for all lags $k = 0, \pm 1, \pm 2, \ldots$ is called the *autocorrelation function*. It is usually displayed in the normalized form of *autocorrelation coefficients*

$$\rho(k) = \frac{R_{xx}(k)}{R_{xx}(0)}$$

The autocorrelation coefficient for a lag $k = 0$ is $\rho(0) = 1$, the largest value the coefficient may attain. The smallest possible value is -1. Generally, for noisy data, the autocorrelation coefficients drop down to zero (Fig. 5.2) for any substantial lag. Pure random noise would have zero correlation between samples not identically equal to each other. The standard deviation of the computed value of $\hat{\rho}(k)$, from a finite sample of T observations, is $(T - k - 1)^{-1/2}$.

Suppose that whenever x_t is positive, so is x_{t+k}, and that whenever x_t is negative, so is x_{t+k}. Then the autocovariance will be large and positive. In this case, pairs of observations, k units of time apart in the sequence, are highly correlated, and one could be used to forecast the other. Similarly if x_t positive usually implies that x_{t+k} is negative (and vice versa), one can still be used to forecast the other. The autocovariance will be large and negative. When the autocovariance is close to zero, then information about one observation doesn't help much in forecasting a later observation in the same sequence.

Exercise. Suppose that the sequence of observations was $x_t = A \sin \omega t + \epsilon_t$, where ϵ_t is a sample from some noise distribution with zero mean and constant variance. Compute $R_{xx}(k)$ in general. What happens if $R_{\epsilon\epsilon}(k) = 0$ for $k \neq 0$?

In practical applications, when you want to compute the autocovariance for a set of observations, proceed as follows. First, plot the observations as a time series to see whether you should expect a secular linear trend or a significant cyclical pattern. If there is a secular trend, fit a straight line to the data by least squares (that is, ordinary regression against the fitting functions $f_1(t) = 1$, $f_2(t) = t$). Adjust the sequence to zero expected value $\mathbf{y} = \mathbf{x} - \hat{\mathbf{x}}$. Compute the autocovariances

$$R_{xx}(k) = \frac{\sum\limits_{j=k+1}^{T} y_j y_{j-k}}{T - 1 - k}$$

The maximum lag should not exceed $k_{max} = T/20$. Even within a span of k_{max} the autocovariances should be treated as zero unless they are either (1) clearly significant when compared with the standard deviation, or (2) clearly part of a cosine pattern.

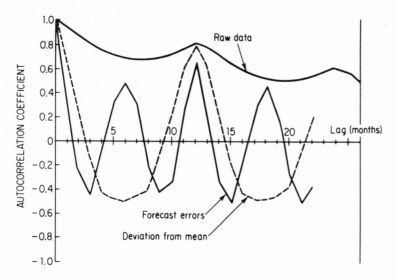

Fig. A.1 Autocorrelation functions for airline passenger data.

Figure A.1 shows three autocorrelation functions computed from the airline passenger data (Fig. 4.10). There is a significant trend, which shows as a high correlation for all lags in the raw data. When the trend is removed by subtracting either the current average rate or the forecast from the data, the periodic nature of the data is much clearer.

Spectral Analysis

Sometimes it is helpful to think of a time series $x(t)$ with zero mean as being made up of several periodic functions plus some additive noise.

$$x(t) = a_1 \cos \omega_1 t + a_2 \cos \omega_2 t + \ldots + a_n \cos \omega_n t + e_t$$

(The Fourier series representation, an infinite series in cosines, can be made to represent any time series arbitrarily closely. See Fig. 4.6.) The frequencies ω_i are all distinct from each other. A more general formulation would include sine terms as well, to allow for relative phase shifts of the various frequencies. These terms just make the algebra a little more tedious. The autocovariance is the average (over all time) of the lagged products

$$R_{xx}(k) = \lim_{T \to \infty} \frac{1}{2T+1} \sum_{t=-T}^{T} x(t+k)x(t)$$

$$= \lim_{T \to \infty} \frac{1}{2T+1} \sum_{t=-T}^{T} \left\{ \sum_{i=1}^{n} \sum_{j=1}^{n} a_i a_j \cos \omega_i t \cos \omega_i(t+k) + \epsilon_t \epsilon_{t+k} \right\}$$

The cross products between the noise and the cosine signal are not shown since their expected value is zero. The expected values of all terms of the form $\cos \omega_i t \cos \omega_j t$ is also zero, for $i \neq j$. Therefore, the autovariance reduces to

$$R_{xx}(k) = \tfrac{1}{2} \sum_{i=1}^{n} a_i^2 \cos \omega_i k + R_{\epsilon\epsilon}(k)$$

At this point, it is usual to make the assumption that the noise has no serial correlation, so that

$$R_{\epsilon\epsilon}(k) = \sigma_\epsilon^2 \delta(k)$$

Note that the autocorrelation function $\rho(k) = R_{xx}(k)/R_{xx}(0)$ will have a local maximum at $k_i = (2\pi/\omega_i)$.

The variance of the observed data is

$$\sigma_x^2 = R_{xx}(0) = \tfrac{1}{2} \sum_{i=1}^{n} a_i^2 + \sigma_\epsilon^2$$

Thus we see, for a sequence of the form assumed above, that the total variance is made up of a series of terms in half the square of the amplitudes at each frequency present. By analogy with the electrical power in a circuit with alternating current passing through a resistance, we call $a_i^2/2$ the *power* in frequency ω_i.

In the case of a purely periodic function there is a "line" in the power spectrum for each frequency present. The power at other frequencies is zero. For an arbitrary stochastic function $x(t)$, the autocovariance function is still defined. The *power spectrum* will be a continuous function of frequencies $P(\omega)$. It is defined as the Fourier transform of the autocovariance function.

$$P(\omega) = \frac{1}{\pi} \int_{-\infty}^{\infty} R_{xx}(t) \cos \omega t \, dt$$

In Chapter 21 we used a similar transform in the design of an optimum linear filter for an autoregressive process. The power spectrum is also very helpful in finding the best model and the initial conditions in a trigonometric model of a time series.

We have seen that the autocovariance function will have local maxima at the periods of the various frequencies present. At those points, the value of the autocovariance function will be

$$R_{xx}(k_i) = \frac{1}{2} \sum_{j=1}^{n} a_i^2 \cos \frac{2\pi\omega_j}{\omega_i} + R_{\epsilon\epsilon}\left(\frac{2\pi}{\omega_i}\right)$$

One may be able to see these maxima in a plot of the autocovariance function, but it will be hard to tell the contribution from one particular frequency. When we take the Fourier transform, the power spectrum will be

$$P(\omega_i) = a_i^2/2$$

Hence it will be much clearer (1) what frequencies are indeed present and (2) what their amplitudes are, if we examine the power spectrum, rather than the autocovariance function.

For example, Fig. A.1 showed the autocorrelation function for the deviation from the mean of the airline passenger data. To the practiced eye the square bottom to the autocorrelation function is an indication of higher harmonics in the waveform. Contrast this with Fig. A.2, however, which shows the power spectrum for the raw data. There are clear spikes for frequencies with periods of six, twelve, and twenty-one months. (The period of fifty-two months per cycle is a low enough frequency to be dealt with adequately by the adaptive forecasting.)

Figure A.3 shows the drastic reduction in power by subtracting the mean. Spikes of six- and twelve-month cycles are apparent in the deviation from the mean. The forecast using the model in Table 12.9 removes almost all the power except the six-month cycles which were not included in the model.

There is still another interest in power spectra. The response of a linear system to any composite signal is the sum of its responses to the elementary components of the signal, by the superposition theorem. Suppose the input signal were $x(t) = A \cos \omega t$. The output from a linear filter will be

$$y(t) = G(\omega)A \cos [\omega t + \phi(\omega)]$$

The *frequency response function* of the linear filter is $\Psi(\omega) = G(\omega)e^{i\phi(\omega)}$. The *gain* $G(\omega)$ is the real part $|\Psi(\omega)|$, and the *phase shift* is the argument

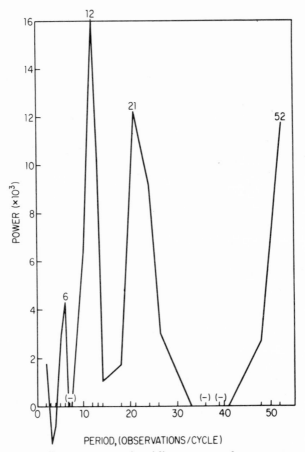

Fig. A.2 Power spectrum for airline passenger data.

$\arg \Psi(\omega)$. When we let $z = e^{i\omega}$, we see that $\Psi(\omega)$ is merely the z-transform of the impulse response, or the *transfer function* of the system (see Appendix B). It follows that the power spectrum of the output is

$$P_y(\omega) = P_x(\omega)|\Psi(\omega)|^2$$

and the variance of the output is

$$\sigma_y^2 = \int_0^\infty P_x(\omega)|\Psi(\omega)|^2 \, d\omega$$

There is difficulty in estimating the power spectrum from a finite number T of observations of a discrete time series (which may be a sampling of a continuous series, but not necessarily so). When there is only a finite number of points, the autocovariance function can be calculated for $k < T$ lags. Since with random noise the variance of the estimated function is

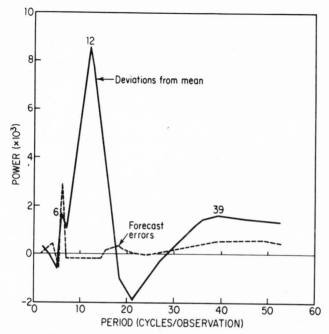

Fig. A.3 Power spectra for reduced airline passenger data.

$1/(T - k - 1)$, it usually isn't practical to estimate $R_{xx}(k)$ for $k > T/20$, and sometimes even for shorter periods. (Another point that worries the electrical engineers is that any frequency higher than the *Nyquist frequency* $\omega_n = \pi$ will be aliased with lower frequencies. We assume that the sequence is discrete in the first place, and hence aren't worried about these higher frequencies.)

The actual power spectrum is

$$P(\omega) = \frac{1}{\pi} \sum_{-\infty}^{\infty} R_{xx}(k) \cos k\omega$$

$$= \frac{1}{\pi} \left[\sigma_x^2 + 2 \sum_{k=1}^{\infty} R_{xx}(k) \cos k\omega \right]$$

But with a finite sample T of observations we can only estimate $P(\omega)$ for the first $K(\leq T/20)$ terms

$$P(\omega) = \frac{1}{\pi} \left[\sigma_x^2 + 2 \sum_{k=1}^{K} R_{xx}(k) \cos k\omega \right]$$

One obvious (but inappropriate) method of estimating the power spectrum is the Schuster *periodogram*. Suppose that $x(t) = x(t + p) + \epsilon(t)$; that is, that the sequence is purely periodic, except for noise. The fundamental frequency corresponding to the period is $\omega_0 = 2\pi/p$. The kth harmonic of this frequency is $\omega_k = 2k\pi/p$. The periodogram in this case is

$$I_p(\omega_k) = \frac{1}{\pi p} \left\{ \left[\sum_{t=1}^{p} x(t) \cos \omega_k t \right]^2 + \left[\sum_{t=1}^{p} x(t) \sin \omega_k t \right]^2 \right\}$$

It can be shown that

$$\lim_{p \to \infty} E[I_p(\omega_k)] = P(\omega_k)$$

That is, the expected value of the periodogram at any frequency approaches the power at that frequency, for large samples. Unfortunately, when a random noise sample is analyzed, the periodogram consists of a sequence of spikes, whereas it is obvious that the power spectrum should be

$$P(\omega) = \frac{\sigma_\epsilon^2}{\omega_n}$$

(where ω_n is the Nyquist frequency) for all frequencies. The reason for this problem was shown by Bartlett* to be that

$$\lim_{p \to \infty} \text{var}\,[I_p(\omega_k)] = 4P^2(\omega_k)$$

That is, the variance of these estimates does not decrease with sample size. This result is somewhat surprising, since, in almost all other statistical estimates, one can be as precise as desired by taking large enough samples.

The solution to the problem is to take local averages over frequencies surrounding the frequency for which the power is being sought. The averaging process is carried out with the aid of a *kernel* or *window*. There is a fairly large literature having to do with the shape and bandwidth of this window.† The selection is a compromise between two conflicting objectives: (1) The power at adjacent frequencies can be estimated with little variance, but the estimates are smudged. It is hard to see differences between power at adjacent frequencies. (2) Another window can focus on a particular frequency, but has a fairly large variance of estimate.

For our purposes the frequencies will generally be fairly obvious, such as an annual cycle with 12 observations where we are trying to decide whether any of the harmonics has significant power. We are not interested in frequencies near these harmonics and can, therefore, stand the "smudging" effect, to get less variance in the estimates. Hence, power spectra are presented here for certain specific frequencies: those with periods of 2, 3,

---

* M. S. Bartlett, "Smoothing Periodograms from Time Series with Continuous Spectra," *Nature*, Vol. 161 (1948), 686–87.

† In particular, see *Technometrics*, Vol. 3, No. 2 (May, 1961) which has papers by Jenkins, Parzen, Tukey, Goodman, and Wonnacott, who seem to be the principal authors on this topic. The references given in those papers seem to exhaust the subject (and possibly even the reader).

4, 5, 6, and 7 observations (for daily records of weekly phenomena); 13, 26, 39, and 52 observations (weekly observations of annual cycles); and 2, 3, 4, 6, 12, 18, 24, 36, and 48 for either monthly observations of annual cycles, or hourly observations of daily cycles.

It is not crucial what the power is, since it will be estimated by the model used in forecasting. It *is* crucial to know all frequencies with significant power, so that the appropriate terms can be included in the model.

The *z*-Transform

"The temptation to form premature theories upon insufficient data is the bane of our profession. . . . I should
like a few more facts before I get so far as a theory."

Valley of Fear

The z-transform, discussed in this appendix, is a useful technique for the analysis of a linear, discrete, time-invariant system. A *discrete* system is sometimes called a *sampled-data* system. The inputs to the system consist of a sequence of numbers, $x(t)$, where the time index, t, takes on integral values from minus infinity to plus infinity. As a result of these inputs, the system provides a sequence of outputs, $y(t)$, at similar instants of time. A *physically realizable system* is one where the output at any time, $y(t)$, depends only on inputs at prior times, $x(t - n)$, where n is non-negative.

Suppose that when the input to the system is a time series $x_1(t)$, the resulting output is $y_1(t)$. Further suppose that if the input were $x_2(t)$, then the resulting output would be $y_2(t)$. Then consider as an input the sequence $x(t) = ax_1(t) + bx_2(t)$, where a and b are constants. The system is said to be *linear* if the resulting output is $y(t) = ay_1(t) + by_2(t)$.

Finally, the system is said to be *time-invariant* if the input $x(t)$ causes an output function $y(t)$ and the same input at some other time $x(t - T)$ produces the same sequence as output with the same change in the origin of time $y(t - T)$.*

The problem of analyzing such systems is representing the output in

* Remark on notation: In some chapters of the text, time sequences have been represented by x_t where the subscript denotes the sequence of the observations. In this appendix, we shall find it convenient to use $x(t)$ for the input functions, and to let a subscript distinguish between different time series; then $y(t)$—with subscripts if necessary—can be used to represent the outputs.

terms of the input, involving the parameters of the system. We could always find these relationships by simulation. But there are infinitely many possible input signals, and the simulation may not show how a particular systems configuration affects the relationships. Therefore it would be hard to decide how to modify the system design to produce a more desirable output.

Any discrete, linear, time-invariant system can be completely described by its impulse response. That is, if we know how a particular system would respond to the impulse $x(t) = \delta(t)$, then we can describe its response to any other function of time $(\delta(0) = 1; \delta(t) = 0 \text{ for } t \neq 0)$. The impulse response will be denoted by $y(t) = h(t)$. Note that for a physically realizable system $h(t) = 0$ for $t < 0$; the system can't respond before the stimulus occurs.

Suppose we know the impulse response $h(t)$ for a discrete, linear, time-invariant system. Any arbitrary input signal $x(t)$ can be represented by

$$x(t) = \ldots x(-n)\,\delta(t+n) + x(-n+1)\,\delta(t+n-1)$$
$$+ \ldots + x(0)\,\delta(t) + \ldots + x(n)\,\delta(t-n) + \ldots$$
$$= \sum_{n=-\infty}^{\infty} x(n)\,\delta(t-n)$$

where now the $\{x(n)\}$ are to be viewed as constant coefficients. Since the system is linear, the output $y(t)$ can be expressed

$$y(t) = \sum_{n=-\infty}^{\infty} x(n)h(t-n)$$

This relation is called the *convolution* of the sequence $\{x(t)\}$ with the sequence $\{h(t)\}$ and can be written for convenience

$$y(t) = x(t) * h(t)$$

Let us now consider the problem of finding the impulse response for a compound system. We start with the concept of a simple system

$$x(t) \longrightarrow \boxed{h(t)} \longrightarrow y(t)$$

for which we know the impulse response $h(t)$ and, therefore, can compute the output signal $y(t)$ given the input $x(t)$, by convolution.

Now consider two systems in parallel,

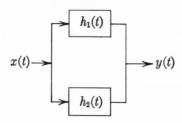

with impulse responses $h_1(t)$ and $h_2(t)$. This compound system has some impulse response $h(t)$, which we should like to express in terms of the known $h_1(t)$ and $h_2(t)$.

The output signal $y(t)$ is the sum of the separate signals from the two branches:

$$y(t) = y_1(t) + y_2(t)$$

where
$$y_1(t) = x(t) * h_1(t)$$

$$y_2(t) = x(t) * h_2(t)$$

Therefore
$$y(t) = x(t) * h_1(t) + x(t) * h_2(t)$$

$$= x(t) * [h_1(t) + h_2(t)]$$

Since
$$y(t) = x(t) * h(t)$$

the desired impulse response for the compound system is the sum of the impulse responses for the parallel branches:

$$h(t) = h_1(t) + h_2(t)$$

The next compound system to consider is two simple systems in series:

$$x(t) \longrightarrow \boxed{h_1(t)} \longrightarrow \boxed{h_2(t)} \longrightarrow y(t)$$

The input to the second branch is $y_1(t) = x(t) * h_1(t)$, so that the output is $y(t) = y_1(t) * h_2(t) = x(t) * h_1(t) * h_2(t)$. The equivalent impulse response for a simple system is therefore the convolution of the impulse responses for the series systems:

$$h(t) = h_1(t) * h_2(t)$$

A great many systems can be analyzed by repeatedly replacing parallel and series systems by their equivalents until a single impulse response is obtained for the whole system. We shall need one more type of compounding, however, the feedback loop:

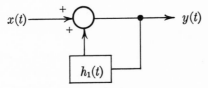

In this case, the output is a function of itself:

$$y(t) = x(t) + h_1(t) * y(t)$$

and there is no simple way of replacing the convolution by some equivalent response function $h(t)$ such that

$$y(t) = h(t) * x(t)$$

In order to solve this problem, we turn to the z-transform.

The *z*-Transform

Given any function $f(n)$ defined for integral arguments, the *z*-transform $F(z)$ is defined by

$$F(z) = \sum_{-\infty}^{\infty} f(n)z^n$$

If $f(n) < a^n$ for large n, then the sum for positive n will converge inside a circle with radius a. If $f(n) < b^{-n}$ for large negative n, then the sum for negative n will converge outside a circle with radius $1/b$. Hence, there is an annulus of convergence, so that the transform exists, if $a > 1/b$. In this appendix, we deal with functions that are identically zero for negative time and that do not grow more rapidly than a^n, so that all transforms needed actually exist.

Recall the definition of convolution

$$y(t) = \sum_{n=-\infty}^{\infty} x(n)h(t-n)$$

Take the *z*-transforms of both sides of this equation:

$$Y(z) = \sum_{n=-\infty}^{\infty} y(n)z^n = \sum_{n=-\infty}^{\infty} z^n \sum_{m=-\infty}^{\infty} x(m)h(n-m)$$

We can let $z^n = z^m \cdot z^{n-m}$, and then let $p = n - m$. The summation on the right side can then be rearranged to yield

$$Y(z) = \sum_{m=-\infty}^{\infty} x(m)z^m \cdot \sum_{p=-\infty}^{\infty} h(p)z^p$$

Therefore, $$Y(z) = X(z) \cdot H(z)$$

The convolution of functions in the time domain is replaced by multiplication of transforms in the transform domain. Transforms offer a convenience to the system designer similar to the convenience of logarithms in arithmetic.

The *z*-transform $H(z)$ of the impulse response $h(t)$ is called the *transfer function*. It can easily be verified that the transform of the sum of two functions is the sum of the transforms of the functions. For two systems in *parallel*, the transfer function is the *sum* of the transfer function for the separate branches:

$$H(z) = H_1(z) + H_2(z)$$

The transfer function for two systems in *series* is the *product* of the individual transfer function:

$$H(z) = H_1(z) \cdot H_2(z)$$

Now we can return to our problem of feedback: Recall that

$$y(t) = x(t) + h_1(t) * y(t)$$

When we take z-transforms of both sides of this equation, we obtain

$$Y(z) = X(z) + H_1(z) \cdot Y(z)$$

which can be solved to yield

$$Y(z) = \frac{X(z)}{1 - H_1(z)}$$

Therefore, we can replace the feedback loop with transfer function $H_1(z)$ by a series system with transfer function

$$H(z) = \frac{1}{1 - H_1(z)}$$

Table of Transform Pairs

Since it is sometimes more convenient to work in the transform domain instead of in the time domain, it will be helpful to have a table of equivalents between common functions $f(t)$ and their transforms $F(z)$. Then when we know the function we can look up its transform, and vice versa.

If the function is a linear combination of the tabulated functions, then its transform will be the same linear combination of the tabulated transforms. A common device in going from the transform domain back to the time domain is to break up a complicated transform into partial fractions, where each term in the result is given in the table.

We can start constructing a table by considering an exponential decay $f(n) = 0(n < 0)$ and $f(n) = \beta^n$, $(n \geqslant 0)$. The transform is

$$F(z) = \sum_{n=0}^{\infty} \beta^n z^n$$

$$= \frac{1}{1 - \beta z}$$

If $\beta = 1$, $f(n) = 1$ for non-negative time. Thus the transform of a step function is

$$F(z) = \frac{1}{1 - z}$$

If $\beta = 0$, $f(n) = 0$, except that $f(0) = 1$. That is, the limiting case of $\beta = 0$ is just an impulse $\delta(n)$ at the origin, and the transform of an impulse is

$$F(z) = 1$$

Table B.1   TIME SERIES USED IN THIS BOOK AND THEIR *z*-TRANSFORMS
(All time functions are identically zero for negative time)

Series	$f(n)$	Transform $F(z)$
Impulse	$f(n) = \delta(n)$	$F(z) = 1$
Step	$f(n) = 1$	$F(z) = \dfrac{1}{1 - z}$
Ramp	$f(n) = n$	$F(z) = \dfrac{z}{(1 - z)^2}$
Parabola	$f(n) = n^2$	$F(z) = \dfrac{z(1 + z)}{(1 - z)^3}$
Single Exponential Decay	$f(n) = \beta^n$	$F(z) = \dfrac{1}{1 - \beta z}$
Double Exponential Decay	$f(n) = (n + 1)\beta^n$	$F(z) = \dfrac{1}{(1 - \beta z)^2}$
Triple Exponential Decay	$f(n) = \dfrac{(n + 1)(n + 2)}{2} \beta^n$	$F(z) = \dfrac{1}{(1 - \beta z)^3}$
Time Advance	$f(n) = g(n + 1)$	$F(z) = \dfrac{1}{z} [G(z) - g(0)]$
Time Delay	$f(n) = g(n - 1)$	$F(z) = zG(z)$
Sine Wave	$f(n) = \sin \omega n$	$F(z) = \dfrac{z \sin \omega}{1 - 2z \cos \omega + z^2}$
Cosine Wave	$f(n) = \cos \omega n$	$F(z) = \dfrac{1 - z \cos \omega}{1 - 2z \cos \omega + z^2}$

For 12 samples per cycle $\omega = \dfrac{2\pi}{12}$

Sine Wave	$f(n) = \sin \dfrac{2\pi n}{12}$	$F(z) = \dfrac{z}{2(1 - \sqrt{3}\, z + z^2)}$
Cosine Wave	$f(n) = \cos \dfrac{2\pi n}{12}$	$F(z) = \dfrac{2 - \sqrt{3}\, z}{2(1 - \sqrt{3}\, z + z^2)}$

These transform pairs are given in Table B.1. The transform pairs for other functions—such as the ramp, parabola, and double and triple exponential decays—can be obtained by successive differentiation. Table B.1 contains all the transform pairs needed for analyzing the systems in this book. Beightler[*] and others have prepared an especially complete table.

* C. S. Beightler, L. G. Mitton, G. L. Nenhauser, "A Short Table of *z*-Transforms and Generating Functions," *Operations Research*, Vol. 9, No. 4 (July–August, 1961), 574–78.

For example,

$$\frac{\beta}{(1 - \beta z)^2} = \sum_{n=0}^{\infty} n\beta^n z^{n-1}$$

Divide both sides by β and change the index of summation to $p = n - 1$,

$$\frac{1}{(1 - \beta z)^2} = \sum_{p=0}^{\infty} (p + 1)\beta^p z^p$$

which yields the transform pair for the double exponential decay.

The effect of a unit delay or advance in time follows directly from the definition of the z-transform. The only other results we shall want are the trigonometric functions $\sin \omega t$ and $\cos \omega t$.

Consider the case of the cosine function

$$f(t) = \cos \omega t = \tfrac{1}{2}(e^{i\omega t} + e^{-i\omega t})$$

The transform is

$$F(z) = \sum_{n=0}^{\infty} \cos \omega z^n$$

$$= \sum_{n=0}^{\infty} \frac{1}{2} (e^{i\omega n} + e^{i\omega n}) z^n$$

$$= \frac{1}{2}\left[\frac{2 - (e^{i\omega} + e^{-i\omega})z}{1 - (e^{i\omega} + e^{-i\omega})z + z^2} \right]$$

$$= \frac{1 - z \cos \omega}{1 - 2z \cos \omega + z^2}$$

The results for $\sin \omega t = -(i/2)(e^{i\omega t} - e^{-i\omega t})$ are obtained in a similar fashion. In many cases such as monthly data from an annual seasonal pattern, or hourly observations of tides, there are 12 observations per cycle, and special forms are given for that case.

Samples of Time Series for Practice

"Data! data! data!" he cried impatiently. "I can't make bricks without clay."

The Copper Beeches

The sixteen sets of data tabulated in this appendix illustrate a few of the many types of discrete time series for which forecasts might be required. They are provided primarily as a basis for the exercises in this book. Additional data with which to practice the use of various techniques can be generated by the methods described in Chapter 24. These sources may provide longer time series that can readily be recovered from existing records, and a richer variety of problems. Ultimately, of course, any methods must be investigated in the context of actual data from the real problem.

Where there is no indication to the contrary, the data in this appendix were generated synthetically. Some actual commercial data have been disguised to protect confidential information.

Table C.1 A SAMPLE SEQUENCE OF DATA

Time	Observation	Time	Observation	Time	Observation	Time	Observation
1	103	26	109	51	90	76	120
2	131	27	109	52	111	77	65
3	130	28	55	53	104	78	103
4	120	29	116	54	113	79	135
5	99	30	68	55	86	80	105
6	111	31	76	56	117	81	108
7	78	32	90	57	153	82	66
8	71	33	130	58	115	83	75
9	110	34	68	59	74	84	80
10	118	35	146	60	100	85	129
11	90	36	91	61	116	86	142
12	71	37	94	62	117	87	139
13	108	38	103	63	123	88	148
14	98	39	65	64	57	89	73
15	85	40	98	65	112	90	101
16	91	41	102	66	87	91	98
17	112	42	119	67	102	92	134
18	94	43	148	68	53	93	108
19	82	44	109	69	85	94	87
20	74	45	122	70	71	95	95
21	64	46	135	71	105	96	51
22	99	47	117	72	85	97	102
23	125	48	90	73	55	98	94
24	89	49	100	74	62	99	147
25	109	50	93	75	52	100	100

Table C.2 A SEQUENCE OF INDIVIDUAL DEMAND TRANSACTIONS*

Date	Demand	Date	Demand	Date	Demand
Jan. 1, 1956	83	May 3, 1956	50	Sept. 4, 1956	25
7	25	5	60	10	25
11	45	9	100	13	30
14	30	11	38	14	25
17	75	17	20	16	75
18	12	18	2	20	140
19	12				
20	25				
Feb. 3, 1956	42	June 2, 1956	250	Oct. 1, 1956	100
6	50	3	40	2	60
9	30	4	20	4	100
14	50	7	12	6	15
17	250	8	75	12	8
19	100	10	15	18	2
20	30	14	12	20	75
		15	30		
		16	250		
		18	8		
		20	40		
Mar. 6, 1956	60	July 2, 1956	75	Nov. 4, 1956	30
9	8	4	108	7	2
10	40	5	12	9	8
12	100	8	30	12	25
18	40	10	50	14	360
20	50	13	40	18	30
		14	60	19	50
		20	2	20	2
Apr. 4, 1956	160	Aug. 3, 1956	50	Dec. 4, 1956	50
8	60	4	20	8	60
10	15	6	72	11	30
11	8	12	20	14	100
14	20	13	45	18	75
20	252	14	44	20	250
		16	250		
		20	115		
Jan. 3, 1957	2	May 2, 1957	25	Sept. 1, 1957	12
5	40	5	12	4	75
8	60	7	30	5	60
11	75	8	20	7	250
12	12	10	250	10	40
13	40	11	50	13	38
14	20	12	75	16	17
16	270	13	12	20	60
17	130	17	30		
18	30	19	12		

* Each month has exactly twenty days, so that weeks include dates 1–5, 6–10, 11–15, and 16–20.

Table C.2 A SEQUENCE OF INDIVIDUAL DEMAND TRANSACTIONS* (cont.)

Date	Demand	Date	Demand	Date	Demand
Feb. 4, 1957	12	June 1, 1957	98	Oct. 6, 1957	12
6	100	4	15	8	25
7	108	6	20	9	83
8	75	8	20	13	2
14	8	12	75	17	135
15	15	15	100	18	20
19	8	19	30	20	15
20	12	20	15		
Mar. 2, 1957	22	July 4, 1957	50	Nov. 1, 1957	100
4	20	7	200	3	40
6	25	13	60	6	25
8	15	15	2	10	95
12	50	17	20	11	40
15	100			12	8
				15	80
				16	40
				19	25
Apr. 1, 1957	20	Aug. 3, 1957	58	Dec. 5, 1957	8
3	12	7	25	8	60
9	100	11	250	12	2
10	38	13	30	18	100
11	8	14	40	20	15
15	250	20	40		
18	40				
19	2				
20	250				
Jan. 2, 1958	75	May 1, 1958	60	Sept. 2, 1958	2
3	100	5	50	3	25
5	12	7	2	5	75
9	75	9	30	7	15
11	60	15	12	10	50
15	40	18	40	14	100
17	30			17	25
20	75			18	265
Feb. 6, 1958	20	June 1, 1958	40	Oct. 1, 1958	25
9	50	5	2	5	30
13	75	9	12	7	30
17	15	12	135	9	2
19	37	13	100	13	8
		15	27	15	135
		16	100	16	100
		17	15	17	50
		18	12	18	62
		20	55		

Table C.2   A SEQUENCE OF INDIVIDUAL DEMAND TRANSACTIONS* (cont.)

Date	Demand	Date	Demand	Date	Demand
Mar. 5, 1958	100	July 6, 1958	2	Nov. 2, 1958	250
7	250	9	58	3	50
9	25	13	95	5	8
10	50	16	60	8	12
11	75	18	8	14	250
14	150			18	15
18	30			20	2
Apr. 2, 1958	28	Aug. 2, 1958	250	Dec. 3, 1958	275
4	40	3	25	5	20
6	250	5	20	8	250
7	100	7	57	9	250
10	75	9	25	10	8
11	15	11	60	13	40
12	270	12	75	17	20
18	25	15	75	18	50
19	60	19	42	19	15
				20	12
Jan. 4, 1959	30	May 2, 1959	60	Sept. 1, 1959	60
5	20	3	125	3	30
6	2	7	4	4	25
10	100	13	100	8	60
12	2	15	60	11	8
13	40	19	12	15	75
17	60			17	50
19	87			20	8
Feb. 1, 1959	115	June 1, 1959	50	Oct. 2, 1959	75
7	8	3	75	3	15
13	20	5	100	4	2
15	30	9	12	8	60
17	60	11	20	11	60
19	30	14	15	12	2
		16	17	18	125
		20	60		
Mar. 1, 1959	35	July 1, 1959	90	Nov. 2, 1959	40
3	75	3	40	4	60
7	250	6	32	6	2
13	52	8	250	8	125
16	15	10	60	10	30
19	25	16	60	13	20
		17	30	17	50
		20	75	18	20

Table C.2 A SEQUENCE OF INDIVIDUAL DEMAND TRANSACTIONS* (cont.)

Date	Demand	Date	Demand	Date	Demand
Apr. 3, 1959	30	Aug. 4, 1959	75	Dec. 2, 1959	60
4	105	5	47	6	20
7	14	9	22	7	250
8	25	12	8	9	75
10	40	14	27	15	15
11	12	15	40	17	2
14	8	17	40	20	25
16	30	19	500		
20	8				

Table C.3   PRODUCTION SCHEDULES FOR REFRIGERATORS AND
NUMBERS OF UNITS WITH LEFT-HAND DOORS

Date	Refrigerators Production Rate	Left-hand Doors Demand	Left-hand Door Installation Rate	Date	Refrigerators Production Rate	Left-hand Doors Demand	Left-hand Door Installation Rate
June, 1957	1000	390	0.390	A		298	0.332
J		323	0.323	S		318	0.353
A		371	0.371	O	900	340	0.378
S		326	0.326	Nov., 1959	1200	497	0.414
O		358	0.358	D		349	0.291
Nov., 1957	1200	538	0.448	J		380	0.317
D		533	0.444	F		379	0.316
J		458	0.382	M		526	0.438
Feb., 1958	1500	414	0.276	A		272	0.227
M		489	0.326	M		401	0.334
A		306	0.204	J		553	0.461
M		654	0.436	July, 1960	1500	527	0.351
J		458	0.305	A		485	0.323
J		507	0.338	S		722	0.481
Aug., 1958	1000	362	0.362	O		474	0.316
S		367	0.367	N		510	0.340
O		306	0.306	Dec., 1960	1750	760	0.434
Nov., 1958	750	223	0.297	J		515	0.294
D		281	0.374	F		560	0.320
J		317	0.423	M		751	0.429
F		238	0.317	Apr., 1961	2000	842	0.421
M		286	0.381	M		818	0.409
A		306	0.408	J		746	0.373
May, 1959	900	307	0.341	J		672	0.336
J		275	0.305	A		854	0.427
J		284	0.315	S		692	0.346

Table C.4   TED PATTON'S RALLY RECORD*

Date	Patton's Raw Score	Numbers of Entries in Rally	Median Score for All Contestants	Patton's Normalized Score
Feb., 1957	721	69	385	0.797
Mar.	97	70	331	−1.041
Apr.	983	69	2250	−1.020
May	738	72	342	0.782
June	355	63	535	−0.963
July	812	66	747	0.117
Aug.	486	73	1870	−2.065
Sept.	166	72	413	−1.190
Dec.	166	72	293	−0.465
Jan., 1958	56	73	338	−1.775
Mar.	168	67	270	−0.461
Apr.	20	67	680	−3.820
May	109	71	427	−1.620
June	197	83	398	−0.802
July	174	71	380	−0.615
Aug.	534	68	2440	−2.900
Oct.	37	68	473	−2.800
Dec.	17	60	172	−2.090
Mar., 1959	60	61	433	−1.640
Apr.	45	64	335	−1.490
May	85	49	310	−1.410
July	940	42	645	0.450
Sept.	670	42	268	1.241
Oct.	131	52	99	0.358
Nov.	15	57	421	−1.620
Dec.	72	45	362	−1.615

* Touring Club of New England, Inc., "Driver-Navigator" for months shown.

Table C.5 INTERNATIONAL BUSINESS MACHINES CORPORATION COMMON STOCK CLOSING PRICES ON NEW YORK STOCK EXCHANGE (TO NEAREST WHOLE DOLLAR)*

Date	Price	Date	Price	Date	Price	Date	Price	Date	Price
June 29, 1959	445	Sept. 7, 1959		Nov. 16, 1959	406	Jan. 25, 1960	418	Apr. 4, 1960	445
30	448	8	406	17	405	26	416	5	450
July 1	450	9	406	18	407	27	419	6	461
2	447	10	413	19	409	28	418	7	471
3		11	411	20	407	29	416	8	467
July 6	451	Sept. 14	410	Nov. 23	409	Feb. 1	419	Apr. 11	462
7	453	15	405	24	425	2	425	12	456
8	454	16	409	25	425	3	421	13	464
9	454	17	410	26		4	422	14	463
10	459	18	405	27	428	5	422	15	
July 13	440	Sept. 21	401	Nov. 30	436	Feb. 8	417	Apr. 18	465
14	446	22	401	Dec. 1	442	9	420	19	464
15	443	23	401	2	442	10	417	20	456
16	443	24	414	3	433	11	418	21	460
17	440	25	419	4	435	12	419	22	458
July 20	439	Sept. 28	425	Dec. 7	433	Feb. 15	419	Apr. 25	453
21	435	29	423	8	435	16	417	26	453
22	435	30	411	9	429	17	419	27	449
23	436	Oct. 1	414	10	439	18	422	28	447
24	435	2	420	11	437	19	423	29	453
July 27	435	Oct. 5	412	Dec. 14	439	Feb. 22		May 2	450
28	435	6	415	15	438	23	422	3	459
29	433	7	412	16	435	24	421	4	457
30	429	8	412	17	433	25	421	5	453
31	428	9	411	18	437	26	419	6	455
Aug. 3	425	Oct. 12	412	Dec. 21	437	Feb. 29	418	May 9	453
4	427	13	409	22	444	Mar. 1	421	10	450
5	425	14	407	23	441	2	420	11	456
6	422	15	408	24	440	3	413	12	461
7	409	16	415	25		4	413	13	463
Aug. 10	407	Oct. 19	413	Dec. 28	441	Mar. 7	408	May 16	463
11	423	20	413	29	439	8	409	17	461
12	422	21	410	30	439	9	415	18	465
13	417	22	405	31	438	10	415	19	473
14	421	23	410	Jan. 1, 1960		11	420	20	473
Aug. 17	424	Oct. 26	412	Jan. 4	437	Mar. 14	420	May 23	475
18	414	27	413	5	441	15	424	24	499
19	419	28	411	6	442	16	426	25	485
20	429	29	411	7	441	17	423	26	491
21	426	30	409	8	437	18	423	27	496
Aug. 24	425	Nov. 2	406	Jan. 11	427	Mar. 21	425	May 30	
25	424	3		12	423	22	431	31	504
26	425	4	407	13	424	23	436	June 1	504
27	425	5	410	14	428	24	436	2	509
28	424	6	408	15	428	25	440	3	511
Aug. 31	425	Nov. 9	408	Jan. 18	431	Mar. 28	436	June 6	524
Sept. 1	421	10	409	19	425	29	443	7	525
2	414	11	410	20	423	30	445	8	541
3	410	12	409	21	420	31	439	9	531
4	411	13	405	22	426	Apr. 1	443	10	529

*From *The Wall Street Journal*.

Date	Price	Date	Price	Date	Price	Date	Price	Date	Price
June 13, 1960	530	Aug. 22, 1960	539	Oct. 31, 1960	511	Jan. 9, 1961	597	Mar. 20, 1961	729
14	531	23	543	Nov. 1	521	10	599	21	722
15	527	24	548	2	520	11	601	22	709
16	525	25	550	3	524	12	608	23	704
17	519	26	548	4	527	13	622	24	702
June 20	514	Aug. 29	550	Nov. 7	528	Jan. 16	613	Mar. 27	699
21	509	30	544	8	539	17	618	28	693
22	505	31	536	9	541	18	622	29	692
23	513	Sept. 1	545	10	537	19	620	30	700
24	525	2	546	11		20	624	31	
June 27	519	Sept. 5	545	Nov. 14	543	Jan. 23	628	Apr. 3	697
28	519	6	536	15	551	24	628	4	702
29	522	7	534	16	541	25	641	5	694
30	522	8	541	17	547	26	630	6	690
July 1		9	541	18	559	27	638	7	693
July 4		Sept. 12	541	Nov. 21	559	Jan. 30	647	Apr. 10	703
5		13	538	22	560	31	636	11	711
6		14	531	23	556	Feb. 1	637	12	716
7		15	521	24		2	641	13	715
8		16	523	25	560	3	640	14	723
July 11	510	Sept. 19	501	Nov. 28	558	Feb. 6	643	Apr. 17	725
12	497	20	505	29	558	7	644	18	721
13	504	21	520	30	557	8	650	19	714
14	510	22	521	Dec. 1	553	9	644	20	712
15	509	23	511	2	554	10	641	21	709
July 18	503	Sept. 26	504	Dec. 5	555	Feb. 13	641	Apr. 24	705
19	500	27	507	6	562	14	642	25	703
20	500	28	502	7	569	15	643	26	711
21	500	29	505	8	585	16	645	27	716
22	495	30	516	9	590	17	643	28	716
July 25	494	Oct. 3	509	Dec. 12	596	Feb. 20	640	May 1	715
26	499	4	507	13	589	21	641	2	709
27	502	5	508	14	583	22		3	707
28	509	6	509	15	584	23	641	4	710
29	525	7	513	16	597	24	650	5	711
Aug. 1	512	Oct. 10	515	Dec. 19	591	Feb. 27	669	May 8	713
2	510	11	520	20	591	28	675	9	709
3	506	12	519	21	589	Mar. 1	675	10	707
4	515	13	526	22	581	2	672	11	700
5	522	14	529	23	588	3	676	12	699
Aug. 8	523	Oct. 17	528	Dec. 26		Mar. 6	673	May 15	699
9	527	18	527	27	592	7	672	16	688
10	523	19	524	28	597	8	681	17	Split 3:2
11	528	20	515	29	594	9	698		
12	529	21	509	30	593	10	700		
Aug. 15	538	Oct. 24	504	Jan. 2, 1961		Mar. 13	708		
16	539	25	502	3	583	14	702		
17	541	26	508	4	592	15	710		
18	543	27	515	5	591	16	727		
19	541	28	507	6	597	17	733		

Table C.5 INTERNATIONAL BUSINESS MACHINES CORPORATION COMMON STOCK CLOSING PRICES ON NEW YORK STOCK EXCHANGE (TO NEAREST WHOLE DOLLAR)* (cont.)

Date	Price	Date	Price	Date	Price	Date	Price
Apr. 24, 1961		July 3, 1961	478	Sept. 11, 1961	541	Nov. 20, 1961	592
25		4		12	545	21	588
26	476	5	479	13	549	22	582
27	479	6	477	14	545	23	
28	479	7	476	15	549	24	576
May 1	479	July 10	475	Sept. 18	547	Nov. 27	578
2	475	11	475	19	543	28	589
3	471	12	473	20	540	29	585
4	475	13	474	21	539	30	580
5	477	14	474	22	532	Dec. 1	579
May 8	478	July 17	474	Sept. 25	517	Dec. 4	584
9	475	18	465	26	527	5	581
10	473	19	466	27	540	6	581
11	467	20	467	28	542	7	577
12	467	21	471	29	538	8	577
May 15	467	July 24	471	Oct. 2	541	Dec. 11	578
16	469	25	467	3	541	12	580
17	460	26	473	4	547	13	586
18	457	27	481	5	553	19	583
19	452	28	488	6	559	15	581
May 22	459	July 31	490	Oct. 9	557	Dec. 18	576
23	462	Aug. 1	489	10	557	19	571
24	459	2	489	11	560	20	575
25	463	3	485	12	571	21	575
26	479	4	491	13	571	22	573
May 29		Aug. 7	492	Oct. 16	569	Dec. 25	
30		8	494	17	575	26	577
31	493	9	499	18	580	27	582
June 1	490	10	498	19	584	28	584
2	492	11	500	20	585	29	579
June 5	498	Aug. 14	497	Oct. 23	590	Jan. 1, 1962	
6	499	15	494	24	599	2	572
7	497	16	495	25	603	3	577
8	496	17	500	26	599	4	571
9	490	18	504	27	596	5	560
June 12	489	Aug. 21	513	Oct. 30	585	Jan. 8	549
13	478	22	511	31	587	9	556
14	487	23	514	Nov. 1	585	10	557
15	491	24	510	2	581	11	563
16	487	25	509	3	583	12	564
June 19	482	Aug. 28	515	Nov. 6	592	Jan. 15	567
20	479	29	519	7		16	561
21	478	30	523	8	592	17	559
22	479	31	519	9	596	18	553
23	477	Sept. 1	523	10	596	19	553
June 26	479	Sept. 4		Nov. 13	595	Jan. 22	553
27	475	5	531	14	598	23	547
28	479	6	547	15	598	24	550
29	476	7	551	16	595	25	544
30	476	8	547	17	595	26	541

When Issued (bracket spanning May 2 – May 16)

Date	Price	Date	Price	Date	Price	Date	Price
Jan. 29, 1962	532	Apr. 9, 1962	521	June 18, 1962	330	Aug. 27, 1962	408
30	525	10	523	19	336	28	393
31	542	11	516	20	328	29	391
Feb. 1	555	12	511	21	316	30	388
2	558	13	518	22	320	31	396
Feb. 5	551	Apr. 16	517	June 25	332	Sept. 3	
6	551	17	520	26	320	4	387
7	552	18	519	27	333	5	383
8	553	19	519	28	344	6	388
9	557	20		29	339	7	382
Feb. 12	557	Apr. 23	519	July 2	350	Sept. 10	384
13	548	24	518	3	351	11	382
14	547	25	513	4		12	383
15	545	26	499	5	350	13	383
16	545	27	485	6	345	14	388
Feb. 19	539	Apr. 30	454	July 9	350	Sept. 17	395
20	539	May 1	462	10	359	18	392
21	535	2	473	11	375	19	386
22		3	482	12	379	20	383
23	537	4	486	13	376	21	377
Feb. 26	535	May 7	475	July 16	382	Sept. 24	364
27	536	8	459	17	370	25	369
28	537	9	451	18	365	26	355
Mar. 1	543	10	453	19	367	27	350
2	548	11	446	20	372	28	353
Mar. 5	546	May 14	455	July 23	373	Oct. 1	340
6	547	15	452	24	363	2	350
7	548	16	457	25	371	3	349
8	549	17	449	26	369	4	358
9	553	18		27	376	5	360
Mar. 12	553	May 21	450	July 30	387	Oct. 8	360
13	552	22	435	31	387	9	366
14	551	23	415	Aug. 1	376	10	359
15	550	24	398	2	385	11	356
16	553	25	399	3	385	12	355
Mar. 19	554	May 28	361	Aug. 6	380	Oct. 15	367
20	551	29	383	7	373	16	357
21	551	30		8	382	17	361
22	545	31	393	9	377	18	355
23	547	June 1	385	10	376	19	348
Mar. 26	547	June 4	360	Aug. 13	379	Oct. 22	343
27	537	5	364	14	386	23	330
28	539	6	365	15	387	24	340
29	538	7	370	16	386	25	339
30	533	8	374	17	389	26	331
Apr. 2	525	June 11	359	Aug. 20	394	Oct. 29	345
3	513	12	335	21	393	30	352
4	510	13	323	22	409	31	346
5	521	14	306	23	411	Nov. 1	352
6	521	15	333	24	409	2	357

Table C.6   UNITED STATES POPULATION*

Census	Population (thousands omitted)	Percentage Increase
1790	3.929	.
1800	5,308	35.1
1810	7,240	36.4
1820	9,638	33.1
1830	12,866	33.5
1840	17,069	32.7
1850	23,192	35.9
1860	31,443	35.6
1870	39,818	26.6
1880	50,156	26.0
1890	62,947	25.5
1900	75,995	20.7
1910	91,972	21.0
1920	105,710	14.9
1930	122,775	16.1
1940	131,669	7.2
1950	150,697	14.5
1960†	179,323	19.0

* *The World Almanac* (New York: *New York World-Telegram and Sun,* 1962).
† Includes Alaska and Hawaii.

Table C.7   REVENUE PASSENGER MILES ON DOMESTIC
SCHEDULED AIRLINES*

Year	Passenger Miles (in millions)	Percentage Increase
1937	0.412	.
1938	0.480	16.5
1939	0.683	42.2
1940	1,052	54.0
1941	1,385	31.6
1942	1,418	2.3
1943	1,634	15.2
1944	2,178	33.2
1945	3,362	54.3
1946	5,948	76.9
1947	6,109	2.7
1948	5,981	−2.1
1949	6,753	12.9
1950	8,003	18.5
1951	10,566	32.0
1952	12,528	18.5
1953	14,760	17.8
1954	16,769	13.6
1955	19,819	18.1
1956	22,362	12.8
1957	25,340	13.3
1958	25,343	.
1959	29,269	15.4
1960	30,514	4.2

* *FAA Statistical Handbook of Aviation.*

Table C.8 A SEQUENCE OF 60 OBSERVATIONS
OF ONE CYCLE OF A WAVEFORM*

t	X_t	t	X_t
1	−3640	31	365
2	−140	32	165
3	10	33	60
4	80	34	−140
5	60	35	−340
6	10	36	−440
7	−140	37	−540
8	−240	38	−620
9	−290	39	−590
10	−240	40	−40
11	−290	41	515
12	−140	42	515
13	60	43	365
14	−40	44	315
15	60	45	315
16	60	46	310
17	−40	47	360
18	−40	48	260
19	−40	49	210
20	−40	50	160
21	−40	51	160
22	1165	52	60
23	1365	53	−40
24	1315	54	−140
25	1265	55	−240
26	1165	56	−440
27	1065	57	−640
28	865	58	−1040
29	715	59	−1340
30	565	60	−2010

* The shape of the waveform should be apparent from a plot of the data.

Table C.9 MONTHLY IMPORTS BY COMPANY B*

Month	1950	1951	1952	1953	1954	1955	1956	1957	1958	1959
Jan.	1935	1950	1895	2146	2195	2043	1880	1752	2260	2250
Feb.	1990	2108	1951	2296	2470	2072	2244	2282	2157	2500
Mar.	3316	3009	2510	3225	3449	2939	3449	3204	3204	3728
Apr.	2901	2699	2252	2927	3101	2591	2794	2812	2770	2914
May	976	2921	2252	3050	2330	2649	2531	2718	3062	2868
June	3563	3368	3322	3160	2430	2945	3204	2652	3177	3048
July	2655	2438	2342	2268	2151	2035	2298	2056	1911	2182
Aug.	2699	2232	2124	2233	2216	2052	2071	1818	1807	2009
Sept.	2827	2797	2839	2899	2469	2703	2400	2250	2275	2459
Oct.	2306	2299	2466	2064	2002	2230	1937	1816	1697	1795
Nov.	2188	2401	2159	2419	2092	2130	1705	1861	1922	2178
Dec.	2825	2619	2940	2949	2506	2591	2701	2764	2332	2331

* Actual company records, with a linear change of scale.

Table C.10 INTERNATIONAL AIRLINES PASSENGERS*

(thousands omitted)

Month	1949	1950	1951	1952	1953	1954	1955	1956	1957	1958	1959	1960
Jan.	112	115	145	171	196	204	242	284	315	340	360	417
Feb.	118	126	150	180	196	188	233	277	301	318	342	391
Mar.	132	141	178	193	236	235	267	317	356	362	406	419
Apr.	129	135	163	181	235	227	269	313	348	348	396	461
May	121	125	172	183	229	234	270	318	355	363	420	472
June	135	149	178	218	243	264	315	374	422	435	472	535
July	148	170	199	230	264	302	364	413	465	491	548	622
Aug.	148	170	199	242	272	293	347	405	467	505	559	606
Sept.	136	158	184	209	237	259	312	355	404	404	463	508
Oct.	119	133	162	191	211	229	274	306	347	359	407	461
Nov.	104	114	146	172	180	203	237	271	305	310	362	390
Dec.	118	140	166	194	201	229	278	306	336	337	405	432
Total	1520	1676	2042	2364	2700	2867	3408	3939	4421	4572	5140	5714

* *FAA Statistical Handbook of Civil Aviation* (several annual issues).

Table C.11   WEEKLY SALES OF ECONOMY ROLLS*

(Warehouse Ten)

Week	Sales	Week	Sales	Week	Sales	Week	Sales
1	10	40	.	79	.	118	.
2	.	41	.	80	.	119	.
3	60	42	40	81	.	120	.
4	12	43	10	82	.	121	.
5	.	44	10	83	12	122	80
6	10	45	.	84	.	123	30
7	10	46	.	85	.	124	.
8	51	47	30	86	10	125	.
9	20	48	80	87	20	126	50
10	10	49	42	88	.	127	51
11	30	50	20	89	30	128	80
12	32	51	10	90	12	129	10
13	.	52	10	91	.	130	.
14	14	53	.	92	32	131	12
15	180	54	.	93	310	132	.
16	.	55	.	94	14	133	.
17	10	56	12	95	30	134	.
18	10	57	23	96	10	135	3
19	12	58	.	97	50	136	10
20	.	59	10	98	30	137	.
21	40	60	.	99	90	138	.
22	.	61	10	100	30	139	1
23	43	62	10	101	10	140	.
24	30	63	30	102	10	141	.
25	2	64	.	103	.	142	.
26	.	65	.	104	20	143	10
27	1	66	12	105	.	144	2
28	.	67	30	106	.	145	30
29	.	68	.	107	10	146	.
30	310	69	90	108	.	147	12
31	.	70	.	109	3	148	.
32	.	71	10	110	.	149	.
33	.	72	.	111	.	150	.
34	.	73	20	112	.	151	.
35	3	74	30	113	10	152	.
36	10	75	20	114	10	153	.
37	2	76	10	115	10	154	.
38	50	77	10	116	.	155	10
39	.	78	40	117	.	156	10

* Actual company records.

Table C.12   WEEKLY SALES OF WARMDOT THERMOSTATS

Week Ending	Sales	Week Ending	Sales	Week Ending	Sales	Week Ending	Sales
Jan. 6	206	Apr. 7	189	July 7	172	Oct. 6	255
13	245	14	244	14	210	13	303
20	185	21	209	21	205	20	282
27	169	28	207	28	244	27	291
Feb. 3	162	May 5	211	Aug. 4	218	Nov. 3	280
10	177	12	210	11	182	10	255
17	207	19	173	18	206	17	312
24	216	26	194	25	211	24	296
Mar. 3	193	June 2	234	Sept. 1	273	Dec. 1	307
10	230	9	156	8	248	8	281
17	212	16	206	15	262	15	308
24	192	23	188	22	258	22	280
31	162	30	162	29	233	29	345

Table C.13   NOISE-FREE DATA

t	$X_t = 500 + 10t$	$X_t = 500 + 10t + \frac{1}{2}(0.4)t^2$
0	500	500.0
1	510	510.2
2	520	520.8
3	530	531.8
4	540	543.2
5	550	555.0
6	560	567.2
7	570	579.8
8	580	592.8
9	590	606.2
10	600	620.0
11	610	634.2
12	620	648.8
13	630	663.8
14	640	679.2
15	650	695.0
16	660	711.2
17	670	727.8
18	680	744.8
19	690	762.2
20	700	780.0

Table C.14 MONTHLY SALES OF WARMDOT FILTERS

Month	1953	1954	1955	1956	1957	1958	1959	1960	1961	1962
Jan.	191	182	199	180	137	184	209	150	169	205
Feb.	158	175	143	173	129	149	145	157	145	125
Mar.	184	155	125	132	164	108	128	162	172	122
Apr.	97	149	148	134	143	114	159	118	102	99
May	124	84	140	81	95	119	117	102	62	134
June	92	36	101	49	95	75	127	116	53	152
July	99	129	105	113	142	104	113	107	124	101
Aug.	113	107	120	139	104	126	69	95	68	151
Sept.	100	135	162	171	122	131	84	146	127	168
Oct.	150	203	147	121	137	184	175	173	140	165
Nov.	228	200	212	129	187	174	180	166	196	158
Dec.	199	193	201	202	188	194	241	167	212	162

Table C.15   INTERVALS BETWEEN SUCCESSIVE DEMANDS FOR BEARING
SHELL HALF HF 2815-343-2678*

Trans-action	Days	Trans-action	Days	Trans-action	Days	Trans-action	Days
1	19	26	2	51	1	76	29
2	5	27	4	52	14	77	5
3	24	28	7	53	1	78	0
4	6	29	10	54	3	79	0
5	17	30	26	55	4	80	1
6	0	31	1	56	5	81	2
7	2	32	1	57	1	82	0
8	0	33	6	58	1	83	4
9	0	34	14	59	0	84	3
10	6	35	8	60	18	85	0
11	0	36	5	61	6	86	0
12	1	37	1	62	8	87	5
13	1	38	7	63	42	88	8
14	6	39	1	64	0	89	0
15	8	40	3	65	17	90	0
16	3	41	0	66	18	91	13
17	0	42	8	67	2	92	0
18	10	43	8	68	0	93	1
19	1	44	0	69	0	94	0
20	15	45	6	70	2	95	0
21	0	46	0	71	5	96	1
22	0	47	15	72	19	97	3
23	0	48	0	73	15	98	10
24	27	49	1	74	0	99	1
25	0	50	40	75	1	100	11

* USN Ships Parts Control Center, Mechanicsburg, Pa.

Table C.16 WARMDOT BUSINESS CONDITIONS

Month	1948	1949	1950	1951	1952	1953	1954	1955	1956	1957
Jan.	169	419	583	432	548	628	510	491	569	564
Feb.	295	359	549	474	581	609	455	503	511	566
Mar.	243	301	513	530	618	615	470	493	567	518
Apr.	374	400	574	492	672	658	513	429	633	450
May	432	475	517	548	690	570	548	403	657	450
June	482	486	483	538	749	551	580	404	595	484
July	520	483	506	475	792	466	465	435	662	547
Aug.	594	524	487	436	766	500	553	536	629	448
Sept.	521	449	536	413	699	419	459	548	630	360
Oct.	553	525	478	480	611	445	408	487	519	328
Nov.	461	531	425	465	627	441	400	569	588	362
Dec.	392	500	538	462	674	462	438	472	636	292

Mathematical Tables

"It is a capital mistake to theorize in advance of the facts."

The Adventure of the Second Stain

In this appendix we provide tables of functions that are most often used in this book.

D.1 The Natural Trigonometric Functions to Ten Places (by degrees, with equivalent number of radius)

D.2 Trigonometric Relationships

D.3 Four-place Mantissas of Common Logarithms, Base 10

D.4 Five-place Natural Logarithms, Base e

D.5 Squares, Cubes, and Roots

D.6 The Normal Distribution, to Eight Places

D.7 The F-distribution

D.8 5000 Random Digits

Table D.1   THE NATURAL TRIGONOMETRIC FUNCTIONS

Angle θ Degrees	Radians	Sin θ		Tan θ		Cot θ		Cos θ			
0	0.00000	0.00000	00000	0.0000	0000	Infinite		1.00000	00000	1.57080	90
1	.01745	.01745	24064	.0174	5506	57.2899	6175	.99984	76952	.55334	89
2	.03491	.03489	94967	.0349	2077	28.6362	5328	.99939	08270	.53589	88
3	.05236	.05233	59562	.0524	0778	19.0811	3670	.99862	95348	.51884	87
4	.06981	.06975	64737	.0699	2681	14.3006	6626	.99756	40503	.50098	86
5	0.08727	0.08715	57427	0.0913	0850	11.4300	5230	0.99619	46981	1.48353	85
6	.10472	.10452	84633	.1053	0534	9.5143	6445	.99452	18954	.46608	84
7	.12217	.12186	93434	.1302	9439	8.1443	4643	.99254	61516	.44862	83
8	.13963	.13917	31010	.1405	4083	7.1153	6972	.99026	80687	.43117	82
9	.15708	.15643	44650	.1708	4957	6.3137	5152	.98768	83406	.41372	81
10	0.17453	0.17364	81777	0.1763	2698	5.6712	8182	0.98480	77530	1.39626	80
11	.19199	.19080	89954	.1943	8031	5.1445	5402	.98162	71834	.37881	79
12	.20944	.20791	16908	.2125	5656	4.7046	3011	.97814	76007	.36136	78
13	.22689	.22495	10543	.2308	1455	4.3314	7588	.97437	00648	.34390	77
14	.24435	.24192	18956	.2493	2800	4.0107	8093	.97029	57263	.32645	76
15	0.26180	0.25881	90451	0.2679	4919	3.7320	5081	0.96592	58263	1.30900	75
16	.27925	.27563	73558	.2870	4400	3.4874	1444	.96126	16959	.29154	74
17	.29671	.29237	17047	.3067	7637	3.2708	5262	.95630	47560	.27409	73
18	.31416	.30901	69944	.3249	1970	3.0776	8354	.95105	65163	.25664	72
19	.33161	.32556	81545	.3443	2761	2.9042	1088	.94551	85756	.23918	71
20	0.34907	0.34202	01433	0.3639	7023	2.7474	7742	0.93969	26208	1.22173	70
21	.36652	.35836	79495	.3838	6403	2.6050	8907	.93358	04265	.20428	69
22	.38397	.37460	65934	.4040	2623	2.4750	8685	.92718	38546	.18682	68
23	.40143	.39073	11285	.4244	7482	2.3558	5237	.92050	48535	.16937	67
24	.41888	.40673	66431	.4452	2869	2.2460	3677	.91354	54576	.15192	66
25	0.43633	0.42261	82617	0.4663	0766	2.1445	0692	0.90630	77870	1.13446	65
26	.45379	.43837	11468	.4877	3259	2.0503	0384	.89879	40463	.11701	64
27	.47124	.45399	04997	.5095	2545	1.9626	1051	.89100	65242	.09956	63
28	.48869	.46947	15628	.5317	0943	1.8807	2647	.88294	75929	.08210	62
29	.50615	.48480	96202	.5543	0905	1.8040	4776	.87461	97071	.06465	61
30	0.52360	0.50000	00000	0.5773	5027	1.7320	5081	0.86602	54038	1.04720	60
31	.54105	.51503	80749	.6008	6062	1.6642	7948	.85716	73007	.02974	59
32	.55851	.52991	92642	.6248	6935	1.6003	3453	.84804	80962	1.01229	58
33	.57596	.54463	90350	.6494	0759	1.5398	6496	.83867	05679	0.99484	57
34	.59341	.55919	29035	.6745	0852	1.4825	6097	.82903	75726	.97738	56
35	0.61087	0.57357	64364	0.7002	0754	1.4281	4801	0.81915	20443	0.95933	55
36	.62832	.58778	52523	.7265	4253	1.3763	8192	.80901	69944	.94248	54
37	.64577	.60181	50232	.7535	5405	1.3270	4482	.79863	55100	.92502	53
38	.66323	.61566	14753	.7812	8563	1.2799	4163	.78801	07536	.90757	52
39	.68068	.62932	03910	.8097	8403	1.2348	9716	.77714	59615	.89012	51
40	0.69813	0.64278	76097	0.8390	9963	1.1917	5359	0.76604	44431	0.87266	50
41	.71558	.65605	90290	.8692	8674	1.1503	6841	.75470	95802	.85521	49
42	.73304	.66913	06064	.9004	0404	1.1106	1251	.74314	48255	.83776	48
43	.75049	.68199	83601	.9325	1509	1.0723	6871	.73135	37016	.82030	47
44	.76794	.69465	83705	.9656	8877	1.0355	3031	.71933	98003	.80285	46
45	0.78540	0.70710	67812	1.0000	0000	1.0000	0000	0.70710	67812	0.78540	45
		Cos ϕ		Cot ϕ		Tan ϕ		Sin ϕ		Radians	Degrees
										Angle ϕ	

Table D.2   TRIGONOMETRIC RELATIONSHIPS

$\pi = 3.14159\ 26535\ 89793$

$\dfrac{1}{\pi} = 0.31830\ 98861\ 83790$

$e = 2.71828\ 18284\ 59045$

1 radian $= 57.29577\ 95131$ degrees

1 degree $= 0.01745\ 32925\ 19943$ radians

Reduction Formulas

Angle	Sin x	Cos x	Tan x
$0° \leqslant x \leqslant 90°$	$\sin x$	$\cos x$	$\tan x$
$90° \leqslant x \leqslant 180°$	$\sin (180 - x)$	$-\cos (180 - x)$	$-\tan (180 - x)$
$180° \leqslant x \leqslant 270°$	$-\sin (x - 180)$	$-\cos (x - 180)$	$+\tan (x - 180)$
$270° \leqslant x \leqslant 360°$	$-\sin (360 - x)$	$\cos (360 - x)$	$-\tan (360 - x)$

Series

$\sin x = \displaystyle\sum_{n=0}^{\infty} \frac{(-1)^n x^{2n-1}}{(2n-1)!}$ converges for all x

$\cos x = \displaystyle\sum_{n=0}^{\infty} (-1)^{n+1} \frac{x^{2n}}{(2n)!}$ converges for all x

$\log_e x = \displaystyle\sum_{n=0}^{\infty} (-1)^n \frac{(x-1)^{n+1}}{n+1}$ converges for $0 < x < 2$

$\sin (x \pm y) = \sin x \cos y \pm \cos x \sin y$

$\cos (x \pm y) = \cos x \cos y \mp \sin x \sin y$

$\sin 2x = 2 \sin x \cos x$

$\cos 2x = \cos^2 x - \sin^2 x$

$\sin 3x = 3 \sin x - 4 \sin^3 x$

$\cos 3x = 4 \cos^3 x - 3 \cos x$

$\sin 4x = 8 \cos^3 x \sin x - 4 \cos x \sin x$

$\cos 4x = 8 \cos^4 x - 8 \cos^2 x + 1$

$\sin 5x = 5 \sin x - 20 \sin^3 x + 16 \sin^5 x$

$\cos 5x = 16 \cos^5 x - 20 \cos^3 x + 5 \cos x$

$\sin 6x = 32 \cos^5 x \sin x - 32 \cos^3 x \sin x + 6 \cos x \sin x$

$\cos 6x = 32 \cos^6 x - 48 \cos^4 x + 18 \cos^2 x - 1$

Table D.3 FOUR-PLACE MANTISSAS OF COMMON LOGARITHMS

N	0	1	2	3	4	5	6	7	8	9
10	.0000	0043	0086	0128	0170	0212	0253	0294	0334	0374
11	.0414	0453	0492	0531	0569	0607	0645	0682	0719	0755
12	.0792	0828	0864	0899	0934	0969	1004	1038	1072	1106
13	.1139	1173	1206	1239	1271	1303	1335	1367	1399	1430
14	.1461	1492	1523	1553	1584	1614	1644	1673	1703	1732
15	.1761	1790	1818	1847	1875	1903	1931	1959	1987	2014
16	.2041	2068	2095	2122	2148	2175	2201	2227	2253	2279
17	.2304	2330	2355	2380	2405	2430	2455	2480	2504	2529
18	.2553	2577	2601	2625	2648	2672	2695	2718	2742	2765
19	.2788	2810	2833	2856	2878	2900	2923	2945	2967	2989
20	.3010	3032	3054	3075	3096	3118	3139	3160	3181	3201
21	.3222	3243	3263	3284	3304	3324	3345	3365	3385	3404
22	.3424	3444	3464	3483	3502	3522	3541	3560	3579	3598
23	.3617	3636	3655	3674	3692	3711	3729	3747	3766	3784
24	.3802	3820	3838	3856	3874	3892	3909	3927	3945	3962
25	.3979	3997	4014	4031	4048	4065	4082	4099	4116	4133
26	.4150	4166	4183	4200	4216	4232	4249	4265	4281	4298
27	.4314	4330	4346	4362	4378	4393	4409	4425	4440	4456
28	.4472	4487	4502	4518	4533	4548	4564	4579	4594	4609
29	.4624	4639	4654	4669	4683	4698	4713	4728	4742	4757
30	.4771	4786	4800	4814	4829	4843	4857	4871	4886	4900
31	.4914	4928	4942	4955	4969	4983	4997	5011	5024	5038
32	.5051	5065	5079	5092	5105	5119	5132	5145	5159	5172
33	.5185	5198	5211	5224	5237	5250	5263	5276	5289	5302
34	.5315	5328	5340	5353	5366	5378	5391	5403	5416	5428
35	.5441	5453	5465	5478	5490	5502	5514	5527	5539	5551
36	.5563	5575	5587	5599	5611	5623	5635	5647	5658	5670
37	.5682	5694	5705	5717	5729	5740	5752	5763	5775	5786
38	.5798	5809	5821	5832	5843	5855	5866	5877	5888	5899
39	.5911	5922	5933	5944	5955	5966	5977	5988	5999	6010
40	.6021	6031	6042	6053	6064	6075	6085	6096	6107	6117
41	.6128	6138	6149	6160	6170	6180	6191	6201	6212	6222
42	.6232	6243	6253	6263	6274	6284	6294	6304	6314	6325
43	.6335	6345	6355	6365	6375	6385	6395	6405	6415	6425
44	.6435	6444	6454	6464	6474	6484	6493	6503	6513	6522
45	.6532	6542	6551	6561	6571	6580	6590	6599	6609	6618
46	.6628	6637	6646	6656	6665	6675	6684	6693	6702	6712
47	.6721	6730	6739	6749	6758	6767	6776	6785	6794	6803
48	.6812	6821	6830	6839	6848	6857	6866	6875	6884	6893
49	.6902	6911	6920	6928	6937	6946	6955	6964	6972	6981
50	.6990	6998	7007	7016	7024	7033	7042	7050	7059	7067
N	0	1	2	3	4	5	6	7	8	9

Table D.3   FOUR-PLACE MANTISSAS OF COMMON LOGARITHMS (cont.)

N	0	1	2	3	4	5	6	7	8	9
50	.6990	6998	7007	7016	7024	7033	7042	7050	7059	7067
51	.7076	7084	7093	7101	7110	7118	7126	7135	7143	7152
52	.7160	7168	7177	7185	7193	7202	7210	7218	7226	7235
53	.7243	7251	7259	7267	7275	7284	7292	7300	7308	7316
54	.7324	7332	7340	7348	7356	7364	7372	7380	7388	7396
55	.7404	7412	7419	7427	7435	7443	7451	7459	7466	7474
56	.7482	7490	7497	7505	7513	7520	7528	7536	7543	7551
57	.7559	7566	7574	7582	7589	7597	7604	7612	7619	7627
58	.7634	7642	7649	7657	7664	7672	7679	7686	7694	7701
59	.7709	7716	7723	7731	7738	7745	7752	7760	7767	7774
60	.7782	7789	7796	7803	7810	7818	7825	7832	7839	7846
61	.7853	7860	7868	7875	7882	7889	7896	7903	7910	7917
62	.7924	7931	7938	7945	7952	7959	7966	7973	7980	7987
63	.7993	8000	8007	8014	8021	8028	8035	8041	8048	8055
64	.8062	8069	8075	8082	8089	8096	8102	8109	8116	8122
65	.8129	8136	8142	8149	8156	8162	8169	8176	8182	8189
66	.8195	8202	8209	8215	8222	8228	8235	8241	8248	8254
67	.8261	8267	8274	8280	8287	8293	8299	8306	8312	8319
68	.8325	8331	8338	8344	8351	8357	8363	8370	8376	8382
69	.8388	8395	8401	8407	8414	8420	8426	8432	8439	8445
70	.8451	8457	8463	8470	8476	8482	8488	8494	8500	8506
71	.8513	8519	8525	8531	8537	8543	8549	8555	8561	8567
72	.8573	8579	8585	8591	8597	8603	8609	8615	8621	8627
73	.8633	8639	8645	8651	8657	8663	8669	8675	8681	8686
74	.8692	8698	8704	8710	8716	8722	8727	8733	8739	8745
75	.8751	8756	8762	8768	8774	8779	8785	8791	8797	8802
76	.8808	8814	8820	8825	8831	8837	8842	8848	8854	8859
77	.8865	8871	8876	8882	8887	8893	8899	8904	8910	8915
78	.8921	8927	8932	8938	8943	8949	8954	8960	8965	8971
79	.8976	8982	8987	8993	8998	9004	9009	9015	9020	9025
80	.9031	9036	9042	9047	9053	9058	9063	9069	9074	9079
81	.9085	9090	9096	9101	9106	9112	9117	9122	9128	9133
82	.9138	9143	9149	9154	9159	9165	9170	9175	9180	9186
83	.9191	9196	9201	9206	9212	9217	9222	9227	9232	9238
84	.9243	9248	9253	9258	9263	9269	9274	9279	9284	9289
85	.9294	9299	9304	9309	9315	9320	9325	9330	9335	9340
86	.9345	9350	9355	9360	9365	9370	9375	9380	9385	9390
87	.9395	9400	9405	9410	9415	9420	9425	9430	9435	9440
88	.9445	9450	9455	9460	9465	9469	9474	9479	9484	9489
89	.9494	9499	9504	9509	9513	9518	9523	9528	9533	9538
90	.9542	9547	9552	9557	9562	9566	9571	9576	9581	9586
91	.9590	9595	9600	9605	9609	9614	9619	9624	9628	9633
92	.9638	9643	9647	9652	9657	9661	9666	9671	9675	9680
93	.9685	9689	9694	9699	9703	9708	9713	9717	9722	9727
94	.9731	9736	9741	9745	9750	9754	9759	9763	9768	9773
95	.9777	9782	9786	9791	9795	9800	9805	9809	9814	9818
96	.9823	9827	9832	9836	9841	9845	9850	9854	9859	9863
97	.9868	9872	9877	9881	9886	9890	9894	9899	9903	9908
98	.9912	9917	9921	9926	9930	9934	9939	9943	9948	9952
99	.9956	9961	9965	9969	9974	9978	9983	9987	9991	9996
N	0	1	2	3	4	5	6	7	8	9

Table D.4 FIVE-PLACE NATURAL LOGARITHMS

log 10 = 2.30258 50930	6 log 10 = 13.81551 05580
2 log 10 = 4.60517 01860	7 log 10 = 16.11809 56510
3 log 10 = 6.90775 52790	8 log 10 = 18.42068 07440
4 log 10 = 9.21034 03720	9 log 10 = 20.72326 58369
5 log 10 = 11.51292 54650	10 log 10 = 23.02585 09299

1.00–4.99

N	0	1	2	3	4	5	6	7	8	9
1.0	0.00000	.00995	.01980	.02956	.03922	.04879	.05827	.06766	.07696	.08618
.1	.09531	.10436	.11333	.12222	.13103	.13976	.14842	.15700	.16551	.17395
.2	.18232	.19062	.19885	.20701	.21511	.22314	.23111	.23902	.24686	.25464
.3	.26236	.27003	.27763	.28518	.29267	.30010	.30748	.31481	.32208	.32930
.4	.33647	.34359	.35066	.35767	.36464	.37156	.37844	.38526	.39204	.39878
.5	.40547	.41211	.41871	.42527	.43178	.43825	.44469	.45108	.45742	.46373
.6	.47000	.47623	.48243	.48858	.49470	.50078	.50682	.51282	.51879	.52473
.7	.53063	.53649	.54232	.54812	.55389	.55962	.56531	.57098	.57661	.58222
.8	.58779	.59333	.59884	.60432	.60977	.61519	.62058	.62594	.63127	.63658
.9	.64185	.64710	.65233	.65752	.66269	.66783	.67294	.67803	.68310	.68813
2.0	0.69315	.69813	.70310	.70804	.71295	.71784	.72271	.72755	.73237	.73716
.1	.74194	.74669	.75142	.75612	.76081	.76547	.77011	.77473	.77932	.78390
.2	.78846	.79299	.79751	.80200	.80648	.81093	.81536	.81978	.82418	.82855
.3	.83291	.83725	.84457	.84587	.85015	.85442	.85866	.86289	.86710	.87129
.4	.87547	.87963	.88377	.88789	.89200	.89609	.90010	.90422	.90826	.91228
.5	.91629	.92028	.92426	.92822	.93216	.93609	.94001	.94391	.94779	.95166
.6	.95551	.95935	.96317	.96698	.97078	.97456	.97833	.98208	.98582	.98954
.7	.99325	.99695	1.00063	1.00430	1.00796	1.01160	1.01523	1.01885	1.02245	1.02604
.8	1.02962	.03318	.03674	.04028	.04380	.04732	.05082	.05431	.05779	.06126
.9	.06471	.06815	.07158	.07500	.07811	.08181	.08519	.08856	.09192	.09527
3.0	1.09861	.10194	.10526	.10856	.11186	.11514	.11841	.12168	.12493	.12817
.1	.13140	.13462	.13783	.14103	.14422	.14740	.15057	.15373	.15688	.16002
.2	.16315	.16627	.16938	.17248	.17557	.17865	.18173	.18479	.18784	.19089
.3	.19392	.19695	.19996	.20297	.20597	.20896	.21194	.21491	.21788	.22083
.4	.22378	.22671	.22964	.23256	.23547	.23837	.24127	.24415	.24703	.24990
.5	.25276	.25562	.25846	.26130	.26413	.26695	.26976	.27257	.27536	.27815
.6	.28093	.28371	.28647	.28923	.29198	.29473	.29746	.30019	.30291	.30563
.7	.30833	.31103	.31372	.31641	.31909	.32176	.32442	.32708	.32972	.33237
.8	.33500	.33763	.34025	.34286	.34547	.34807	.35067	.35325	.35584	.35841
.9	.36098	.36354	.36609	.36864	.37118	.37372	.37624	.37877	.38128	.38379
4.0	1.38629	.38879	.39128	.39377	.39624	.39872	.40118	.40364	.40610	.40854
.1	.41099	.41342	.41585	.41828	.42070	.42311	.42552	.42792	.43031	.43270
.2	.43508	.43746	.43984	.44220	.44456	.44692	.44927	.45161	.45395	.45629
.3	.45862	.46094	.46326	.46557	.46787	.47018	.47247	.47476	.47705	.47933
.4	.48160	.48387	.48614	.48840	.49065	.49290	.49515	.49739	.49962	.50185
.5	.50408	.50630	.50851	.51072	.51293	.51513	.51732	.51951	.52170	.52388
.6	.52606	.52823	.53039	.53256	.53471	.53687	.53902	.54116	.54330	.54543
.7	.54756	.54969	.55181	.55393	.55604	.55814	.56025	.56235	.56414	.56653
.8	.56862	.57070	.57277	.57485	.57691	.57898	.58104	.58309	.58515	.58719
.9	.58924	.59127	.59331	.59534	.59737	.59939	.60141	.60342	.60543	.60744

Table D.4 FIVE-PLACE NATURAL LOGARITHMS (cont.)

5.00–9.99

N	0	1	2	3	4	5	6	7	8	9
5.0	1.60944	.61144	.61343	.61542	.61741	.61939	.62137	.62334	.62531	.62728
.1	.62924	.63120	.63315	.63511	.63705	.63900	.64094	.64287	.64481	.64673
.2	.64866	.65058	.65250	.65441	.65632	.65823	.66013	.66203	.66393	.66582
.3	.66771	.66959	.67147	.67335	.67523	.67710	.67896	.68083	.68269	.68155
.4	.68640	.68825	.69010	.69194	.69378	.69562	.69745	.69928	.70111	.70293
.5	.70475	.70656	.70838	.71019	.71199	.71380	.71560	.71740	.71919	.72098
.6	.72277	.72455	.72633	.72811	.72988	.73166	.73342	.73519	.73695	.73871
.7	.74047	.74222	.74397	.74572	.74746	.74920	.75094	.75267	.75440	.75613
.8	.75786	.75958	.76130	.76302	.76473	.76644	.76815	.76985	.77156	.77326
.9	.77495	.77665	.77834	.78002	.78171	.78339	.78507	.78675	.78842	.79009
6.0	1.79176	.79342	.79509	.79675	.79840	.80006	.80171	.80336	.80500	.80665
.1	.80829	.80993	.81156	.81319	.81482	.81645	.81808	.81970	.82132	.82294
.2	.82455	.82616	.82777	.82938	.83098	.83258	.83418	.83578	.83737	.83896
.3	.84055	.84214	.84372	.84530	.84688	.84845	.85003	.85160	.85317	.85473
.4	.85630	.85786	.85942	.86097	.86253	.86408	.86563	.86718	.86872	.87026
.5	.87180	.87334	.87487	.87641	.87794	.87947	.88099	.88251	.88403	.88555
.6	.88707	.88858	.89010	.89160	.89311	.89462	.89612	.89762	.89912	.90061
.7	.90211	.90360	.90509	.90658	.90806	.90954	.91102	.91250	.91398	.91545
.8	.91692	.91839	.91986	.92132	.92279	.92425	.92571	.92716	.92862	.93007
.9	.93152	.93297	.93442	.93586	.93730	.93874	.94018	.94162	.94305	.94448
7.0	1.94591	.94734	.94876	.95019	.95161	.95303	.95445	.95586	.95727	.95869
.1	.96009	.96150	.96291	.96431	.96571	.96711	.96851	.96991	.97130	.97260
.2	.97408	.97547	.97685	.97824	.97962	.98100	.98238	.98376	.98513	.98650
.3	.98787	.98924	.99061	.99198	.99334	.99470	.99606	.99742	.99877	2.00013
.4	2.00148	.00283	.00418	.00553	.00687	.00821	.00956	.01089	.01223	.01357
.5	.01490	.01624	.01757	.01890	.02022	.02155	.02287	.02419	.02551	.02683
.6	.02815	.02916	.03078	.03209	.03340	.03471	.03601	.03732	.03862	.03992
.7	.04122	.04252	.04381	.04511	.04640	.04769	.04898	.05027	.05156	.05284
.8	.05412	.05540	.05668	.05796	.05924	.06051	.06179	.06306	.06433	.06560
.9	.06686	.06813	.06939	.07065	.07191	.07317	.07443	.07568	.07694	.07819
8.0	2.07944	.08069	.08194	.08318	.08443	.08567	.08691	.08815	.08939	.09063
.1	.09186	.09310	.09433	.09556	.09679	.09802	.09924	.10047	.10169	.10291
.2	.10413	.10535	.10657	.10779	.10900	.11021	.11142	.11263	.11384	.11505
.3	.11626	.11746	.11866	.11986	.12106	.12226	.12346	.12465	.12585	.12704
.4	.12823	.12942	.13061	.13180	.13298	.13417	.13535	.13653	.13771	.13889
.5	.14007	.14124	.14242	.14359	.14476	.14593	.14710	.14827	.14943	.15060
.6	.15176	.15292	.15409	.15524	.15640	.15756	.15871	.15987	.16102	.16217
.7	.16332	.16447	.16562	.16677	.16791	.16905	.17020	.17134	.17248	.17361
.8	.17475	.17589	.17702	.17816	.17929	.18042	.18155	.18267	.18380	.18493
.9	.18605	.18717	.18830	.18942	.19054	.19165	.19277	.19389	.19500	.19611
9.0	2.19722	.19834	.19944	.20055	.20166	.20276	.20387	.20497	.20607	.20717
.1	.20827	.20937	.21047	.21157	.21266	.21375	.21485	.21594	.21703	.21812
.2	.21920	.22029	.22138	.22246	.22354	.22462	.22570	.22678	.22786	.22894
.3	.23001	.23109	.23216	.23324	.23431	.23538	.23645	.23751	.23858	.23965
.4	.24071	.24177	.24284	.24390	.24496	.24601	.24707	.24813	.24918	.25024
.5	.25129	.25234	.25339	.25444	.25549	.25654	.25759	.25863	.25968	.26072
.6	.26176	.26280	.26384	.26488	.26592	.26696	.26799	.26903	.27006	.27109
.7	.27213	.27316	.27419	.27521	.27624	.27727	.27829	.27932	.28034	.28136
.8	.28238	.28340	.28442	.28544	.28646	.28747	.28849	.28950	.29051	.29152
.9	.29253	.29354	.29455	.29556	.29657	.29757	.29858	.29958	.30058	.30158

Table D.5   SQUARES, CUBES, AND ROOTS

n	n^2	$\sqrt{n}$	$\sqrt{10n}$	n^3	$\sqrt[3]{n}$	$\sqrt[3]{10n}$	$\sqrt[3]{100n}$
1	1	1.000 000	3.162 278	1	1.000 000	2.154 435	4.641 589
2	4	1.414 214	4.472 136	8	1.259 921	2.714 418	5.848 035
3	9	1.732 051	5.477 226	27	1.442 250	3.107 233	6.694 330
4	16	2.000 000	6.324 555	64	1.587 401	3.419 952	7.368 063
5	25	2.236 068	7.071 068	125	1.709 976	3.684 031	7.937 005
6	36	2.449 490	7.745 967	216	1.817 121	3.914 868	8.434 327
7	49	2.645 751	8.366 600	343	1.912 931	4.121 285	8.879 040
8	64	2.828 427	8.944 272	512	2.000 000	4.308 869	9.283 178
9	81	3.000 000	9.486 833	729	2.080 084	4.481 405	9.654 894
10	100	3.162 278	10.00000	1 000	2.154 435	4.641 589	10.00000
11	121	3.316 625	10.48809	1 331	2.223 980	4.791 420	10.32280
12	144	3.464 102	10.95445	1 728	2.289 428	4.932 424	10.62659
13	169	3.605 551	11.40175	2 197	2.351 335	5.065 797	10.91393
14	196	3.741 657	11.83216	2 744	2.410 142	5.192 404	11.18689
15	225	3.872 983	12.24745	3 375	2.466 212	5.313 293	11.44714
16	256	4.000 000	12.64911	4 096	2.519 842	5.428 835	11.69607
17	289	4.123 106	13.03840	4 913	2.571 282	5.539 658	11.93483
18	324	4.242 641	13.41641	5 832	2.620 741	5.646 216	12.16440
19	361	4.358 899	13.78405	6 859	2.668 402	5.748 897	12.38562
20	400	4.472 136	14.14214	8 000	2.714 418	5.848 035	12.59921
21	441	4.582 576	14.49138	9 261	2.758 924	5.943 922	12.80579
22	484	4.690 416	14.83240	10 648	2.802 039	6.036 811	13.00591
23	529	4.795 832	15.16575	12 167	2.843 867	6.126 926	13.20006
24	576	4.898 979	15.49193	13 824	2.884 499	6.214 465	13.38866
25	625	5.000 000	15.81139	15 625	2.924 018	6.299 605	13.57209
26	676	5.099 020	16.12452	17 576	2.962 496	6.382 504	13.75069
27	729	5.196 152	16.43168	19 683	3.000 000	6.463 304	13.92477
28	784	5.291 503	16.73320	21 952	3.036 589	6.542 133	14.09460
29	841	5.385 165	17.02939	24 389	3.072 317	6.619 106	14.26043
30	900	5.477 226	17.32051	27 000	3.107 233	6.694 330	14.42250
31	961	5.567 764	17.60682	29 791	3.141 381	6.767 899	14.58100
32	1 024	5.656 854	17.88854	32 768	3.174 802	6.839 904	14.73613
33	1 089	5.744 563	18.16590	35 937	3.207 534	6.910 423	14.88806
34	1 156	5.830 952	18.43909	39 304	3.239 612	6.979 532	15.03695
35	1 225	5.916 080	18.70829	42 875	3.271 066	7.047 299	15.18294
36	1 296	6.000 000	18.97367	46 656	3.301 927	7.113 787	15.32619
37	1 369	6.082 763	19.23538	50 653	3.332 222	7.179 054	15.46680
38	1 444	6.164 414	19.49359	54 872	3.361 975	7.243 156	15.60491
39	1 521	6.244 998	19.74842	59 319	3.391 211	7.306 144	15.74061
40	1 600	6.324 555	20.00000	64 000	3.419 952	7.368 063	15.87401
41	1 681	6.403 124	20.24846	68 921	3.448 217	7.428 959	16.00521
42	1 764	6.480 741	20.49390	74 088	3.476 027	7.488 872	16.13429
43	1 849	6.557 439	20.73644	79 507	3.503 398	7.547 842	16.26133
44	1 936	6.633 250	20.97618	85 184	3.530 348	7.605 905	16.38643
45	2 025	6.708 204	21.21320	91 125	3.556 893	7.663 094	16.50964
46	2 116	6.782 330	21.44761	97 336	3.583 048	7.719 443	16.63103
47	2 209	6.855 655	21.67948	103 823	3.608 826	7.774 980	16.75069
48	2 304	6.928 203	21.90890	110 592	3.634 241	7.829 735	16.86865
49	2 401	7.000 000	22.13594	117 649	3.659 306	7.883 735	16.98499
50	2 500	7.071 068	22.36068	125 000	3.684 031	7.937 005	17.09976

Table D.5   SQUARES, CUBES, AND ROOTS (cont.)

n	n^2	$\sqrt{n}$	$\sqrt{10n}$	n^3	$\sqrt[3]{n}$	$\sqrt[3]{10n}$	$\sqrt[3]{100n}$
50	2 500	7.071 068	22.36068	125 000	3.684 031	7.937 005	17.09976
51	2 601	7.141 428	22.58318	132 651	3.708 430	7.989 570	17.21301
52	2 704	7.211 103	22.80351	140 608	3.732 511	8.041 452	17.32478
53	2 809	7.280 110	23.02173	148 877	3.756 286	8.092 672	17.43513
54	2 916	7.348 469	23.23790	157 464	3.779 763	8.143 253	17.54411
55	3 025	7.416 198	23.45208	166 375	3.802 952	8.193 213	17.65174
56	3 136	7.483 315	23.66432	175 616	3.825 862	8.242 571	17.75808
57	3 249	7.549 834	23.87467	185 193	3.848 501	8.291 344	17.86316
58	3 364	7.615 773	24.08319	195 112	3.870 877	8.339 551	17.96702
59	3 481	7.681 146	24.28992	205 379	3.892 996	8.387 207	18.06969
60	3 600	7.745 967	24.49490	216 000	3.914 868	8.434 327	18.17121
61	3 721	7.810 250	24.69818	226 981	3.936 497	8.480 926	18.27160
62	3 844	7.874 008	24.89980	238 328	3.957 892	8.527 019	18.37091
63	3 969	7.937 254	25.09980	250 047	3.979 057	8.572 619	18.46915
64	4 096	8.000 000	25.29822	262 144	4.000 000	8.617 739	18.56636
65	4 225	8.062 258	25.49510	274 625	4.020 726	8.662 391	18.66256
66	4 356	8.124 038	25.69047	287 496	4.041 240	8.706 588	18.75777
67	4 489	8.185 353	25.88436	300 763	4.061 548	8.750 340	18.85204
68	4 624	8.246 211	26.07681	314 432	4.081 655	8.793 659	18.94536
69	4 761	8.306 624	26.26785	328 509	4.101 566	8.836 556	19.03778
70	4 900	8.366 600	26.45751	343 000	4.121 285	8.879 040	19.12931
71	5 041	8.426 150	26.64583	357 911	4.140 818	8.921 121	19.21997
72	5 184	8.485 281	26.83282	373 248	4.160 168	8.962 809	19.30979
73	5 329	8.544 004	27.01851	389 017	4.179 339	9.004 113	19.39877
74	5 476	8.602 325	27.20294	405 224	4.198 336	9.045 042	19.48695
75	5 625	8.660 254	27.38613	421 875	4.217 163	9.085 603	19.57434
76	5 776	8.717 798	27.56810	438 976	4.235 824	9.125 805	19.66095
77	5 929	8.774 964	27.74887	456 533	4.254 321	9.165 656	19.74681
78	6 084	8.831 761	27.92848	474 552	4.272 659	9.205 164	19.83192
79	6 241	8.888 194	28.10694	493 039	4.290 840	9.244 335	19.91632
80	6 400	8.944 272	28.28427	512 000	4.308 869	9.283 178	20.00000
81	6 561	9.000 000	28.46050	531 441	4.326 749	9.321 698	20.08299
82	6 724	9.055 385	28.63564	551 368	4.344 481	9.359 902	20.16530
83	6 889	9.110 434	28.80972	571 787	4.362 071	9.397 796	20.24694
84	7 056	9.165 151	28.98275	592 704	4.379 519	9.435 388	20.32793
85	7 225	9.219 544	29.15476	614 125	4.396 830	9.472 682	20.40828
86	7 396	9.273 618	29.32576	636 056	4.414 005	9.509 685	20.48800
87	7 569	9.327 379	29.49576	658 503	4.431 048	9.546 403	20.56710
88	7 744	9.380 832	29.66479	681 472	4.447 960	9.582 840	20.64560
89	7 921	9.433 981	29.83287	704 969	4.464 745	9.619 002	20.72351
90	8 100	9.486 833	30.00000	729 000	4.481 405	9.654 894	20.80084
91	8 281	9.539 392	30.16621	753 571	4.497 941	9.690 521	20.87759
92	8 464	9.591 663	30.33150	778 688	4.514 357	9.725 888	20.95379
93	8 649	9.643 651	30.49590	804 357	4.530 655	9.761 000	21.02944
94	8 836	9.695 360	30.65942	830 584	4.546 836	9.795 861	21.10454
95	9 025	9.746 794	30.82207	857 375	4.562 903	9.830 476	21.17912
96	9 216	9.797 959	30.98387	884 736	4.578 857	9.864 848	21.25317
97	9 409	9.848 858	31.14482	912 673	4.594 701	9.898 983	21.32671
98	9 604	9.899 495	31.30495	941 192	4.610 436	9.932 884	21.39975
99	9 801	9.949 874	31.46427	970 299	4.626 065	9.966 555	21.47229
100	10 000	10.00000	31.62278	1 000 000	4.641 589	10.00000	21.54435

Table D.6   THE NORMAL DISTRIBUTION

Variable $x = \mu + k\sigma$

Mean μ,   Standard deviation σ

Probability Density $p(k) = \dfrac{1}{\sqrt{2\pi}} e^{-k^2/2}, \qquad p(-k) = p(k)$

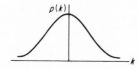

Probability (Cumulative) $F(k) = \displaystyle\int_{-\infty}^{k} p(t)\,dt, \qquad F(-k) = 1 - F(k)$

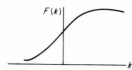

Partial Expectation $E(t > k) = \displaystyle\int_{k}^{\infty} (t - k)p(t)\,dt$

$$= p(k) - k[1 - F(k)]$$

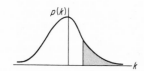

Variate k	Density $p(k)$		Probability $F(k)$		Partial Expectations			
					$E(t > k)$		$E(t > -k)$	
0.00	0.39894	228	0.50000	000	0.39894	228	0.39894	228
0.05	.39844	391	.51993	881	.37444	085	.42444	085
0.10	.39695	255	.53982	784	.35093	503	.45093	503
0.15	.39447	933	.53961	769	.32542	198	.47542	198
0.20	.39104	269	.57925	971	.30689	463	.50689	463
0.25	0.38666	812	0.59870	633	0.28634	470	0.53634	470
0.30	.38138	782	.61791	142	.26676	125	.56676	125
0.35	.37524	035	.63683	065	.24813	108	.59813	108
0.40	.36827	014	.65542	174	.23043	884	.63043	884
0.45	.36052	696	.67364	478	.21366	711	.66366	711
0.50	0.35206	533	0.69146	246	0.19779	656	0.69779	656
0.55	.34294	386	.70884	031	.18280	603	.73280	603
0.60	.33322	460	.72574	688	.16867	273	.76867	273

Table D.6 THE NORMAL DISTRIBUTION (cont.)

Variate k	Density $p(k)$		Probability $F(k)$		Partial Expectations $E(t > k)$		$E(t > -k)$	
0.65	.32297	236	.74215	389	.15537	239	.80537	239
0.70	.31225	393	.75803	635	.14287	938	.84287	938
0.75	0.30113	743	0.77337	265	0.13116	692	0.88116	692
0.80	.28969	155	.78814	460	.12020	723	0.92020	723
0.85	.27798	489	.80233	746	.10997	173	0.95997	173
0.90	.26608	525	.81593	987	.10043	113	1.00043	113
0.95	.25405	906	.82894	387	.09155	574	1.04155	574
1.00	0.24197	072	0.84134	475	0.08331	547	1.08331	547
1.05	.22988	214	.85314	094	.07568	013	1.12568	013
1.10	.21785	218	.86433	394	.06861	951	1.16861	951
1.15	.20593	627	.87492	806	.06210	354	1.21210	354
1.20	.19418	605	.88493	033	.05610	245	1.25610	245
1.25	0.18264	909	0.89435	023	0.05058	688	1.30058	688
1.30	.17136	859	.90319	952	.04552	797	1.34552	797
1.35	.16038	333	.91149	201	.04089	754	1.39089	754
1.40	.14972	747	.91924	334	.03666	815	1.43666	815
1.45	.13943	057	.92647	074	.03281	314	1.48281	314
1.50	0.12951	760	0.93319	280	0.02930	680	1.52930	680
1.55	.12000	900	.93942	924	.02612	432	1.57612	432
1.60	.11092	083	.94520	071	.02324	197	1.62324	197
1.65	.10226	492	.95052	853	.02063	699	1.67063	699
1.70	.09404	908	.95543	454	.01828	780	1.71828	780
1.75	0.08627	732	0.95994	084	0.01617	379	1.76617	379
1.80	.07895	016	.96406	968	.01427	558	1.81427	558
1.85	.07206	487	.96784	323	.01257	485	1.86257	485
1.90	.06561	581	.97128	344	.01105	435	1.91105	435
1.95	.05959	471	.97441	194	.00969	799	1.95969	799
2.00	0.05399	097	0.97724	987	0.00849	071	2.00849	071
2.05	.04879	202	.97981	778	.00741	847	2.05741	847
2.10	.04398	360	.98213	558	.00646	832	2.10646	832
2.15	.03955	004	.98422	239	.00777	818	2.15777	818
2.20	.03547	459	.98609	655	.00488	700	2.20488	700
2.25	0.03173	965	0.98777	553	0.00423	459	2.25423	459
2.30	.02832	704	.98927	589	.00366	159	2.30366	159
2.35	.02521	822	.99061	329	.00315	945	2.35315	945
2.40	.02239	453	.99180	246	.00272	043	2.40272	043
2.45	.01983	735	.99285	719	.00233	747	2.45233	747
2.50	0.01752	830	0.99379	033	0.00200	413	2.50200	413
2.55	.01544	935	.99461	385	.00171	467	2.55171	467
2.60	.01358	297	.99533	881	.00146	388	2.60146	388
2.65	.01191	224	.99597	541	.00124	708	2.65124	708
2.70	.01042	093	.99653	303	.00106	011	2.70106	011

Table D.6 THE NORMAL DISTRIBUTION (cont.)

Variate k	Density p(k)		Probability F(k)		Partial Expectations			
					$E(t>k)$		$E(t>-k)$	
2.75	0.00909	356	0.99702	024	0.00089	922	2.75089	922
2.80	.00791	545	.99744	487	.00076	109	2.80076	109
2.85	.00687	277	.99781	404	.00064	278	2.85064	278
2.90	.00595	253	.99813	419	.00054	168	2.90054	168
2.95	.00514	264	.99841	113	.00045	547	2.95045	547
3.00	0.00443	185	0.99865	010	0.00038	215	3.00038	215
3.05	.00380	976	.99885	579	.00031	992	3.05031	992
3.10	.00326	682	.99903	240	.00026	726	3.10026	726
3.15	.00279	426	.99918	365	.00022	276	3.15022	276
3.20	.00238	409	.99931	286	.00018	524	3.20018	524
3.25	0.00202	905	0.99942	298	0.00015	374	3.25015	374
3.30	.00172	257	.99951	658	.00012	728	3.30012	728
3.35	.00145	873	.99959	594	.00010	513	3.35010	513
3.40	.00123	222	.99966	307	.00008	666	3.40008	666
3.45	.00103	828	.99971	971	.00007	128	3.45007	128
3.50	0.00087	268	0.99976	737	0.00005	848	3.50005	848
3.55	.00073	166	.99980	738	.00004	785	3.55004	785
3.60	.00061	190	.99984	089	.00003	910	3.60003	910
3.65	.00051	046	.99986	888	.00003	187	3.65003	187
3.70	.00042	478	.99989	220	.00002	592	3.70002	592
3.75	0.00035	260	0.99991	158	0.00002	103	3.75002	103
3.80	.00029	195	.99992	765	.00001	802	3.80001	802
3.85	.00024	113	.99994	094	.00001	375	3.85001	375
3.90	.00019	866	.99995	190	.00001	107	3.90001	107
3.95	.00016	326	.99996	092	.00000	889	3.95000	889
4.00	0.00013	383	0.99996	833	0.00000	715	4.00000	715

Table D.7   THE F-DISTRIBUTION*

$$\text{The } F\text{-ratio} = \frac{\text{larger variance}}{\text{smaller variance}}$$

(If variances were estimated for samples from the same distribution, then the ratio would exceed tabulated entry by chance P % of time.)

Degrees of Freedom in Denominator	P	Degrees of Freedom in Numerator

Degrees of Freedom in Denominator	P	5	10	20	40	120	∞
5	25	1.89	1.89	1.88	1.88	1.87	1.87
	10	3.45	3.30	3.21	3.16	3.12	3.10
	5	5.05	4.74	4.56	4.46	4.40	4.36
	2.5	7.15	6.62	6.33	6.18	6.07	6.02
	1.0	10.97	10.05	9.55	9.29	9.11	9.02
	0.5	14.94	13.62	12.90	12.53	12.27	12.14
	0.1	29.75	26.92	25.39	24.60	24.06	23.79
10	25	1.59	1.55	1.52	1.51	1.49	1.48
	10	2.52	2.32	2.20	2.13	2.08	2.06
	5	3.33	2.98	2.77	2.66	2.58	2.54
	2.5	4.24	3.72	3.42	3.26	3.14	3.08
	1.0	5.64	4.85	4.41	4.17	4.00	3.91
	0.5	6.87	5.85	5.27	4.97	4.75	4.64
	0.1	10.48	8.75	7.80	7.30	6.94	6.76
20	25	1.45	1.40	1.36	1.33	1.31	1.29
	10	2.16	1.94	1.79	1.71	1.64	1.61
	5	2.71	2.35	2.12	1.99	1.90	1.84
	2.5	3.29	2.77	2.46	2.29	2.16	2.09
	1.0	4.10	3.37	2.94	2.69	2.52	2.42
	0.5	4.76	3.85	3.32	3.02	2.81	2.69
	0.1	6.46	5.08	4.29	3.86	3.54	3.38
40	25	1.39	1.33	1.28	1.24	1.21	1.19
	10	2.00	1.76	1.61	1.51	1.42	1.38
	5	2.45	2.08	1.84	1.69	1.58	1.51
	2.5	2.90	2.39	2.07	1.88	1.72	1.64
	1.0	3.51	2.80	2.37	2.11	1.92	1.80
	0.5	3.99	3.12	2.60	2.30	2.06	1.93
	0.1	5.13	3.87	3.15	2.73	2.41	2.23
120	25	1.35	1.28	1.22	1.18	1.13	1.10
	10	1.90	1.65	1.48	1.37	1.26	1.19
	5	2.29	1.91	1.66	1.50	1.35	1.25
	2.5	2.67	1.26	1.82	1.61	1.43	1.31
	1.0	3.17	2.47	2.03	1.76	1.53	1.38
	0.5	3.55	2.71	2.19	1.87	1.61	1.43
	0.1	4.42	3.24	2.53	2.11	1.76	1.54
∞	25	1.33	1.25	1.19	1.14	1.08	1.00
	10	1.85	1.60	1.42	1.30	1.17	1.00
	5	2.21	1.83	1.57	1.39	1.22	1.00
	2.5	2.57	2.05	1.71	1.48	1.27	1.00
	1.0	30.2	2.32	1.88	1.59	1.32	1.00
	0.5	3.35	2.52	2.00	1.67	1.36	1.00
	0.1	4.10	2.96	2.27	1.84	1.45	1.00

* Based on E. S. Pearson and H. O. Hartley, eds., *Biometrika Tables for Statisticians*, Vol. I (Cambridge: Cambridge University Press, 1958), table 18.

Table D.8 RANDOM DIGITS

$$(R_0 = 5 \times 10^{10} + 1, \qquad K = 10^5 + 11)$$

66666	44432	10909	63708	81551	85375	10487	00271	36939	79842
86817	49102	75280	14794	16494	72749	04594	98444	09841	04766
13987	30970	88830	06838	01975	16040	13799	62695	09602	25129
90975	60836	30357	06639	72794	98049	48901	11824	43020	15729
40581	89500	58663	60999	43752	81577	00702	44631	96896	31368
65605	47762	12546	96717	09647	09422	40000	39915	38030	06844
48847	46423	10808	20593	45280	04385	17597	56478	13223	56959
53106	76281	52247	19426	05451	69267	64292	33119	49273	76511
21184	08137	15664	60018	24960	86866	90884	88638	52981	40302
75880	92791	59860	89168	18607	19983	88175	21835	11147	03130
19994	61043	23633	33676	81192	11419	26964	11510	90572	99797
36326	23693	25785	00341	87515	83972	58050	16463	38054	45101
87676	71541	65114	75965	92376	40443	12235	75494	80394	33844
16843	75387	20422	27347	30575	63633	00318	07403	24392	40824
46629	86032	50507	01287	16912	16340	13098	10990	56848	20843
79833	34274	94170	24584	46187	41365	21377	65055	44563	08700
99255	30914	70212	04040	93200	61508	75953	28398	34335	19194
67695	66752	77431	26454	12751	79570	07628	39819	52965	47127
27953	12588	94629	58625	39640	78349	27201	18118	07253	67297
02828	19222	80604	47355	88667	20646	25471	62095	84000	34506
95122	17454	74158	19443	54632	49262	73240	50549	50004	83552
87634	18084	94089	81689	12335	86995	21307	42282	52066	29237
43164	11913	39198	20892	16576	36646	00471	76093	16986	66359
04512	69739	88286	03854	02155	81016	21534	70782	51565	69720
94478	42363	00151	77374	83872	82903	75294	25149	42601	94118
15861	60585	13595	68252	56527	85108	32553	17994	56895	74355
51463	35205	47416	83287	94920	10432	44110	08117	41247	25229
64083	57023	00416	09281	53851	61673	40764	34318	22457	41542
96521	96839	51393	13033	68120	21632	33317	15397	07326	98092
71577	05453	59148	41342	52527	53110	12568	50154	82652	49681
92051	13666	62482	21010	01872	98905	49316	17389	15236	31107
40742	32276	80193	58836	90955	81818	94363	75902	51878	57172
80452	52084	11083	41620	74576	04650	78508	64493	19379	22675
53980	43890	33950	36161	87535	50199	12550	01962	24537	02415
84126	58494	07596	89261	44632	81266	87291	87108	54153	51194
73690	26696	70819	27719	40667	40652	73529	98733	75027	03810
05471	59296	42420	58335	50440	51155	22066	95636	33960	75065
42271	47095	21200	67908	28751	15576	63701	16617	57750	59757
26889	60891	85957	23240	10401	16716	09233	80476	53198	32688
82125	51485	95493	71130	10188	17373	49464	86013	07104	48656
10779	49677	88606	38378	22913	60348	55193	12028	86268	42463
95651	66267	84098	31783	23376	68442	77219	17321	37491	28907
99540	92055	80767	38147	66377	44453	46344	40692	87571	02790
65248	97841	57414	24269	86716	71182	73366	00941	43309	38910
15574	34425	72840	36948	99193	11430	49087	96868	91505	92069
53318	32608	65843	02986	98608	07995	44306	07273	98960	97065
61280	03188	55225	29182	59761	83678	09822	90956	12472	68700
02260	36966	39784	02336	37452	41280	76437	86717	58842	01772
19057	04742	98322	89247	66481	63599	54950	13355	44870	71083
34473	57316	89637	36717	61648	13436	36160	69672	57357	31432

Table D.8 RANDOM DIGITS (cont.)

51307	25488	52530	71545	17753	33592	90869	34467	63101	17618
52359	20058	05802	00531	09596	46865	69875	66540	08903	44443
00429	31826	48251	10474	91977	56056	03980	04691	21563	06705
38317	31593	58679	68176	99696	43966	03983	67720	07881	79206
88822	70157	95884	20436	47553	73393	60683	54427	54658	16744
54746	78319	98668	94053	30348	87138	44882	43612	28692	54121
18888	66879	85829	95829	22881	08002	07379	94075	76784	06135
44048	26637	56168	12563	79952	38783	78973	44616	25734	67588
73026	28393	88486	11055	36361	62282	70466	14035	82343	13278
28622	22947	41581	38104	06908	41300	72657	01132	33409	98007
13635	41100	54255	20512	86393	18635	56345	84707	45733	56573
10867	93650	45306	65078	49616	17088	72332	23560	66115	03778
83117	71398	13536	58602	51377	39460	51416	56490	21355	34420
73185	45144	37743	67883	26476	68549	04399	02299	18254	23301
03871	65688	76728	39723	89713	67156	22080	59786	43610	25220
77975	63830	69292	00921	35888	78082	75258	07751	64224	74976
78296	50370	34233	58276	39801	24125	14735	04994	26896	87371
67636	16108	70353	98590	56252	08086	71310	90315	58427	57203
88794	31845	56450	88662	20041	12766	55782	82514	65615	59274
64570	48379	51326	75292	45968	00963	58953	80391	35261	48382
97764	96511	93779	85279	28833	15478	51621	62746	34165	59329
71176	87041	02610	25425	43437	79112	84588	88379	09128	06913
47605	10769	76620	82529	44578	94663	88653	96090	86948	85936
69853	38495	94607	23391	67057	44932	74615	04679	74426	71196
60719	21019	15373	94810	25674	92720	33276	12946	58362	17495
23003	89141	77716	23588	15229	80825	35435	99691	05556	59631
39505	53662	00438	16524	10522	32048	31891	23714	62809	12406
73025	05380	82337	60418	66353	49190	53446	23814	56919	70618
66362	15096	02214	22069	17522	15049	10898	18793	94687	09069
42318	33610	18870	48279	78829	92426	95049	07450	62913	82557
03692	91722	71103	65847	45074	24122	76698	68585	28398	25884
33284	00232	77715	81572	91057	32935	06644	60998	37940	53849
93894	49940	37504	82256	71578	21666	15689	23489	18340	61251
28322	11647	29272	34698	21437	73116	14632	74858	76398	22892
59367	36151	11817	85698	55434	50083	94272	13905	98915	93570
89831	54253	23940	62055	68369	95368	25411	19430	52689	08087
02513	76753	84442	70571	35042	31772	58848	50233	84521	81241
60213	94451	92121	98045	10253	62093	25382	45114	21211	07834
05731	78147	25779	11277	28802	69132	35815	22873	69559	62664
61866	78641	44214	57066	05489	15690	80945	82310	16366	00533
31420	26733	86228	62214	35114	44565	31574	02225	28430	56239
97192	33224	70619	33520	92477	78558	38501	41417	52552	44584
21982	88912	96188	57783	32378	20470	32525	38688	15532	60366
48590	64598	41736	01805	89617	53099	24448	12837	24171	78387
99816	11082	66061	12385	78994	39246	05969	62664	65267	53445
78459	59164	07965	16323	95309	21712	45187	66969	05621	20342
67321	19644	86246	20418	13362	23295	95604	84552	92033	93876
29201	83322	99706	11472	87953	46796	87118	54213	51304	68849
06899	20998	27143	56284	53882	75016	30531	94752	90232	20060
23215	83473	27359	01654	25949	70753	16642	04969	95618	03308

Bibliography

"If the art of the detective began and ended in reasoning from an armchair, my brother would be the greatest criminal agent that ever lived. But he has no ambition and no energy. He would not even go out of his way to verify his solution; and would rather be considered wrong than take the trouble to prove himself right."

The Greek Interpreter

The development of any new idea depends heavily on the ideas that preceded it. Wherever a remark in this book stemmed from a specific reference, a footnote gives the necessary details. This bibliography is intended as a general reading list for the student who wants to recapitulate for himself the ontogeny of current techniques of statistical forecasting.

Books marked with an asterisk (*) have particularly good bibliographies of journal articles.

I am deeply indebted to Mrs. Elizabeth J. Hutton for her patience, industry, and ingenuity in assembling these references.

Forecasting or Prediction

Abramson, Adolph G. and R. H. Mack, *Business Forecasting in Practice*. New York: Wiley, 1956

Adams, Robert William, "The Use of Economic Models in Forecasting." Unpublished doctoral dissertation, M.I.T. 1951.

American Management Association, Company Organization for Economic Forecasting, Rev. Report No. 28. New York: AMA, 1957.

———, Materials and Methods of Sales Forecasting, Special Report No. 27. New York: AMA, 1957.

———, *Sales Forecasting; Uses, Techniques, and Trends*, Special Report No. 16. New York: AMA, 1956.

Bassie, V. Lewis, *Economic Forecasting*. New York: McGraw-Hill, 1958.

———, *Uncertainty in Forecasting and Policy Formation*. Austin, Tex.: University of Texas Bureau of Business Research, 1959.

Bates, Philip Knight, Jr., "A Dynamic Study of Self-Induced Seasonal Cycles." Unpublished master's thesis, M.I.T., 1960.

Berger, Richard, "Several of the Forecasting Techniques in Use Today," *Com. Fin. Chron.*, May 14, 1959, pp. 22–23.

Biggs, Robert M., *National-Income Analysis and Forecasting*. New York: Norton, 1956.

Box, G. E. P. and G. M. Jenkins, "Some Statistical Aspects of Adaptive Optimization and Control," *Jour. Roy. Stat. Soc.*, Apr. 5, 1962.

*Bratt, Elmer C., *Business Cycles and Forecasting*, 5th ed., Homewood, Ill.: Irwin, 1961.

———, *Business Forecasting*. New York: McGraw-Hill, 1958.

———, "Methodology in Long-Range Business Forecasting," *Com. Fin. Chron.*, Feb. 4, 1960, pp. 10–11.

Brown, R. G., "Less Risk in Inventory Estimates," *Har. Bus. Rev.*, July–Aug., 1959, pp. 104–16.

———, *Statistical Forecasting for Inventory Control*. New York: McGraw-Hill, 1959.

——— and R. F. Meyer, "The Fundamental Theorem of Exponential Smoothing," *Operations Research*, Vol. 9, No. 5 (Sept.–Oct., 1961), 673–87.

Business Week, "Business Forecasting; A Special Report," Sept. 24, 1955, pp. 90–122.

Chambers, Edward J., *Economic Fluctuations and Forecasting*. Englewood Cliffs, N.J.: Prentice-Hall, Inc., 1961.

Colm, Gerhard, "Economic Projections: Tools of Economic Analysis and Decision Making," *Amer. Econ. Rev.*, May, 1958, pp. 178–87.

Conference on Research in Income and Wealth, *Long-Range Economic Projection: Studies in Income and Wealth*, Vol. 16. Princeton, N.J.: Princeton University Press, 1954.

———, *Short-Term Economic Forecasting: Studies in Income and Wealth*, Vol. 17. Princeton, N.J.: Princeton University Press, 1955.

Controllership Foundation, *Business Forecasting; A Survey of Business Practices and Methods*. New York: 1950.

Cox, D. R., "Prediction by Exponentially Weighted Moving Averages and Related Methods," *Jour. Roy. Stat. Soc.* (Ser. B), Vol. 23, No. 2 (1961), 414–22.

Crawford, C. M., "Sales Forecasting: Methods of Selected Firms," University of Illinois, Bureau of Economic and Business Research, *Bulletin* No. 78, Urbana, Ill., 1955.

Croxton, F. E. and D. J. Cowden, *Practical Business Statistics*. Englewood Cliffs, N.J.: Prentice-Hall, Inc., 1960.

Dauten, Carl A., *Business Fluctuations and Forecasting*. Chicago: South-Western Publishing Co., 1954.

Dewey, Edward R. and E. F. Dakin, *Cycles, The Science of Prediction*. New York: Holt, 1947.

Eiteman, Wilford J., *Business Forecasting*. Ann Arbor, Mich.: Masterco Press, 1954.

Goldberg, Melvin J., "How Top Management Forecasts the Future," *Dun's Rev. Mod. Ind.*, September, 1958, pp. 33ff.

Goodman, Oscar R., *Sales Forecasting: A Case Study Approach*. Madison, Wisc.: University of Wisconsin Bureau of Business Research and Service, 1954.

Gordon, Robert A., *Business Fluctuations*. New York: Harper, 1952.

Grayson, Henry, *Economic Planning under Free Enterprise*. Washington, D.C.: Public Affairs, 1954.

Juster, Francis T., *Consumer Expectations, Plans, and Purchases*. Princeton, N.J.: Princeton University Press, 1959.

Klein, Lawrence R. and A. S. Goldberger, *An Econometric Model of the U.S., 1929–1952*. Amsterdam: North-Holland Publishing Co., 1955.

Lazer, William, "Perspectives of Sales Forecasting," *Bus. Topics*, Michigan State University Bureau of Business and Economic Research, Winter, 1959, pp. 41–51.

Lewis, John P., *Business Conditions Analysis*. New York: McGraw-Hill, 1959.

————, *Recent Development in Economic Forecasting*. Indiana University, Bloomington School of Business, 1955.

Likert, Rensis and Samuel P. Hayes, *Psychological Surveys in Business Forecasting*. Foundation for Research on Human Behavior, 1958.

Luedicke, Heinz E., *How to Forecast Business Trends; A Special Report for Executives*. New York: *Jour. Com.*, 1954.

MacNiece, E. H., *Production Forecasting, Planning, and Control*. 3rd ed. New York: Wiley, 1961.

Maisel, Sherman J., *Fluctuations, Growth, and Forecasting: The Principles of Dynamic Business Economics*. New York: Wiley, 1957.

Meyer, R. F., "An Adaptive Method of Short-Term Forecasting," International Federation of Operational Research Societies, Oslo, July, 1963.

Moore, G. H., "Statistical Indicators of Cyclical Revivals and Recessions," National Bureau of Economic Research, *Occasional Paper* No. 31, 1950.

Muth, J. F., "Optimal Properties of Exponentially Weighted Forecasts," *Amer. Stat. Assoc. Jour.*, Vol. 55, No. 290 (June, 1960), 299–306.

National Bureau of Economic Research, "Measuring Recessions," *Occasional Paper* No. 61, Princeton, N.J.: 1958.

———, *Quality and Economic Significance of Anticipations Data.* Princeton, N.J.: 1960.

National Planning Association, "Long-Range Projections for Economic Growth: The American Economy in 1970," *Planning Pamphlet*, No. 107. Washington, D.C.: 1959.

Newbury, Frank D., *Business Forecasting; Principles and Practices.* New York: McGraw-Hill, 1952.

Orcutt, G. H., *et al.*, *Microanalysis of Socioeconomic Systems.* New York: Harper, 1961.

Platt, H. M., "Economic Indicators; Their Use in Business Forecasting," Dartmouth College, Amos Tuck School of Business Administration, *Tuck Bulletin*, No. 21, 1959.

Roos, Charles F., "Survey of Economic Forecasting Techniques," *Econometrica*, October, 1955, pp. 363–95.

Saunders, L. R., "The Prediction of a Random Time Series Affected by a Prescribed Time Function," *Aust. Jour. Stat.*, Vol. 4, No. 1 (April, 1962), 11–24.

Shapiro, I. I., *The Prediction of Ballistic Missile Trajectories from Radar Observations.* New York: McGraw-Hill, 1957.

Shiskin, J., "Electronic Computers and Business Indicators," National Bureau of Economic Research, *Occasional Paper* No. 57, 1957.

——— and H. Eisenpress, "Seasonal Adjustments by Electronic Computer Methods," National Bureau of Economic Research, *Technical Paper* No. 12, 1958.

Silk, Leonard S., *Forecasting Business Trends.* New York: McGraw-Hill, 1956.

Snyder, Richard M., *Measuring Business Change.* New York: Wiley, 1955.

Spencer, Milton H. and Louis Siegelman, *Managerial Economics: Decision Making and Forward Planning.* Homewood, Ill.: Irwin, 1959.

———, *et al.*, *Business and Economic Forecasting: An Econometric Approach.* Homewood, Ill.: Irwin, 1961.

Theil, H., *Economic Forecasts and Policy.* Amsterdam: North-Holland, 1958.

University of Chicago, *Jour. Bus.*, "Eleven Articles on Forecasting," January, 1954.

Weintraub, Sidney, *Forecasting the Price Level, Income Distribution and Economic Growth*. Philadelphia, Chilton, 1959.

Wright, Wilson, *Forecasting for Profit: A Technique for Business Management*. New York: Wiley, 1947.

Sampled-data Systems

Cosgriff, R. L., *Nonlinear Control Systems*. New York: McGraw-Hill, 1958.

Doyle, A. C., *Sherlock Holmes* (various).

Goode, H. H. and R. E. Machol, *Systems Engineering*. New York: McGraw-Hill, 1957.

Jury, Eliahu I., *Sampled-Data Control Systems*. New York: Wiley, 1958.

Laning, J. H. and R. H. Battin, *Random Processes in Automatic Control*. New York: McGraw-Hill, 1955.

Mishkin, Eli, ed., *Adaptive Control Systems*. New York: McGraw-Hill, 1961.

Ragazzini, John R. and Gene Franklin, *Sampled-Data Control Systems*. New York: McGraw-Hill, 1958.

Sittler, R. W., "Lectures on Sampled-Data Systems," M.I.T. Lincoln Laboratory, *Memorandum* No. 2M 0671, Aug. 22, 1957.

Tou, Julius T., *Digital and Sampled-Data Control Systems*. New York: McGraw-Hill, 1959.

Truxal, J. G., *Control System Synthesis*. New York: McGraw-Hill, 1955.

Vassian, H. J., "Application of Discrete Variable Servo Theory to Inventory Control," *Oper. Res. Soc. Amer. Jour.*, Vol. 3 (August, 1955), 272.

Time-series Analysis

Arrow, Kenneth, and J. M. Hoffenberg, *A Time Series Analysis of Interindustry Demands*. Amsterdam: North-Holland, 1959.

Blackman, R. B. and J. W. Tukey, *Measurement of Power Spectra from the Point of View of Communications Engineering*. New York: Dover, 1959.

Cunningham, L. and W. Hynd, "Random Processes in Problems of Air Warfare," *Jour. Roy. Stat. Soc.*, Supplement No. 1, pp. 62–85, 1946.

Davenport, W. B. and W. L. Root, *An Introduction to the Theory of Random Signals and Noise.* New York: McGraw-Hill, 1958.

Davis, Harold T., *The Analysis of Economic Time Series.* New Haven: Yale University, Cowles Commission, 1941.

Grenander, Ulf, *Probability and Statistics.* New York: Wiley, 1960.

——— and Murray Rosenblatt, *Statistical Analysis of Stationary Time Series.* New York: Wiley, 1957.

*Hannan, E. J., *Time Series Analysis.* London: Methuen, 1960.

Jackson, D., *Fourier Series—Orthogonal Polynomials.* New York: American Mathematical Society, 1941.

Jones, R. H., "Stochastic Processes on a Sphere as Applied to Meteorological 500 mb Forecasts," Brown University Symposium, June 12, 1962.

Koopmans, Tjalling C., *Statistical Inference in Dynamic Economic Models.* New York: Wiley, 1950.

Maverick, Lewis A., *Time Series Analysis: Smoothing by Stages.* Southern Illinois University Press: 1945.

Morgenstern, Oskar, "A New Look at Economic Time Series Analysis," Princeton University Econometric Research Program, *Research Memorandum* No. 19.

Nyquist, H., "Certain Topics in Telegraph Transmission Theory," *Trans. AIEE,* April, 1928, 617–44.

Quenouille, M. H., *Analysis of Multiple Time Series.* New York: Hafner, 1957.

Steiner, Peter O., *Introduction to the Analysis of Time Series.* New York: Holt, Rinehart, and Winston, 1956.

Wiener, Norbert, *Extrapolation, Interpolation, and Smoothing of Stationary Time Series.* New York: Wiley, 1949.

Wold, H., *A Study in the Analysis of Stationary Time Series,* 2nd ed.; Appendix by Peter Whittle. Stockholm: Almquist and Wiksell, 1954.

Yule, G. U., "Why Do We Sometimes Get Nonsense Correlations between Time Series," *Jour. Roy. Stat. Soc.,* Vol. 89 (New Ser.), 61–64, 1926.

Harmonic Analysis

Bartlett, M. S., "Smoothing Periodograms from Time Series with Continuous Spectra," *Nature,* Vol. 161 (1948), 666–68.

Besicovitch, A. S., *Almost Periodic Functions.* New York: Dover, 1955.

Bochner, Solomon, *Harmonic Analysis and the Theory of Probability*. Berkeley, Calif.: University of California, 1955.

———, *Lectures on Fourier Integrals*. Princeton, N.J.: Princeton University Press, 1959.

Bohr, H., *Almost Periodic Functions*. New York: Chelsea, n.d.

Byerly, William E., *Elementary Treatise on Fourier's Series and Spherical, Cylindrical, and Ellipsoidal Harmonics*. New York: Dover, 1959.

Cuceia, C. L., *Harmonics, Sidebands, and Transients in Communication Engineering*. New York: McGraw-Hill, 1952.

Cunningham, W. J., *Introduction to Nonlinear Analysis*. New York: McGraw-Hill, 1958.

Harrington, Roger F., *Time-Harmonic Electromagnetic Fields*. New York: McGraw-Hill, 1961.

Heble, M. P., "A Regression Problem Concerning Stationary Processes," *Trans. Amer. Math. Soc.*, Vol. 99 (May, 1961), 350–71.

Lee, Y. W., *Statistical Theory of Communication*. New York: Wiley, 1960.

Loomis, Lynn H., *Introduction to Abstract Harmonic Analysis*. New York: Van Nostrand, 1953.

Murnaghan, F. D., *Introduction to Applied Mathematics*. New York: Wiley, 1948.

Riesz, Frigyes and Bela Sz-Nagy, *Functional Analysis*. New York: Ungar, 1955.

Titchmarsh, Edward C., *Eigen Function Expansions Associated with Second-Order Differential Equations:* Part 1; Part 2. New York: Oxford University Press, 1946, 1958.

Whittaker, E. T. and G. N. Watson, *Modern Analysis*, 4th ed. Cambridge: Cambridge University Press, 1927.

Communication Filters

Baghdady, Elie J., *Lectures on Communication System Theory*. New York: McGraw-Hill, 1961.

Grabbe, E. M., S. Ramo, and D. E. Wooldridge, eds., *Handbook of Automation, Computation, and Control*. New York: Wiley, 1958.

*Middleton, David, *An Introduction to Statistical Communication Theory*. New York: McGraw-Hill, 1960.

Shannon, Claude E. and Warren Weaver, *Mathematical Theory of Communication*. University of Illinois, 1949.

Storer, James E., *Passive Network Synthesis*. New York: McGraw-Hill, 1957.

Wiener, Norbert, *Non-Linear Problems in Random Theory*. New York: Wiley, 1958.

Multiple Regression

Ezekiel, Mordecai and Karl A. Fox, *Methods of Correlation Analysis and Regression Analysis*, 3rd ed., New York: Wiley, 1959.

Freiberger, W., M. Rosenblatt, and J. van Ness, "Regression Analysis of Vector Valved Random Processes," *Jour. Soc. Ind. Appl. Math.*, Vol. 10, No. 1 (March, 1962), 89–102.

Graybill, Franklin A., *An Introduction to Linear Statistical Models*, Vol. 1. New York: McGraw-Hill, 1961.

Hoel, Paul G., *Introduction to Mathematical Statistics*, 2nd ed., New York: Wiley, 1954.

Lyle, Philip, *Regression Analysis of Production Cost and Factory Operations*. New York: Hafner, 1957.

Plackett, R. L., *Principles of Regression Analysis*. New York: Oxford University Press, 1960.

Scheid, F. J., "The Under-Over-Under Theorem," *Amer. Math. Monthly*, Vol. 68, No. 9 (November, 1961), 862–71.

Williams, E. J., *Regression Analysis*. New York: Wiley, 1959.

Statistical Decision Theory

Anscombe, F. J., "Rejection of Outliers," *Technometrics*, Vol. 2, No. 2 (May, 1960), 123–24.

Bellman, Richard E., *Adaptive Control Processes*. Princeton, N.J.: Princeton University Press, 1961.

———, *Dynamic Programming*. Princeton, N.J.: Princeton University Press, 1957.

Bierman, Harold, L. E. Fouraker, and R. K. Jaedicke, *Quantitative Analysis for Business Decisions*. Homewood, Ill.: Irwin, 1961.

Blackwell, D. and M. A. Girshick, *Theory of Games and Statistical Decision*. New York: Wiley, 1954.

Bowman, E. H. and R. B. Fetter, eds., *Analyses of Industrial Operations*. Homewood, Ill.: Irwin, 1959.

Bross, Irwin, *Design for Decision*. New York: Macmillan, 1953.

Chernoff, Herman and L. E. Moses, *Elementary Decision Theory*. New York: Wiley, 1959.

Churchman, C. West, *Prediction and Optimal Decision*. Englewood Cliffs, N.J.: Prentice-Hall, Inc., 1961.

Coppock, J. D., *Economics of the Business Firm*. New York: McGraw-Hill, 1959.

Davidson, Donald, *et al.*, *Decision Making; An Experimental Approach*. Stanford, Calif.: Stanford University Press, 1957.

Derman, Cyrus and Morton Klein, *Probability and Statistical Inference for Engineers*. New York: Oxford University Press, 1959.

Dresher, Melvin, *Games of Strategy: Theory and Applications*. Englewood Cliffs, N.J.: Prentice-Hall, Inc., 1961.

Forrester, Jay W., *Industrial Dynamics*. Cambridge, Mass.: M.I.T. Press, 1961.

Grayson, Charles J., *Decisions under Uncertainty; Drilling Decisions by Oil and Gas Operators*. Boston: Harvard University, Division of Research, 1960.

Holt, Charles C., *et al.*, *Planning Production, Inventories, and Work Force*. Englewood Cliffs, N.J.: Prentice-Hall, Inc., 1960.

Howard, Ronald A., *Dynamic Programming and Markov Processes*. Cambridge, Mass.: M.I.T. Press, 1960.

Willner, D., ed., *Decisions, Values, and Groups*, Proceedings of an Interdisciplinary Research Conference, University of New Mexico. New York: Pergamon Press, 1960.

Kemeny, John G., *et al.*, *Introduction to Finite Mathematics*. Englewood Cliffs, N.J.: Prentice-Hall, Inc., 1957.

Kozelka, Robert M., *Elements of Statistical Inference*. Reading, Mass.: Addison-Wesley, 1961.

Kurnow, Ernest, *Statistics for Business Decisions*. Homewood, Ill.: Irwin, 1959.

Lindsay, Franklin A., *New Techniques for Management Decision Making*. New York: McGraw-Hill, 1958.

Luce, R. and H. Raiffa, *Games and Decisions*. New York: Wiley, 1957.

Machol, Robert E., *Information and Decision Processes*. New York: McGraw-Hill, 1960.

Manne, Alan Sussmann, *Economic Analysis for Business Decisions*. New York: McGraw-Hill, 1961.

Raiffa, Howard and Robert Schlaifer, *Applied Statistical Decision Theory*. Cambridge, Mass.: Harvard University, Division of Research, 1961.

Schlaifer, Robert, *Introduction to Statistics for Business Decisions*. New York: McGraw-Hill, 1961.

————, *Probability and Statistics for Business Decisions*. New York: McGraw-Hill, 1959.

Simon, Herbert A., *Models of Man*. New York: Wiley, 1957.

Solomon, Herbert, ed., *Studies in Item Analysis and Prediction*. Stanford, Calif.: Stanford University Press, 1961.

Swets, John A., "Detection Theory and Psychophysics: A Review," *Psychometrika*, Vol. 26 (March, 1961), 49–63.

Thrall, R. M., *et al.*, *Decision Processes*. New York: Wiley, 1954.

Wald, Abraham, *Statistical Decision Functions*. New York: Wiley, 1950.

Weiss, Lionel, *Statistical Decision Theory*. New York: McGraw-Hill, 1961.

Heuristic Programming

Ashby, W. Ross, *Design for a Brain*, 2nd ed. rev. New York: Wiley, 1960.

Friedberg, R. M., B. Dunham, and J. H. North, "A Learning Machine: Part II," *IBM Jour. Res. Dev.*, Vol. 3 (July, 1959), 282–87.

Gelernter, H. L. and N. Rochester, "Intelligent Behavior in Problem-Solving Machines," *IBM Jour. Res. Dev.*, Vol. 2 (October, 1958), 336–45.

Hawkins, J. K., "Self-Organizing Systems: A Review and Commentary," *IRE Proc.*, Vol. 49 (January, 1961), 31–48.

Joseph, R. D., "Contributions to Perceptron Theory," *U.S. Government Research Reports*, Vol. 35 (Jan. 13, 1961), 80–81(a).

Malin, D., "Computers: Key to Total Systems Control," *Proc. Eastern Joint Computer Conference*. Washington, D.C.: American Federation of Information-Processing Societies, 1961.

*Minsky, Marvin, "Steps Toward Artificial Intelligence," *IRE Proc.*, January, 1961.

Sebestyen, G. S., "Recognition of Membership in Classes," *IRE Trans. Information Theory*, Vol. IT-7 (January, 1961), 44–50.

Stevens, M. E., "A Machine Model of Recall," *Proc. Intl. Conf. Information Processing, UNESCO*, Paris, June 15–20, 1959.

Watanabe, M. S., "Information—Theoretical Aspects of Inductive and Deductive Inference," *IBM Jour. Res. Dev.*, Vol. 4 (April, 1960), 208–31.

Yovits, Marshall C. and Scott Cameron, "Self-Organizing Systems," *Proceedings of an Interdisciplinary Conference*, May, 1959. New York: Pergamon Press, 1960.

Glossary of Symbols

a	vector of coefficients, 163
$\hat{a}_T$	estimated coefficient at time T, 61
$\hat{b}_T$	estimated trend at time T, 61
e	exponential base (2.71828 . . .), 120, 437
$e_\tau(t)$	forecast error for a lead time τ, 291
$E(t > k)$	partial expectation, 371
$\mathcal{E}[x]$	expected value of x, 101
$f(k)$	partial expectation, 373
$\mathbf{f}(t)$	vector of fitting functions, 162
$f_i(t)$	the ith fitting function at time t, 76
F	matrix of weighted fitting functions, 163
$F(k)$	probability, 377
$F_x(j\omega)$	Fourier transform, 276
$\mathcal{F}$	matrix of fitting functions, 162
$\mathbf{g}(t)$	data vector, 164
$G(\omega)$	gain, 397
h_n	impulse response, 407
$\mathbf{h}$	smoothing vector, 175
$H(z)$	transfer function, 146
L	transition matrix, 165
M_t	moving average, 98
$M_t^{[2]}$	double moving average, 127
MSE	mean square error, 119
$\mathbf{p}(t)$	probability vector, 201
$\mathbf{P}$	probability vector, 83
$P(t)$	probability of arriving home before t, 55
$P_y(\omega)$	power spectrum, 398
$R_{xx}(\tau)$	autocovariance, 47
$S_t(x)$	exponential smoothing operator, 101
$S_t^{[p]}(x)$	pth order exponential smoothing, 128
t	time index in general
T	time of the most recent observation
$\displaystyle \binom{t}{k} = \frac{t!}{(t-k)!k!}$	binomial coefficient, 66
u	unit vector, 200
V	variance-covariance matrix, 229
W	weighting matrix, 391
W_T	weighted moving average, 125
x_t or $x(t)$	observed data, 25
$\hat{x}_\tau(T)$ or $\hat{x}(T+\tau)$	forecast made at time T for a lead time τ, 272
$\hat{x}_t^{(n)}$	estimate of the nth derivative, 132
$\overline{x_t x_{t-k}}$	average lagged product, 119
$Y(T)$	sum of the forecast errors, 290
α	smoothing constant, 101
$\beta = 1 - \alpha$	discount factor, 92
$\delta(t)$	Dirac delta function, impulse, 112
$\Delta(t)$	mean absolute deviation, 283
Δ^n	nth difference, 63
ϵ_t	noise sample, 60
θ	phase angle, 116
$\theta(x)$	probability distribution, 253
$\xi(t)$	process generating observed data, 60
$\rho(k)$	autocorrelation coefficient, 394
σ^2	variance, 47
σ_τ	standard deviation of forecast errors over the lead time, 365
$\Psi(\omega)$	frequency response function, 397

Index

accumulative forecast, 219
accuracy, 91, 118
action, 357
adaptive smoothing, 170
Aeronautical Radio, Inc., 64
air traffic control, 24, 64
airlines, domestic, 64, 427
ALGOL, 342
aliasing, 43
all-time supplies, 259
alternatives, 324
amplification, 32
amplitude, 116
analog computer, 104
anomaly, 300
Anscombe, F. J., 32
antifreeze, 372
appliances, 27
assignable cause, 298
autocorrelation, 110, 309, 389
    coefficient, 394
autocovariance, 309, 394
Automobile Manufacturers Association,
    259
autoregressive process, 167, 308
auxiliary slip, 329
available stock, 249
average, 97
average age of data, 107

backorders, 370
ballistic missiles, 12, 52, 93, 226
Bartlett, M. S., 400
batteries, 292
Bayesian statistics, 200
Beightler, C. S., 410
binomial coefficient, 63, 66, 166
binomial distribution, 27, 201
binomial theorem, 194
Bode-Shannon filters, 312

Bradford, G. A., 104
Business Week, 94

canonical form, 189
Cantor, Sol, 6
Cape Canaveral, 93
census, 64
central limit theorem, 246
characteristic function, 275
Chebyshev polynomials, 92
chi-squared distribution, 295
Christiana Securities, 45
class intervals, 83
class limits, 200
COBOL, 342
coefficients, 95, 97, 162
Commissaryman, 3
composite models, 181
compound interest, 64
confidence limits, 295
constant model, 60
consumption, 26
continuous exponential smoothing, 104
continuous process, 24
control, 357
control points, 31
convergence, 170
convolution, 112, 406
coordinate transformation, 39
Copernicus, 226
correlated samples, 353
correlation, 110
cost function, 372
covariance matrix, 228, 393
Cox, D. R., 122
criteria, 8, 91, 338
Crook, G. J., 150, 247, 288
cumulative forecasts, 219
curve fitting, 87
curve plotting, 33
cycle, 57, 214

damping, 183
data generator, 347
data processing system, 205
data vector, 169
degree of polynomial, 62
degrees of freedom, 62
delay, 32
demand-during-a-lead-time, 205, 251
department store, 6
D'Esopo, D. A., 138
differences, 34
discount factor, 92, 101
discount store, 6
discounted sum of squares, 162
discrete forecasts, 219
discrete system, 405
discrete time series, 21, 24
distribution function, 27, 253
    (*see also*, specific types of probability
    distributions)
distribution, physical, 27
Dobbie, J. M., 182
double exponential smoothing, 128
double moving average, 127
double smoothing, 124

earth-centered coordinates, 226
Econometric Society, 5
economy rolls, 81
electrocardiogram, 24
epidemic, 95
equivalent moving averages, 108
equivalent value of smoothing constant,
    147
error, forecast, 175, 237, 268, 389
error rate, 32
estimate, 59
evaluation of alternatives, 334
event, 199
expedite, 250
exponential, 166
exponential distribution, 203, 284, 351
exponential models, 64, 194
exponential notation, 179
exponential smoothing, 101
exponentially damped sinusoids, 183

F-distribution, 447
Feller, W., 259

filter, 315, 394
financial investments, 194
fire control system, 104
fitting functions, 76, 159
Fleet Supply Office, 3
flexibility, 91
flood control, 364
forecast, 2, 59, 219
forecast equation, 175
forecast error (*see* error)
Forrester, J. W., 3, 17
FORTRAN, 335, 342
Fourier series, 69, 166, 396
Fourier transform, 276, 397
Freeberger, W., 336
frequency response function, 397
function matrix, 169
fundamental theorem of exponential
    smoothing, 133

gain, 397
gamma distribution, 79
garment trade, 35
gasoline consumption, 26
Gauss, K. F., 352
gaussian noise, 59
GECOM, 342
general exponential smoothing, 174, 197
geometric smoothing, 105
GIGO, 23
Glassey, C. R., 105
golf, 385
Graves, H. S., 204
Greenberger, M., 350
gross national product, 160
growing sine, 183
guess, 257
guesstimate, 4
guided missiles, 6, 93

Halley's comet, 67
handicaps, 383
harmonics, 166
heliocentric coordinates, 226
hi-fi system, 325
histogram, 33
horizon, 272
horse races, 385
Howard, R. A., 96
Hutton, Mrs. E. J., 453

impulse response, 112, 145, 406
independence, 390
industrial dynamics, 3
information, 326
initial conditions, 102, 130, 292
installation rates, 35
interarrival times, 26, 203
international airline passengers, 75, 427
International Business Machines Corporation:
    stock, 60, 422
    reference manual, 350
interpolation, 243
inventory control system, 30, 205, 249
irregular, 57

joint probability distribution, 250
Jones, R. H., 76

Kendall, M. G., 158
Kepler's laws, 12, 52
kernel, 400
Korean War, 317

lagged product, 309, 394
lead time, 43, 213, 245, 258, 365
leading indexes, 5, 76
learning curves, 26
least squares, 92, 124, 162
Lee, Y. W., 312
limits, class, 83
linear combinations, 109, 310
linear models, 60, 124
linear system, 405
Little, Arthur D., Inc., 64
logarithms:
    common, 438
    natural, 440
lognormal distribution, 40

Magee, J. F., 249
maneuvering, 221
manufacturing cycle, 250
margin for error, 287
matrix inversion, 354
maximum likelihood, 92
maximum reasonable demand, 250
McCracken, D. D., 335

mean absolute deviation, 281–2, 345
mean square error, 119
measurement, 26
Meyer, R. F., 122, 133. 168, 317
Mercury Project, 52
Middleton, D., 312
Milne, W. E., 244
model, 59
modes of operation, 298
modular system, 326
modulus, 350
moment, 277
moment generating function, 275
monitor, 298
Moran, P. A. P., 364
moving average, 97
multiple regression, 77, 162
multiple smoothing, 133
Muth, J. F., **122**, 317

naive forecasts, 5
National Bureau of Economic Research, 160
New York Stock Exchange, 99
newsboy problem, 15
newsprint, 27
noise, 59, 267, 389
noise generator, 349
nomograph, 40
normal distribution, 283, 352, 444
normality of forecast errors, 275
Nyquist, H., 43
Nyquist frequency, 70, 399

observation, 59
Occam's razor, 70
oil field equipment, 38
open-loop characteristics, 5
opinion polls, 5
optimum safety stock, 374
Orcutt, G. H., 350
order points, 257, 369
orthogonal fitting functions, 235
Osborne, M. F. M., 33
oscillations, 74

parabola, 115
parameters, 267
partial expectation, 371

Patton, E. J., 39, 275, 383, 421
percentile, 84, 243
periodic function, 66, 166, 183
periodogram, 399
phase angle, 116
phase shift, 397
physically realizable system, 405
pipeline, 27
poisson distribution, 79
Polya, G., 335
polynomial model, 62, 132, 165, 180
population, 64, 194, 293, 426
population estimates, 366
power, 396
prediction, 2, 103, 222
prediction bias, 38
prior estimate, 200
probability distribution, 266
   (*see also*, specific distribution form)
probability model, 199, 243
probit, 40
process, 59, 97, 357
proportional control, 103

quadratic, 62, 115
quadratic costs, 378
quality measurements, 26
quasi-continuous process, 25
quasi-random sequence, 350
Quebec woodsmen, 204
queues, 217, 250

radar, 44
Raiffa, H., 359, 371
raincoat problem, 15
rallies, 39, 275, 383, 421
ramp, 114
RAND Corporation, 349
random digits, 448
random number generator, 349
random walk, 95
ranked samples, 253
rate of response, 91
realizability, 315
recursion, 142
refrigerator doors, 36, 420
regression, 389
relative error, 273

reorder level, 249
repair parts, 32, 259
research, 334
residual, 125, 161, 267, 389
responses, 302
ring gear, 38
Roos, C. S., 4
Rosenblatt, M., 336
Rotenberg, A., 350
rubber stamp of operations research, 44,
   118, 275, 372, 374

SAGE air defense system, 93
safety factor, 235, 258, 286, 372
sales year-to-date, 251
sampled data system, 405
sampling interval, 24, 42
Sanders, L. R., 317
satellites, 93
scanning rate, 45
Scheid, F. J., 92
Schlaifer, R., 359
screening unusual data, 32
seasonal, 57
seismograph, 24, 314
selection, 336
serial correlation, 110
service bureau, 334
Shapiro, I. I., 39
shop dates, 252
shotgun problem, 16
signal-to-noise ratio, 314
simplicity, 91
simulation, 29, 157, 232, 237, 278, 305
sinusoidal models, 180
Sittler, R. W., 312
slack time, 217
slanted chart, 273
Smithsonian Astrophysical Laboratory, 93
smoothing, 87, 101, 170, 197
smoothing constant, 101
spectral analysis, 389
speed of response, 298
spherical harmonics, 76
sporadic data, 38, 205
sporting events, 26
sports car rallies, 39
spot forecast, 219
standard score, 40, 383

Starr, M. K., 363
Statistical Forecasting for Inventory Control, 40, 320, 353
statistical inference, 357
step function, 113
step response, 152
stochastic processes, 167
stock market, 24
stockout, 369
storks' nests in Copenhagen, 390
Strong, P. F., 353
subroutines, 337
successive differences, 63
Sullivan, Joan, 179
summary, 143
superposition theorem, 278
supply ships, 30
synthetic data, 339
system performance, 370
systematic vs. random variation, 34

TABSOL, 342
tally, 204
Taylor series, 132, 195
Technometrics, 400
temperature, 24
test sample, 337
textile industry, 74
Thoreau, H. D., 323
tide, 67
time intervals, 26, 203
time-invariant system, 405
time series analysis, 24
time to convergence, 170
Touring Club of New England, Inc., 39, 383, 421
tracking signal, 281, 287, 296
trading volumes, 26
transfer function, 112, 146, 398
transfer matrix, 299
transformations, 35

transients, 29, 150
transition matrix, 165
trend, 57
Trendline Corporation, 99
triangular distribution, 352
trignometric functions, 66, 166, 436
triple coefficient smoothing, 141
triple smoothing, 137
two-bin system, 249

uniform distribution, 284, 351
unit stock record, 249

variable lead times, 367
variance, 228
variance-covariance matrix, 228, 393
variance of coefficient, 156
vector smoothing, 201
von Neumann, J., 352
Votaw, D. F., 353

Wall Street Journal, 94, 160
warranty card, 27
weather data, 26, 76
weights, 101, 310
whiskey, 265
whitening, 315
Wiener, N., 311
Wiener filters, 394
window, 400
work sheet, 326

yields, 26
Yule, G. U., 77

z-transform, 112, 408
Zeitlin, D., 135